THE DRUMMER

&

THE GREAT MOUNTAIN

a Guidebook to Transforming Adult ADD/ADHD

MICHAEL JOSEPH FERGUSON

Dedicated to John Roche
(1925 - 2013)
a lifelong
beacon of support
and unconditional love

TABLE OF CONTENTS

A NOTE ABOUT TERMINOLOGY

Throughout this book, I use the term "hunter-type" in place of Attention Deficit Disorder (ADD) / Attention Deficit Hyperactivity Disorder (ADHD). I base this expression on Thom Hartmann's "Hunter-Farmer Theory," first proposed in his 1993 book, "Attention Deficit Disorder: A Different Perception."

As will be explored, I believe "hunter-type" is a far more precise term in depicting the *many* facets of someone usually diagnosed with ADD/ADHD.

Although I am fully aware that science and medicine require certain terminology in order to conduct studies and identify specific health-related issues, the expression ADD/ADHD falls far short in expressing the many complexities and subtleties of someone diagnosed as such. These terms reference only the challenges: focus and hyperactivity. Even in this, they aren't very accurate, given people with ADD/ADHD typically have a capacity for *hyperfocus* – an ability to spend extended periods of time on subjects they find of interest to them.

Therefore, I share the belief that ADD/ADHD – for most people – is a neurological type, *not* a pathology. This is made absolutely clear by the fact that some of humanity's greatest thinkers, artists, and entrepreneurs are (or would have been) diagnosed with ADD/ADHD.

This neurological type comes with *both* great gifts and great challenges, therefore the metaphor of "hunter-type," from my perspective, seems to be a far more useful ground to build from.

PREFACE

The very fact that you're reading this book right now is, I believe, a testimony to the effectiveness of what is contained within it. I have little doubt that, had I not integrated this information into my day-to-day life, I would never have been able to complete it.

This book is written from the perspective of a fellow traveler, someone who has shared your same challenges and gifts. Over time – and through *necessity* – I've created a kind of map for navigating our particular neurological type.

Along my journey, I've had the good fortune to work with numerous other ADD/ADHD types. They have taught me volumes about myself, and how we – as a collective – function. I've also had the great privilege of being a life coach to a number of them, watching their lives shift and grow as they've adopted many of the suggestions contained in this book.

It is my fervent belief that people with ADD/ADHD are actually the recipients of a most wonderful gift – a highly specialized neurological system that nature has fine-tuned over millennia. However, in order to fully realize this gift, we need a clear understanding of what it is and how to nurture it.

There are many streams that feed into this book. From the groundbreaking work of Thom Hartmann, the originator of the hunter-farmer theory – to Julia Ross and her writings on the connection between nutrition, brain chemistry, and addiction. From psychologist Dr. Marshall Rosenberg, whose "nonviolent communication" process is the basis for the "Navigating Emotions" chapter – to Michael Meade, storyteller, mythologist, and writer, whose work with inner-city kids has transformed countless lives, and inspired the title, and central theme of this book. Dr. Kevin McCauley's work on "the brain chemistry of the addiction" provided numerous pivotal insights, and greatly influenced the chapter on addiction.

All of these luminaries have, in their own way, shown themselves to be true healers of the human spirit, and whose work, invaluable, in both its breadth and effectiveness.

I'm *deeply* grateful for all of those who contributed to, and supported me, in the completion of this book: Julie and Jim Ferguson, John Roche (Uncle John), Mary Ferguson, Lori Ferguson, Jill Jancic, Sandy Jancic, Warren Goldie, Questa Li, Greg and Anne Hogan, Alli Brook, John Whitten, Pat Roche, Doro Kiley, Joshua and Luna Canter, Garrett Bodman, Brian Self, Leo Sofer, Victor Sagalovsky, Mark Roussey, Kristen Watson Geering, Andrew Jones, Rick Guerrero, Jason Weber, and the countless others who offered me encouragement and support. I am eternally grateful.

THE DRUMMER AND
THE GREAT MOUNTAIN

The Drummer awoke at dawn and surveyed the vast plains around him. The morning dew glistened on tips of grass as far as the eye could see. To the east, in the distance, arose the Great Mountain, his intended destination.

To get there, the Drummer would have to pass through the dark forest, home to ill-tempered, menacing creatures of immense size and strength, reputed to destroy all who enter their domain.

The Drummer paused at the edge of the forest, laid down his spear and shield, and moved swiftly into the trees, armed with only his drum. Cleverness, not brute-force, would be his greatest ally in the upcoming confrontation.

After walking some distance without spying a single giant, he stopped in a clearing and began to drum with such a thunder that birds flew from the trees and animals scurried for cover.

A Giant sleeping nearby jolted awake. He was as tall as a fir tree. Straightening the huge straw hat on his head, he bellowed, "Impudent wretch! How dare you awaken me from my mid-morning nap! Why are you making such a racket?"

Facing the Giant squarely, the Drummer said, "I am drumming to show the way to the many thousands who are following me."

"Hrmph!" snorted the Giant. "What do they want in my forest?"

"To put an end to you and rid these woods of such foul creatures!"

"How do you propose to do such a thing?" laughed the Giant. "I will trample all of you like ants beneath my feet."

"I wouldn't advise it," replied the Drummer. "If you bend down to grab hold of us, we are fast and will jump away and hide. And when you lay down to sleep, we'll come at you from every thicket and hiding place. Each of us carries a steel hammer, which we'll repeatedly thump and beat at your skull."

The Giant paused and thought to himself, "Perhaps I should fear these crafty little creatures. If I meddle with them, it may turn out badly for me. I can strangle wolves and bears but I cannot protect myself from these tiny folk."

When he spoke next, his tone was congenial. "Listen, little fellow," he said. "Perhaps it is as you say. If I promise to leave you and your comrades in peace, will you do the same for me?"

"I'll make you a deal," the Drummer replied. "You have long legs and can move quickly through this forest. Carry me to the Great Mountain, and I will call them off, as you request."

The Giant, feeling pleased with his negotiation skills, placed his open hand on the ground. The Drummer stepped onto his palm and was lifted high up onto the brim of the Giant's hat.

With great strides, the Giant began moving swiftly through the forest. From the Drummer's vantage point, high above the tops of the trees, he could see for miles and miles all around him. Such breathtaking views he'd never witnessed in all his years.

Soon, the Great Mountain came into view.

1

INTRODUCTION

This book starts with the assumption that you're more interested in living a fulfilling life than you are in just treating symptoms. Yet another method of "fixing yourself" is not what you're after. It also presupposes that there may be effective natural (non-pharmaceutical) means of minimizing your challenges with focus, consistency, motivation, and hyperactivity.

As the "The Drummer" story illustrates, each one of us is actively engaged in a struggle of some kind. *How* we face this struggle is up to us. Perhaps there is a way of transforming the "giant" problems we face on a daily basis into something that will carry us to our intended destination.

Finding a Better Way

As with a growing number of people, I find the label "Attention Deficit/Hyperactivity Disorder" (ADD/ADHD) falls far short in describing the many facets of someone with our particular neurological makeup. It focuses solely on symptoms and offers little in the way of personal empowerment. It fails to provide any kind of broader perspective in which to see ourselves and the specific gifts we have to contribute to the world around us.

The phenomenon of ADD/ADHD, over the past few decades, has existed mainly within the domain of chronic diseases and birth defects. It's generally considered to be an aberration to the norm, a condition that must be treated with drugs in order that the afflicted may integrate more fluidly within society. Sadly, the indoctrination to this particular point-of-view now starts at a very young age.

However, it seems to be more than just coincidence that ADD/ADHD symptoms are often shared by the most creative and imaginative among us. Although we come in all shapes and sizes, from introverts to extroverts, both women and men – we're commonly the artists, musicians, filmmakers, writers, entrepreneurs, marketing geniuses, actors, standup comedians, high-tech innovators, medics, sales people, and professional athletes.

Unfortunately, we're also the prison inmates, the homeless, and the addicts – in much higher numbers than in the general population. For us, the line between great success and extreme hardship seems to be gossamer thin, and (if we're honest with ourselves) many of us know this all too well.

Excerpt from an interview with Bono
on the Charlie Rose show:

Charlie Rose: If you didn't do this [music],
what would you do?

Bono: I might be sleeping in a
bag down on the corner.

Charlie: Oh, come on... you'd be teaching, or...

Bono: I'm not messin'! I'm not messin'... I have one of those kinds of personalities that I... I could have gone wrong in my life... I have the energy to run myself into the ground.

I don't know what I would have done. I feel like this band saved my life... I don't feel like I have a choice but to sing.

What accounts for this strange dichotomy? Clearly there's a link between creativity, mastery, and ADD/ADHD. It's also undeniable that this biological package often comes with a generous portion of addiction and depression. A quick jaunt through history, studying the lives of famous artists and innovators, confirms this phenomena. What strange biochemical and genetic concoction could create such enigmatic members of society?

I'm One of You

Since I was a kid, I knew I was going to be an artist of some kind. I loved music, and all of my heroes were creative types. I had countless interests, and would flit from one to another: from music, to computers, to science fiction, to model planes... However, looking back, I had the ability, at quite a young age, to hyperfocus on things I really found interesting. I would go *all in*. I'd be consumed with learning everything about my object of focus. It was borderline obsessive. I know this is a tendency shared by many of us diagnosed with ADD/ADHD.

I could shut the rest of the world out, and just live in my inner world of creative thought and imagination. Childhood was rough, and I did the bare minimum necessary to make it through school. Homework, in particular, was excruciating. Focusing on anything that I didn't find interesting was mentally painful. While I fit many of the classic ADD symptoms, I dodged the Ritalin bullet, mainly because I wasn't excessively hyperactive.

Apart from my creative interests, the rest of life felt barren, gray, and depressing. I was (and still am), hypersensitive and a bit socially awkward. I felt like an alien – some strange being from another planet. I didn't feel equipped to make it in this world. The people around me seemed so different. Deep down, I assumed I was just "messed up" in some peculiar way.

However, in my early teens, when I took up the guitar, my life began to change. I started to feel the respect of my peers. My creative gifts matured as I began to make full use of my unusual tendencies. My college career lasted a total of one month. I felt lost there. The lack of structure, and the specific kind of self-discipline necessary to navigate this world evaded me. I was left with the thought, "what's going to happen to me?" I clearly don't have what it takes to make it in "the real world."

As in many subsequent moments in my life, my creative gifts (the fruits of my distractive/hyperfocus nature) came to the rescue. I met a guy who was making his living as a 3D computer animation artist. The moment I realized that someone could actually *get paid* to do this, that was all I needed to know. I was all in.

I acquired the necessary software, and got down to business. I stayed up into the wee hours of the morning every night immersing myself in this new world. I knew, deep down, "this is something I can get good at." Sure enough, within just a few months, I had put together my animation "demo reel." I shopped it around, and quickly got hired at a video production facility in Southern California. This was the beginning of my career making a living doing what I truly enjoyed.

My "play" became my job.

This was also the first time I really faced my giant. From a mythological perspective, this was the definitive beginning of my journey. I started to see, rather quickly, weak points: consistency, stability, and keeping to my commitments. I had lots of creative juice and talent, but I really struggled with follow-through, and keeping to a schedule I set for myself.

As with many creative professions, my work hours were rather flexible. All that mattered was *I get the project done on time.* For the most part, how I got there was up to me. Similar to my experience with college, the need for a self-imposed schedule was quite challenging. Sometimes I'd miss deadlines, and I'd often get into last-minute marathon work sessions that left me feeling wasted for many days after. Getting sick following these "crunch times" was quite common. Undeniably, the intensity and the stress were lowering my immune system.

I had no choice but to seek out wise counsel. This eventually came in the form of devouring every personal growth and nutrition book I could get my hands on. Making the conscious decision to take better care of my health (both physically and emotionally) was a pivotal decision in my life. The effects of this decision were far-reaching, and started me on a completely different trajectory. Through placing a much stronger emphasis on health and nutrition, I was able to create regular routines that exponentially increased my productivity, providing much needed stability and consistency.

However, this was just the beginning. It has taken me many years, much trial-and-error, countless emotional melt-downs, and immense personal struggles, to arrive at a place of truly understanding how I function. Challenges still occur, but it's much easier to come back to a place of balance because I now have effective systems in place that compensate for my weak points.

Transforming ADD/ADHD, Not "Healing" It

This book is about *transforming* your ADD/ADHD, not healing or curing it. While this may sound like a subtle distinction, I believe having this perception is crucial in making *lasting* positive change. If you were born Scottish, would you want to "heal" yourself of your Scottishness? As I can personally attest to, so much energy can get wasted in seeking out a cure for something that actually just needs to be managed.

The benefits of our specific wiring are intrinsically bound up with our challenges. Remove the one, and you often lose the other. This is a frequent complaint of people who have taken ADD/ADHD medications for long periods of time. They report "not feeling like themselves anymore."

> ## "...he not busy being born is busy dying."
> ## – Bob Dylan

This book is about developing effective strategies and habits that work for you *as you are now.* If we spend our entire life in the "what's wrong with me" mode, we forget to truly live.

Going from ADD/ADHD to Hunter-type

As will be discussed in the following chapter, Thom Hartmann's "hunter-farmer theory" is the most vivid analogy I've come across in describing the many facets of our particular neurological makeup. Throughout most of this book, I use the term "hunter-type" in place of ADD/ADHD – terms only used when referring to symptoms.

From my experience, perceiving yourself from this broader *metaphorical* point-of-view can help in rearranging your "inner furniture" a bit more easily. If you label yourself with having a pathology, it's easy to blame all your problems on the "disorder." Having a more expansive perspective on *why* you may have certain tendencies can offer more of a bird's eye view on your life, possibly assisting you in making good "life decisions," not just "treatment decisions."

A Holistic/Whole Systems Approach to ADD/ADHD

Your life is a series of interlocking, interconnected pieces. Any real transformation can only occur through examining the *whole* picture – seeing the points of intersection, and how these can be ever-so-slightly adjusted to make improvements to your life as a collective unity. This book is written with this perspective in mind. It provides a comprehensive holistic method of transforming ADD/ADHD.

What Will Be Covered

Here's a brief overview of the topics to be covered:

- Why do ADD/ADHD-types tend to be creative, out-of-the-box, individuals? ["Hunter-Farmer Theory" and "Hunter-type Brain" chapters]

- What is it *specifically* about our brain chemistry that makes us unique, and how do we use this information to construct effective daily habits? ["Hunter-type Brain" and "Exercise, Diet, and Supplements" chapters]

- Why are we more prone to addiction? ["Addiction" chapter]

- How do I structure my life in ways that will make me more consistent, energized, and overall more successful. ["Exercise, Diet, and Supplements" and "Creating an Effective Support System" chapters]

- How do the foods I eat affect my mood, ability to focus, and my general brain chemistry? Which foods minimize (or exasperate) ADD/ADHD challenges? ["Exercise, Diet, and Supplements" chapter]

- How can I use technology in an empowering way to make my life more enjoyable and manageable? ["Time Management" and "Tips and Practices" chapters]

- How do I successfully manage my inner life? Which simple practices can I put in place to create day-to-day clarity and emotionally stability? ["Navigating Emotions" chapter]

- How do I make a living as an ADD/ADHD creative type? ["The Creative Life" chapter]

- How do I create an effective support structure, even if I don't have the money to pay for a professional life coach? ["Creating A Support System" chapter]

- What are some simple mindfulness practices that can provide me with greater focus and increase my overall well-being? ["Spirituality" chapter]

- How do I create a "life vision" for myself, and how do I stick with these goals once I've made them? ["Life Visioning" chapter]

- How do I build an effective exercise program that minimizes my ADD/ADHD challenges and maximizes my productivity? How can I motivate myself to stick with it once it's in place? ["Exercise, Diet, and Supplements" chapter]

- Which dietary supplements can I take that minimize my ADD/ADHD challenges, and maximize my productivity and focus? ["Exercise, Diet, and Supplements" chapter]

- How do I create a time management system that is best suited for me and my tendencies – one that assists me in being more proactive, providing a bit more *choice* in my day-to-day life? ["Time Management" chapter]

Who Is This Book For?

This book covers a wide-range of topics and can benefit:

- Anyone diagnosed (or self-identified) with ADD/ADHD.

- Spouses, partners, or parents of those who fall into the ADD/ADHD spectrum, looking for ways to effectively support their loved ones.

- Artists, musicians, entrepreneurs, or anyone whose creativity is their life's passion that also struggle with consistency, structure, self-motivation, and possibly addictive tendencies.

- People taking ADD/ADHD medication (possibly from a young age) who are looking for effective natural alternatives.

How to Use This Book

This book is designed to function in a number of ways. It can be used as a step-by-step guidebook. Read through each chapter, take notes, do the exercises, then begin to integrate the information into your day-to-day life.

It also can be used as a reference book, providing very specific information on diet, nutrition, biochemistry, and support strategies.

You may also find it useful as a kind of divination device. Keep this book by your bedside. Crack it open to a random page and see if it offers up some insight into what life may be throwing at you in the moment.

Primarily, this book is meant to provide you with a *long-term* support strategy. It's not a "quick fix" magical system guaranteed to transform all of your woes. I think we all can agree that life rarely works that way, and most rigid systems will fall by the wayside once they don't pan out in the way they've promised.

Use this information to spark your own creativity and ingenuity. Let it help you build systems that will *last*, and support you in living a more balanced and fulfilled life – the quintessential "Great Mountain."

2

THE HUNTER-FARMER THEORY

Is ADD/ADHD merely a disorder, a dysfunctional condition that affects 10 to 20% of the population? Or is it something else?

The hunter-farmer theory of ADD/ADHD was first proposed by Thom Hartmann in his 1993 book, "Attention Deficit Disorder – A Different Perception."

Up until approximately 10,000 years ago – a blip on the human evolutionary map – human beings needed to be hunters in order to survive. Once agriculture was adopted, the survival landscape shifted. Existence was now predicated upon people staying in one place, doing the same tasks, day-in and day-out, in order to provide for themselves.

Picture this:

> It's 12,000 years ago. The sun is just rising up above the grasslands. In the distance, four buffalo, who've wandered off from their herd, are eating wild grasses and slowly meandering their way eastward.

Armed with spears, you and your hunting party, consisting of five others from your tribe, creep slowly toward the unsuspecting animals. These buffalo are heaving masses of muscle and flesh that could easily trample you to death.

All of your senses are heightened and alert. Nothing else exists in the world but the task at hand. With a slight nod of your head, three of the others move to one side of the herd and start to yell and wave their arms, which frightens one of the buffalo to run *directly towards you.*

You watch with a focused, unwavering gaze as the the giant bull approaches you, running at a clip of 30 miles an hour. At just the precise moment, you throw your spear, which pierces deep into the animal's flesh. Your accomplice also throws his spear, bringing down the beast only a few feet in front of you.

Just then, you notice out of the corner of your eye, another bull is barreling towards you. Quickly, you shift your weight, and dive to one side, barely missing the sharp pointed horns of the animal.

As the dust settles, the hunting party gathers around the fallen animal, thanking it for giving its life to nourish you and your family. You then commence the preparations for bringing it back to your campsite.

This one buffalo provides food for you and the families of your tribe for many days. It also provides fur and leather for clothes and shelter building, and horns for tool making.

Back at the campsite, it's time to rest. It's not even mid-day. The hunt has only taken up part of the morning, but the food provided will last days. The rest of your time is spent in shared ritual, art, toolmaking, and tending to your tribal responsibilities.

Now, let's zoom ahead a few thousands years.

> You're a farmer. You and your family tend two acres of land – growing wheat, barley, beans, and some herbs, with some domesticated livestock. On the outskirts of your land you've planted fruit trees. You wake up at the crack of dawn, just as you've done every day for more years than you can count. After breakfast, you go into the field and begin sowing seeds. It's a long and tedious process, but it provides food for your family.
>
> Countless tasks need to get done by the end of each day. One by one, you go through your daily routine. It's backbreaking work, but by the end of the day, you feel satisfied with what you've accomplished.
>
> What keeps you going is the *vision* of harvest time, when the crops will have matured enough for picking and processing. The fruit trees on the edge of your land may not bear fruit for four or five years. In the meantime you must ensure they are well-watered and not trampled on by animals.

Let's take a closer look at these two very different lifestyles.

The *hunter* requires a very specific set of traits in order to survive and complete the task at hand:

- Hyper-focus for short, intense periods of time.

- An ability to be "distractible" – scanning the horizon for game, or for a potential threat.

- Sensitivity to the surrounding environment – listening for the slightest twig break, or sensing the most infinitesimal movement.

- The capacity to be completely "in the moment."

- Energy output consisting of times of *high energy*, followed by times of relaxation after the hunt.

- Your time horizon is *minutes and seconds*, not months or years.

Whereas the *farmer* requires a nearly opposite set of skills:

- An ability to do the same task day-in and day-out.

- A capacity to maintain focus and *not* get distracted. This translates into having successful crops – which your *very survival* depends upon.

- A steady, day-in and day-out, *even* energy output.

- A time horizon that consists of *months and years*. Rewards happen much slower, and there is a need for always coming back to "the big picture."

Most of our ancestors were farmers, but *all* of our ancestors were hunters. No matter your nationality, or the color of your skin, every human being on the planet is descended from hunter-gatherers.

Simply put, the hunter-farmer theory proposes – people with ADD/ADHD are actually *hunter-types*. We have inherited certain genetic traits and tendencies from our hunter ancestors that would have been positive attributes necessary for survival.

With some awareness, these same traits (which are often labeled "ADD/ADHD" symptoms), can also be extremely valuable in the modern world as well.

Scientific Backing for the Theory

There's a growing body of evidence that appears to validate the hunter-farmer theory of ADD/ADHD. In his most recent book on the subject, "The Edison Gene," Thom Hartmann cites numerous recent scientific studies that lend credence to the theory.

One key point really stands out for me:

Indigenous children from hunter-gatherer cultures still in existence today have statistically higher rates of ADHD than the general population.

A recent study conducted by the University of Alberta in Canada, entitled, "ADHD Characteristics in Canadian Aboriginal Children," concluded:

> "The number of Aboriginal children found to have symptoms associated with ADHD is significantly higher than expected based on prevalence rates in the general population."

Another study found that ADHD rates among children in remote tribes in the Amazon rainforest, between the ages of 7 and 16, were notably higher than in "modern" societies.

As will be discussed in later chapters, mimicking the diet and exercise patterns of hunter-gatherers can be an effective treatment strategy for ADD/ADHD symptoms. All this lends further evidence to the hunter-farmer theory being a potentially accurate *scientific* explanation for ADD/ADHD.

The Hunter-Farmer Theory as a "Working Model"

Whether or not it's proven by science is not of prime importance. The hunter-farmer theory offers a rich and supportive *psychological* model for ADD/ADHD. It places ADD/ADHD challenges within a clear context, and provides a strong direction to move in – from dietary choices, exercise routines, even insights into time management.

> "Everybody is a genius.
> But if you judge a fish by
> its ability to climb a tree,
> it will live its whole life believing
> that it is stupid."
> **– Albert Einstein**

It comes back to this simple point:

> *You can either perceive yourself as "broken,"*
> *or as someone uniquely gifted.*

One perception – the hunter-farmer model – offers the potential for empowerment, self-esteem, and hope. Whereas the model which labels us with a pathology – "Attention Deficit *Disorder*" – relies on finding some kind of cure – something that will somehow "fix" the way we are.

No one would criticize Albert Einstein for not being able to fix a car, or Mozart for his inability to run the four-minute mile. Why should you force yourself into roles and lifestyles that were not created with your unique gifts in mind?

Our Institutions Tend to Favor Farmer-types

With the hunter-farmer theory in mind, it's clear to see that our institutions are typically designed for (and favor) people with more farmer-type tendencies – people who can get up and do the same kinds of tasks day-in and day-out.

This is especially true of our school system, which requires its participants to sit still and pay attention for long periods of time. This environment runs completely counter to the natural inclinations of a hunter-type, who usually prefers movement and *active* learning.

Hunter-Gatherer Societies, Ritual, and Creativity

Let's dig deeper. In studying the hunter-gatherer societies still around today, in places like Indonesia and South America, we find that survival (acquiring food and shelter) occupies a relatively small percentage of time. The rest of the day is spent on art, play, community interaction, and ritual.

This *may* account for why hunter-types tend to gravitate towards the arts. Our brains seem to be hard-wired for this activity over a millennia of repetition.

Female Hunter-types

Hunter-type tendencies are not just limited to males. Many women exhibit hypersensitivity, hyper-creativity, and challenges with distraction and staying focused on a task for extended periods of time, as male hunter-types do.

And contrary to popular belief, it was not uncommon for women in hunter-gatherer societies to be hunters as well. They would typically hunt smaller game, while *also* tending to children, and gathering wild fruits and vegetables as well.

Hunter-types in the Present Day

The modern survival landscape has shifted *dramatically* since the dawn of the industrial age, a mere 250 years ago. "Survival" in modern times has become extremely abstract. We no longer build a shelter somewhere out on large swaths of pristine land, populated by wild animals and free-growing fruit trees and herbs.

Survival now means:

- Find a "job."

- Do some usually repetitive activity – oftentimes for a large organization owned by people you'll never meet.

- Receive pieces of paper that can be *exchanged* for food and shelter. Or even more abstract, money is reduced to just blips on a computer screen that denote "credits" that can be accessed through your ATM card.

We, as a society, now live almost *completely* in the abstract, having successfully divorced ourselves from any vestige of natural living. However, especially for us hunter-types, these ancient modes of being still very much live within us, and still dictate our behaviors.

It's no wonder we hunter-types struggle in the modern world. It takes a great amount of effort to push against our natural tendencies in an effort to pay our bills and feel somewhat "normal" in a society that clearly was not designed with us in mind.

The Wise Means of Survival in the Modern World

For us hunter-types to thrive in the modern world, certain key skills may need to be cultivated in order to have the freedom necessary to carve out a life that is most suited for our natural tendencies. Understanding how to earn money (which directly equates with food, shelter, etc.) – *without* being forced to take a job ill-suited for you – is an essential skill to develop.

Whereas our ancient hunter ancestors required the knowledge of how to track game, build efficient shelters, and know which plants were edible, the wise means of survival in our modern world looks more like:

- Knowing how to market your skills and talents.

- Effective time management techniques.

- Having a basic understanding of business, and how to create income from non-traditional sources (if necessary).

- Knowing how to take your ideas to fruition in ways that bring in *at least* enough money to sustain yourself.

All these will be covered in-depth in later chapters.

Hunter-types in Today's Hyper-connected World

Successful hunter-types are all around us. Scratch below the surface of any innovator, famous artist, or "big thinker", and you'll undoubtedly find someone that has all the classic ADD/ADHD issues:

1. Distractibility

2. Challenge with staying organized

3. Impulsivity

And yet, many have managed to overcome these challenges through good systems, effective support from co-workers, and oftentimes, a keen focus on their physical health.

We live in a hyper-connected world. Now, perhaps more than any other time in history, us hunter-types are needed for developing broad, outside-the-box solutions to the massive problems facing our world today.

Lost in a "Farmer's World"

For many of us hunter-types, school was a challenge. And, for many of us, these past difficulties manifest as low self-esteem well into adulthood. Our self-confidence is further eroded as we struggle to cope with the endless list of mundane day-to-day action items necessary for modern life.

If you're one of the lucky ones, you've managed to maximize your creative gifts to compensate. You may have developed some effective coping mechanisms, and perhaps you have a mate that helps keep life "manageable."

However, there are countless numbers of us who haven't been so fortunate. The tendency to self-medicate in not-so-healthy ways is another method of coping with ADD/ADHD challenges. Unfortunately, these means are rarely satisfying, and can often completely ruin our lives.

Hunter Tendencies Manifest in Different Ways for Different People

Not all hunter-types are hyperactive, outgoing, risk-takers. One can look at the differences between the ADD and ADHD diagnosis from this perspective. Some people, like myself, would fall more in the ADD (versus ADHD) category. I can be hypersensitive, interested in many different things, prone to periods of hyperfocus, sometimes challenged by swings in energy and emotions, but do *not* experience the same levels of hyperactivity that others do. People like me are often most challenged with being *overly* creative, and have to struggle, at times, to move *enough* in a straight line to complete tasks and projects.

Hunters, Adaptation, and Creativity

Creativity, especially to our ancient ancestors, wasn't just a pleasurable experience. It meant having a leg up as a species. Here again, it was about survival.

Our ability, as humans, to be creative – to develop better methods of hunting, harvesting food, and predicting weather patterns and the movement of game – directly supported the species.

Creativity usually involves out-of-the-box thinking, connecting two things together that weren't connected before. Here is where hunter-types clearly show their value to the tribe. An interest in many different subjects (which is often the result of distractibility) leads to a broader perspective, and the potential to connect things together that weren't connected before.

Two other traits – distractibility and risk-taking – are *essential* ingredients necessary for the process of innovation to occur. People *not* willing to do things the same way as everyone else make new discoveries. And this has been true for millennia.

However, if everyone in the population were hunter-types, nothing would ever get done. There would be very little order or structure. So, it would seem, nature keeps only a relatively small number of us in the general population. According to recent studies on ADD/ADHD, this ranges from 10 to 20 percent.

Hunter-types in Our Modern School System

Over the past few years, there has been a gradual, but noticeable shift in public and private schools, exploring new ways of teaching. There is a growing recognition that certain children learn differently than others. Charter schools, Montessori, Waldorf, and numerous other private schools are now finding great success in doing more "experiential" learning. This kind of hands-on education is ideal for hunter-types, potentially establishing effective learning patterns that can last a lifetime. For adults, trade schools can be alternative learning environments where hunter-types thrive.

Hunters Learn By "Doing"

As a general rule, hunter-types tend to do much better with hands-on *experiential* learning. When a task is interesting, the hunter brain can "lock on" to it, often resulting in a tremendous amount of focus.

For me, once I got out of high school and entered college, I felt lost. It wasn't until I started my own business that I began to explore – in detail – exactly how I best learned new things.

I learn by *doing,* and if something is inspiring to me, I will spend countless hours voraciously devouring every aspect of that subject. A good example of this was my experience with learning how to use spreadsheets.

I never took accounting in high school because it sounded mind-numbingly boring. However, when I started my own business, it became essential learning because it directly related to the success of the company.

I dove in headlong. I found it surprisingly interesting – especially given it wasn't a "homework assignment." I could see the *practical application* this skill had in my life, and I was fully engaged in the learning process.

Hunter-types, Domesticated

Genetically speaking, dogs are nearly identical to wolves, from the Chihuahua to the Great Dane. However, the typical modern dog, placed in the wild, would not survive. It relies entirely on humans for its food and shelter.

> **"He's a jaguar lost in a living room, see what he has done."**
> **– Greg Brown,**
> *from the song "Ships"*
> *referring to Elvis Presley*
> *in his later years*

We hunter-types, by the time we're adults, have often become domesticated.

Children who've been branded with the ADHD label tend to have boundless energy, and are still deeply in touch with their *wildness* and vitality. However, over time, as we're forced to "sit still" and rearrange our natural tendencies in order to fit in, we often lose connection with this life-giving wilderness inside us.

Many of us were also medicated out of it. In the short-term, we were more focused and productive, but (as is often reported by people who have been on ADD/ADHD drugs for long periods of time) some part of our core personality gets deadened. As adults, we often have access to only a fraction of that vitality and aliveness we had as children.

⌒

Staying Clear about "The Goal"

Simply replacing the term ADD/ADHD with "hunter-type" is not the goal. It's about taking personal responsibility. There is an inner strength that comes from fully honoring who we are – both our challenges *and* our strengths – accepting the entirety of our being.

Taking some cues from our ancient hunter ancestors, there are some key activities that may help minimize our ADD/ADHD challenges and maximize our gifts:

- Eating a healthy diet, consisting of higher protein and lower carbohydrates.

- Engaging in cardio exercise at regular intervals throughout the week.

- Learning to work in spurts (the hunt).

- Leaning on our creativity (in whatever form it may take) to assist us in earning a good living.

From a broader perspective, I believe one of the greatest gifts we hunter-types can offer the world is *inspiration*. Artists, musicians, actors, entrepreneurs, teachers – in whatever your calling – make it a goal to reconnect yourself to that same aliveness that was *essential* for our ancestors' survival. In the face of immense adversity, they drew upon their innate gifts in order that you could be alive here today.

And, quite literally, their blood still pumps through your veins.

3

AM I A HUNTER-TYPE?

Hunter-types, ADD, and ADHD

If you're able to *name* something, you can examine it in greater detail. It's no longer something nebulous and without form. This is the gift the medical diagnosis of ADD/ADHD has brought to the table. For many of us, the diagnosis of ADD/ADHD provided a good deal of solace. It allowed us to put a name to the challenges we've been facing since we were children.

> "I can guarantee you: I would be immediately diagnosed as a severe case, because being a child (and even as an adult) I pay attention to everything and nothing."
> **– Paulo Coelho**,
> *author of "The Alchemist"*
> *writing about Attention-deficit Disorder*

However, on the downside, the labels "Attention Deficit Disorder (ADD)" and "Attention Deficit Hyperactivity Disorder (ADHD)" are both quite limited in their scope. They may be helpful for physicians in prescribing medication, but they do very little in providing a meaningful lens to see the *entirety* of our unique traits through.

I've met and worked with many successful people who have ADD/ADHD-like traits that would not label themselves as such. They don't feel they have a "disorder," but willingly acknowledge they do things differently. Their success, in the face of their ADD/ADHD challenges, is often the result of:

1. How they've structured their lives.

2. How they perceive themselves.

3. How they take care of their physical health.

This is why I much prefer the term "hunter-type" over ADD/ADHD. This metaphor provides a much broader, higher resolution perspective on a specific neurological type that a very high percentage of artists, entrepreneurs, and great creative minds have shared in common throughout history. It's a psychological (not a medical) model that also offers up some key insights in terms of dietary choices and ways of structuring your life to be more suited to your natural tendencies.

Am I a Hunter-type?

Many of us were diagnosed with ADD (or ADHD) at a young age, while others may be exploring these terms for the first time.

I've put together a simple quiz, based on the common strengths and challenges associated with both ADD/ADHD and this broader idea of a "hunter-type." **This quiz *does not* provide a medical diagnosis of ADD/ADHD**, but *will* let you know if the information in this book could potentially be helpful to you.

Hunter-Type Quiz

In the quiz on the following page, check all statements you feel accurately identify you and your patterns.

Tabulating Your Score

Add up your answers. If you answered "yes" to over 22 questions, you are most likely a "hunter-type" and could benefit from much of the information and exercises in this book.

AM I A HUNTER-TYPE? - QUIZ

☐ I work best in short bursts. Long-term projects are a challenge for me.

☐ I have a very active imagination. I spend a lot of time day-dreaming.

☐ I regularly experience "brain fog." When I try to focus on certain tasks, my thinking gets diffused and muddled.

☐ I get bored easily, and prefer having many different interests. I feel confined if I have to do the same thing over and over again.

☐ I'm spontaneous. I often make impulsive decisions. Sometimes this works out well, but there have been times when the consequences of this behavior caused suffering.

☐ I find it very difficult to motivate myself to complete day-to-day mundane tasks (laundry, paying bills, etc.).

☐ I have a hard time sitting still. I feel my best when I'm moving.

☐ I tend to be sensitive to noise.

☐ I often wait until the very last minute before completing an important task. Then, when I'm in the state of "urgency," the task finally gets done. This is a common occurrence.

☐ I have a consistent challenge with longer-term planning (more than a day or two out). Setting and keeping goals is very difficult for me.

☐ I have a hard time winding down at the end of the day. I tend to stay up late, or need to use food (or drugs) to help me "mellow out."

☐ I've used alcohol or drugs to help me focus. When I'm "under the influence," I can think much clearer and I get more done.

☐ I have a hard time concentrating on someone speaking to me in an environment where other people are talking around me.

☐ I'm a highly creative person. I value creativity over practicality.

☐ I am noticeably cyclical. I have distinct "up times" and "down times" – both on a daily and a weekly basis.

☐ I'm an out-of-the-box, imaginative thinker. I come up with lots of ideas, but I'm often challenged with follow-through. I have numerous projects that I haven't completed.

☐ I'm prone to "blow ups" and "melt downs" in relationship. It's a common pattern.

☐ My thoughts tend to be boundary-less. They all flow together, which can often lead to confusion and overwhelm.

☐ I have a very harsh inner-critic.

☐ I spend countless hours doing things I'm interested in, despite any negative consequences (missing appointments, avoiding important practical concerns, etc.).

- [ ] I've developed at least one skill to a great deal of mastery.

- [ ] When I'm "on," I'm *really* "on." On a good day, my abilities are quite impressive, and others have mentioned this.

- [ ] I often feel overwhelmed.

- [ ] I'm autodidactic – I prefer learning on my own than in a structured learning environment.

- [ ] I tend to float from task to task, completing only the ones that seem interesting to me.

- [ ] I have a challenge with prioritizing and ordering tasks.

- [ ] I think better when I'm moving (walking, driving, etc.).

- [ ] I get many "good ideas" in the shower or on long drives.

- [ ] My home, vehicle, and work space, tend to be in disorder. I have to exert a great deal of effort to keep things clean.

- [ ] I tend to really "burn" on a project – spending lots of time and energy on it – barely resting or eating. Then I crash, and need to "go offline" for a couple of days to sleep and rejuvenate.

- [ ] I'm a good problem solver, and tend to come up with ingenious solutions.

- [ ] I can be a "big picture" person – able to see how things interconnect.

- [ ] I highly value individuality and uniqueness.

- [ ] When I'm on a "low ebb," I struggle with depression.

- [ ] I continually underestimate how long things will take.

- [ ] When I'm "on" I feel energetic and charismatic.

- [ ] I have significant challenges with finances. I've bounced checks, had credit problems, been late paying bills, and have a very hard time making and keeping to a budget.

- [ ] In school, I had/have a hard time completing homework. Keeping with regular study habits has been difficult.

- [ ] My mind is often "racing." I have a hard time shutting it off.

- [ ] Consistency is a big challenge for me.

- [ ] The day after a cardio workout (running, sports, etc.), I find it easier to focus for longer periods of time.

- [ ] I tend to interrupt people, or answer their question before they've finished talking.

- [ ] I've had challenges with addiction (alcohol, drugs, sex addiction, gaming addiction, etc.).

Count up your answers. If you answered "yes" to over 22 questions, you are most likely a hunter-type.

What Is ADD/ADHD?

To have a clearer understanding of what the terms ADD/ADHD actually imply, it's helpful to start with the medical definition.

According to the *DANA Guide To Brain Health:*

> "The label *attention deficit/hyperactivity disorder* (ADHD) refers to a family of chronic neurobiological disorders that interfere with people's capacity to attend to tasks, regulate their activity, and inhibit their behavior in ways appropriate to their ages and circumstances..."

Typically, ADD/ADHD symptoms break out into the following categories:

- Challenges with maintaining focus

- Impulsivity and risk taking behavior

- Hyperactivity

The "Diagnostic and Statistical Manual of Mental Disorders", defines three different types of ADHD:

- Predominantly Inattentive Type

- Predominantly Hyperactive-Impulsive Type

- Combined Type

Basically, these translate to:

- *Predominantly Inattentive Type*
  Distractibility and challenges with focus (ADD)

- *Predominantly Hyperactive-Impulsive Type*
  Challenges with hyperactivity and impulsive behavior (ADHD)

- *Combined Type*
  A combination of both types (ADD/ADHD)

While the terms ADD and ADHD are often used interchangeably, ADHD typically refers to people who have ADD symptoms (challenges with focus) *plus* problems with hyperactivity and impulsiveness.

ADD/ADHD is a symptom-based diagnosis. Meaning, if you are having these specific problems, you fit the diagnosis. As of now, there is no blood test or brain scan used to diagnose ADD/ADHD.

For some people, their ADD/ADHD symptoms are the result of brain damage. By most accounts, these are the minority. Studies have shown that ADD/ADHD is predominantly genetic. It's common for someone with ADD/ADHD symptoms to have at least one parent with the same challenges.

The Shortcomings of the Medical Assessment

While an ADD/ADHD diagnosis may be a good place to start, it does little to point out the many strong suits of people with this particular neurological type.

Also, any reference to ADD/ADHD assumes that our modern way of living is the benchmark for what is "normal." This is a *big* assumption.

> Is it normal to sit in a cubicle (probably with little to no access to direct sunlight) for eight hours a day?

> Is it normal to ingest foods laden with countless foreign chemicals, assuming our body will be able to effectively process them with no loss in focus or impulse control?

> Is it normal to sit still in a classroom environment for long periods of time, staying focused, *and* retaining the bulk of what is being presented?

I would offer, part of the process of transforming your ADD/ADHD challenges begins with a re-perceiving of the world around you, and your engagement with it.

Could there be some specific gifts to how you're "wired" that could potentially benefit the rest of us?

In the following chapter, we'll explore in much more detail, the brain chemical aspects of hunter-types. This information can be used to create a much clearer understanding of what makes us tick, and how to construct an exercise, diet, and supplement plan to maximize our productivity and effectiveness.

This Isn't Something New

The archetype of the scattered genius, the brilliant but disorganized artist (often with alcohol or drug problems) – these are nothing new. History is strewn with obvious examples of hunter-types. These are often people at the top of their field – people who produced new inventions, groundbreaking works of art, or entirely new ways of looking at the world.

> "Rocks in my path? I keep them all.
> With them I shall build my castle."
> **– Nemo Nox**

The Many Facets of a Hunter-Type

To gain a more refined picture of what exactly constitutes a "hunter-type", take a look at the two charts on the following pages that outline the "strengths" and "challenges" of a hunter-type.

Keep in mind, "hunter-type" is a broad category, and you may find yourself identifying with some aspects, while not identifying with others. For example, my challenges lie more in the ADD spectrum. I typically don't have issues with hyperactivity (ADHD).

Identifying Your Strengths and Areas You'd Like To Improve

Based on your quiz results, if you've identified yourself as a "hunter-type", it can be helpful to explore what *specific* areas of your life you'd most like to improve. Identifying your top *strengths* is equally useful. This information can give you a kind of "personal map" to work from as you read through this book.

STRENGTHS & CHALLENGES

Review the items on the quiz you answered "yes" to – both your "Strengths" and "Challenges." On a piece of paper, or on your computer, write out a list of areas in your life you want to improve. This can be something as general as:

"I want to get better at paying my bills on time"

or,

"I'm interested in starting my own business and I really want to optimize my health so I can be more productive and consistent."

Next, make a list of your top five strengths. *Leaning on your strengths* can be a very successful life strategy for us hunter-types. If you only focus on areas you need to improve in, you may lack the confidence to move forward. No one wants to be constantly reminded of their weaknesses. Avoid doing this to yourself.

Once you've completed, look over what you've written. Reference this "personal map" as you review the rest of the information in this book. It will offer you *specific* areas of your life to apply this information to.

STRENGTHS

Creative	Adaptive / Resourceful
Artistic – commonly excel in the arts: writing, music, visual arts, craft and design, etc.	Excellent problem-solvers.
Spontaneous	Flexible – able to change direction quickly when necessary.
Entrepreneurial	Quick thinking – fast on their feet.
Imaginative	Versatile
Often multi-talented.	Skillful at overcoming obstacles by finding an innovative solution.

Imaginative / Nonlinear Thinkers	Adventurous
Talent for conceptualizing.	Continually drawn to investigate new places, ideas, and ways of being.
Capable of seeing the "big picture."	Not contained by societal or conceptual boundaries.
Skilled at brain-storming and generating ideas.	Feel most "alive" exploring new things.
Imaginative – and at their best – visionary.	Not afraid to speak their mind.
Capable of seeing many sides of a situation.	Have many interests.
Able to work on numerous projects at once.	

Initiators	Passionate
Often the founders of new businesses and organizations.	Hard workers – passionate about what they love.
Thinks big, dreams big.	Focused on mastery.
Often leaders in their fields of interest.	Have times of seemingly boundless energy.
Constantly absorbing and integrating new ideas, then shares them with others.	Low tolerance for mediocrity.
	Meticulous attention to detail (in certain areas).

Autodidactic (Self Learners)	Inspirational
Self-directed	Good at motivating and inspiring others.
Learn best "hands-on."	Energetic
Tend to follow their "inner calling" regardless of outward pressures.	Often charismatic.
Drawn to self-study or apprenticeship verses structured learning environments.	High self-esteem when doing what their passionate about.
	Confident in their areas of expertise.
	Can excel in certain leadership roles.

STRENGTHS

Socially Adaptive	Empathic
Relate to many different types of people.	Compassionate
Make new acquaintances easily.	Make good mentors.
Often excel at sales and customer relations.	Sensitive to the well being of others.
Fun to be around.	Often drawn towards service and "big picture" causes.
Good conversationalists.	
Tend to have good people skills and sense of humor.	

Intuitive	Comfortable With "Big" Challenges
Capable of following their "gut" intuition to successful outcomes.	Capable of taking on large situations.
Can feel a connection to something "bigger than themselves."	Good in a crisis and emergency situations.
Often drawn to matters of the spirit.	Not afraid to take action.
	Can be a stabilizing presence during difficult situations.

CHALLENGES

Focus

Struggle with sustaining attention on a task for extended periods of time.

Mundane tasks (paying bills, opening the mail, etc.) can feel overwhelming. These tasks are often the objects of procrastination, in spite of unwanted consequences.

Tendency to daydream and "zone out."

Highly distractible, especially in environments with lots of movement or noise.

Difficulty following directions.

Challenge with maintaining focus on the person who is talking to you, especially in a noisy or distractible environment.

"Caught" by Stimuli

Complete absorption in stimulating experiences (watching TV, using the internet, video games) for hours at a time.

This occurs to the point where the results are detrimental to health, relationships, work, etc.

There is a seeming inability to pull yourself away from the object of stimulation, even though there is a desire to do so.

Disorganization

An overall challenge staying organized (home, work, etc.)

Work space, home, car, are cluttered and messy.

Challenge with prioritizing tasks.

Continually late for appointments.

Consistently losing or misplacing items.

Follow-through / Completion

Have many projects going at once, but few actually getting done.

Moving from one task or project to the next without completing the previous one.

Challenge completing a project when it no longer feels interesting or stimulating.

"Fluid" Perception of Time

Continually underestimating how long tasks will take.

Long-term planning can be immensely challenging (anything beyond a week or two ahead).

Procrastination

Continually putting off tasks (especially mundane tasks) until the very last minute.

When a task becomes "urgent," it finally gets done.

Impulsiveness

Recklessness – acting before considering the potential negative consequences of the action.

Blurting out things in conversation that others consider "insensitive" or "inappropriate."

Continually interrupts others during a conversation.

Hyperactivity

Gets bored easily.

Tendency to feel restless.

Mind is always racing.

Continual craving for stimulation and excitement.

CHALLENGES

Emotional

Chronic low-self esteem based on perceived underachievement.

Easily stressed-out.

Can easily go into overwhelm.

Regular mood swings, often quite pronounced.

Challenge with maintaining consistency – wake up in the morning feeling completely different than the day before. Intentions from previous day feel completely inaccessible in the moment.

Difficulty staying motivated.

Explosive temper (have a "short fuse").

Relationship Problems

Unconscious tendency to create drama.

Prone to infidelity.

Challenge with listening to partner when they're talking.

Seemingly small problems in relationship blow up into major arguments.

Codependent tendencies.

Addiction

Overall tendency towards addiction.

Substance abuse.

Compulsive eating / sugar addiction (possibly leading to obesity and other health problems).

Addiction to extreme behaviors (adrenaline junky, sex addiction, etc.)

Addiction to mentally stimulating experiences (video game addiction, internet addiction, etc.)

Work Life

Challenge with keeping a job that requires regular hours and repetitive tasks.

Difficulty following directions.

Continually miss work deadlines.

Challenges with follow-through.

Poor organization, and disorder of work space.

Financial

Credit Problems.

Challenge paying bills on time.

Continual late fees, parking tickets, etc.

Bounces checks regularly.

Feel overwhelmed by financial matters in general, especially the little details.

School

Easily distracted in class.

Challenge paying attention to the teacher.

Inability to complete homework, or maintain effective study habits.

Feel overwhelmed in unstructured learning environments that require self-discipline and personal organization.

Sensitivity

Irritability to noise.

Hypersensitivity to environment.

Difficulty working in noisy or distracting environments.

Moving Forward

Knowing you have unique challenges, possibly not shared by the people around you, is essential. However, *identifying* yourself with these challenges, without seeing the many benefits that go with them, may not be the most empowering strategy.

In moving forward, I encourage you to explore the concept of "hunter-type" in more detail. While it may not be a perfect model, it can go a long way in expanding your awareness of how best to navigate your life, taking into account your strengths, while offering *numerous* ways of minimizing potential weak points.

HUMAN BRAIN.

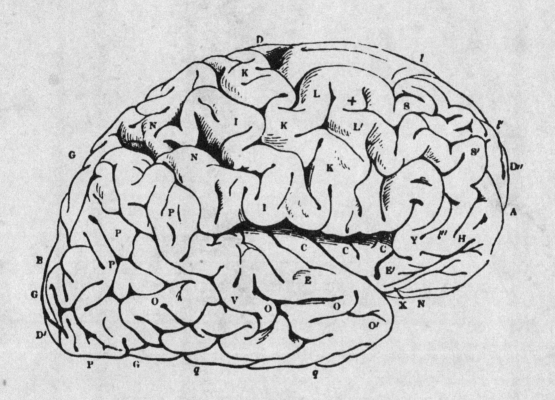

4

THE HUNTER-TYPE BRAIN

To gain a clearer understanding of "what makes us tick" as hunter-types, it's important to look at what's happening under the hood – namely, how our brain may be functioning differently than other people.

While the hunter-farmer theory is a good starting point for re-perceiving your ADD/ADHD challenges, understanding a bit about brain chemistry can provide you with more *accuracy* when implementing the specific strategies discussed later in the book.

With a deeper understanding of how your brain is functioning, you'll feel far more in control of your life. For example, when you're feeling lethargic and scattered, you'll know you're not just "being lazy," there's something happening – biochemically – that has led to your current mental/emotional state. You'll then be able to take some decisive actions towards getting yourself going again.

This chapter includes information based on some of the latest findings in brain research. As time goes on, science may make new discoveries, or fine-tune a few of these points. However, the basic principles discussed can provide a good foundation to work from.

NEUROTRANSMITTERS – YOUR BRAIN'S ELECTRICAL SYSTEM

The first step in our journey of exploring the "hunter-type brain" starts with getting a basic understanding of neurotransmitters.

Neurotransmitters are the brain's circuitry – carrying all of our thoughts and emotions through vast neural networks. They are literally the "wires" that transmit electrical signals throughout the brain – storing memories, processing endless visual and auditory signals, and making up the very core of thought and perception.

There are two neurotransmitters that are *primary* in affecting mood, focus, and motivation: dopamine and serotonin. There are numerous others, but these are the two that seem to impact us hunter-types the most.

Dopamine: Focus, Motivation, and Learning

Dopamine, in many ways, is what rules the modern world. And it's at the very root of what we call "desire."

Dopamine levels in your brain, to a very large degree, dictate: *focus*, *motivation*, and *learning*.

For starters, your brain needs an adequate level of dopamine in your frontal lobe in order to focus on a thought for an extended period of time. Dopamine also motivates us to "take action" – from something as simple as getting off the couch, to the self-discipline required to study for a test, or rehearse two hours for an upcoming play. Dopamine is wired into our deepest centers of physical motion, and this relationship is ancient.

When you are low in dopamine, you can feel fuzzy, muddled, and unmotivated.

If a task or idea is "interesting," it stimulates a small release of dopamine – which, in turn, increases our ability to focus on it. However, if a task or thought is not stimulating, it can be extremely difficult to access the focus necessary to stay with it for any length of time.

In this way, dopamine affects our very thought patterns. Especially when our dopamine levels are low, our brain is drawn to those thoughts that stimulate dopamine. Therefore, the influence dopamine exerts on our lives is truly astounding.

The Big Question

So, what is it *specifically* about our brains (as hunter-types) that makes us predisposed to:

- Creativity

- Impulsiveness, restlessness, and risk-taking

- Challenges with focus for longer periods of time

- An ability to hyperfocus on tasks we find interesting and engaging

- Challenges with being consistent

- Addictions and addictive behaviors

And, why is it that countless famous artists, musicians, inventors, entrepreneurs, and writers, all seem to share these common ADD/ADHD traits?

What Makes Us Unique — Lower Levels of Dopamine

Based on all of the current scientific evidence, ADD/ADHD symptoms are primarily the result of genetically lower levels of dopamine. Other brain chemicals (such as norepinephrine) also play a role, but lower levels of dopamine most accurately correspond to ADD/ADHD challenges. Recent studies may indicate we have less dopamine *receptors*, so we require more dopamine to achieve the same results. As will be discussed, this condition also provides us with some hidden benefits as well.

The culprit appears to be a variation in a specific gene that determines dopamine functioning in the brain – the DRD4 gene (the so-called "adventure gene"). Because this tendency is genetic, it gets passed down from generation to generation.

This would account for our challenges with focus, but what about hyperactivity? How would a brain with lower levels of dopamine have given us a survival "leg up" in our ancient hunter-gatherer past? And how could this condition possibly be of benefit to us now?

On-board Dopamine vs "Stimulated" Dopamine

Consider the difference between these two brain states:

> 1. Stable and *more even* dopamine levels.

> 2. Lower levels of dopamine that push us to seek out "stimulation" as a means of triggering a dopamine release.

Going back to the hunter-farmer model...

A "farmer-type" is someone with a *more even* temperament – someone that can get up and do the same kinds of tasks day-in and day-out. They, most likely, have *higher* overall levels of dopamine – enough for them to maintain focus on a task for longer periods of time. These people would not be predisposed to look *externally* for stimulation to trigger a dopamine release. Their glass is already full.

Whereas a hunter-type, because we have *lower* levels of dopamine, will be drawn to seek out stimulation as an unconscious means of increasing our dopamine levels.

The Potential Benefits of Lower Dopamine Levels

Recent studies have shown that the specific variation of the DRD4 gene that contributes to lower levels of dopamine occurred less than 40,000 years ago. It was a gene mutation that, because it may have provided a survival advantage, was perpetuated by natural selection.

Let's revisit the lifestyle and needs our ancient hunter ancestors. In order for the tribe to survive and flourish, someone needed to go out and hunt for food. The bigger the game animal, the more food for the tribe.

If there were people in the tribe that had naturally lower levels of dopamine, these people would be drawn to high-stimulation activities. They would be restless. Something like "the hunt" –

DOPAMINE RELEASE GRAPH

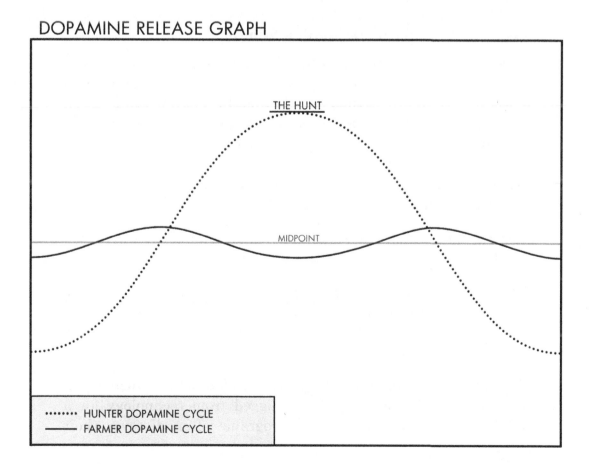

THE HUNT

MIDPOINT

•••••• HUNTER DOPAMINE CYCLE
—— FARMER DOPAMINE CYCLE

especially going after larger game animals – would be the stimulation they required to raise their dopamine levels.

Therefore, low dopamine could have directly translated into: *successful hunters.*

These would be people in the tribe that were of great value. It would also make them attractive mates. This gene would then get passed down through natural selection. This condition of low dopamine may also have made these people more drawn to procreation (another dopamine releasing activity), further spreading the gene into the collective gene pool.

A farmer-type, with higher levels of dopamine in their brain, would not be so restless, and not so drawn to place themselves in potentially life-threatening situations.

Creative Thought as Dopamine Stimuli

However, external stimuli is not the only thing that can trigger a dopamine release. Our *thoughts* can also do this – specifically, novel or "stimulating" thoughts. It would seem our brain, in an effort to stabilize our dopamine levels (and in the absence of external stimulation) will be drawn to creative thought-patterns. If a thought arises that is interesting or "unique," this triggers a small release of dopamine, allowing us to stay with it, and expand on it.

If we're not stimulated by an activity, or something *externally*, our brain seems to be drawn to conjuring something *internally*.

This could account for why people with ADD/ADHD tend to be creatively predisposed. This could also explain our tendency to hyperfocus, staying with an engaging activity for many hours, barely noticing the time pass.

Similarly, it's common for people to report a notable increase in their creativity once they've unplugged from technology for a few days. Patients in recovery programs often discover their new-found sobriety leads them to being *even more creative* than when they were addicts. The brain is still left with a condition it has to contend with, and takes a different tack.

It's this "pressure to normalize" dopamine levels that seems to be a determining factor in why people diagnosed with ADD/ADHD may be predetermined to be "creative." And this is most likely the result of one of nature's key processes at work – *homeostasis*.

All living systems find equilibrium through homeostasis. Just as your body seeks to normalize its temperature at 98.6° Fahrenheit (37°C), so too (it would seem) does our brain continually attempt to raise its dopamine levels to a certain predetermined level.

Low Dopamine, Restlessness, Stimulation Seeking, and Innovation

Restlessness not only makes us hunter-types more prone to risk-taking, it also creates the conditions for us to be *inventive*. Because our brain is seeking out stimulation to raise dopamine levels, "trying new things" is one effective tactic for doing this.

Both for our ancient ancestors, and in modern life, "trying new things" is the basis of any new innovation. It's the fertile ground from which new and better ways of doing things emerge.

In our modern world, this is where our genetic predisposition can (and has) led us hunter-types into roles as visionaries and innovators. Spending a little time examining the lives of people known for their creativity, you'll find a large percentage of them have all the classic ADD/ADHD challenges.

However, if we stay caught in addictive behaviors that monopolize all of our time and energy – if we're constantly stuck in self-destructive patterns – we'll never experience the conditions necessary for this inventiveness to fully emerge.

Symptoms of Low Dopamine and Other Causes

Our brain is in a constant state of transformation. Neurotransmitters levels ebb and flow like the tides. Therefore, there are times when our brain has higher or lower levels of dopamine (and other brain chemicals) depending on factors such as diet, exercise, and chemicals we put into our bodies.

When we're in a lower dopamine state, our ability to focus on our environment, or to "lock on" to tasks, activities, and even conversations, gets impaired. Lower levels of dopamine can make concentration and focus quite difficult, and when we're *really* low in dopamine for extended periods of time, it may also trigger depressive states.

Specifically, the hallmarks of low dopamine are:

- Distractibility

- Impulsivity and hyperactivity

- Challenge with maintaining focus

- Feeling overwhelmed

- Lethargy and low motivation

However, because everyone's brain is unique, some hunter-types, when low in dopamine, lean more towards states of lethargy and low motivation, and not necessarily towards hyperactivity.

Besides a genetic predisposition to lower levels of dopamine, other factors can also deplete dopamine:

- Poor nutrition and diet

- Stress

- Drug abuse

- Long periods of hyper-stimulation

- Lack of sleep

Impulse Control and Low Dopamine

"Lack of impulse control" is another main component of the ADHD diagnosis. This refers to the seeming inability, at certain times, to stop engaging in an activity we don't want to be engaged in. It can be something as benign as not being able to get up from watching TV when you have other things to do, to the extreme of chemical addiction.

I'm sure you're familiar with the experience of watching a television program for a few hours and, in your mind, you are screaming "I really need to get up now!" But, you just can't seem to *will* yourself to do it. Low dopamine levels are most likely to blame.

"Getting Caught" by External Stimuli in the Modern World

The condition of "lower dopamine levels" is a double-edged sword. On the one hand, it has the potential to make us hunter-types more creative and willing to take risks that others would not. On the other hand, it leaves us *wide open* to be caught by external stimuli.

Today's world is defined by excessive external stimulation: movies, video games, the internet (including internet porn), smart phones, etc... It's no wonder why hunter-types are so prone to being caught in addictive behaviors.

We hunter-types know *painfully well* how challenging it can be to tear ourselves away from something we find externally stimulating. And this can often lead us down some pretty dark alleyways. If not all-out "life ruining," they are at least the source of shame and endless frustration.

Here's the key:

By keeping your on-board levels of dopamine up, you are less susceptible to "getting caught" by external stimuli.

This is the basis for nearly all of the recommendations contained in the chapter on Exercise, Diet, and Supplements. The goal is to incorporate healthy *ongoing* habits and practices that keep your dopamine levels up, while still allowing you access to your innate creative tendencies.

Serotonin – The "Good Mood" Neurotransmitter

Serotonin is another key neurotransmitter that can exert a powerful influence on us hunter-types.

Serotonin affects *overall* mood. If your serotonin levels are reasonably *up*, you'll feel happy and have an overall sense of well-being.

When serotonin levels are low, the results can be:

- Depression

- Anxiety

- Chronic fatigue (feeling "warn out" even if you're getting proper sleep)

- Dark moods

- Disrupted sleep schedule

- Tendency to be socially withdrawn

- Trouble concentrating

- An obsession on negative thoughts and painful memories

- "Evil thoughts" (thoughts of harming someone)

- Escape fantasies

- Dramatic and urgent "need-for-change" episodes

When serotonin levels are low, normal personality traits may become exaggerated. Penny-pitchers become obsessed with saving money. Perfectionists become obsessed with cleaning.

Not surprisingly, low serotonin is also one of the root components of Obsessive Compulsive Disorder (OCD). OCD medication usually focuses on raising serotonin levels.

Low dopamine and low serotonin often go hand-in-hand – and are often the result of a less-than-optimum diet and exercise routine.

Anti-depressants are usually designed to raise serotonin levels – unfortunately, they can also have countless side effects. I've personally watched good friends go through extreme emotional suffering as the result of poorly prescribed anti-depressants.

Most of us have seen the TV commercials for anti-depressants that involve five seconds of product promotion, and 25 seconds of warnings. More importantly, anti-depressants *never* address the nutrient deficiencies that are *often* at the root of depression.

We'll go further into healthy ways of maintaining balanced serotonin levels in the Exercise, Diet, and Supplements chapter later in the book.

It's About <u>Effectiveness</u>

Admittedly, this discussion of neurotransmitters contains oversimplifications. The complicated and interconnected cascade of brain chemicals we experience on a daily basis is virtually impossible to grasp in its entirety. Science is still in its infancy in fully understanding the intricacies of the human brain.

Furthermore, as mentioned in the previous chapter, the hunter-farmer theory is still just a *theory*. It has yet to be fully validated by science. However, the goal is not to learn endless facts and statistics about your brain, it's about having a basic conceptual model to work with.

For example, when you are feeling lethargic and unable to focus, you may say to yourself:

> "OK, I'm probably low in dopamine right now. When was the last time I exercised? Am I getting enough protein? What steps can I take *right now* to remedy this situation?"

Or, if you're feeling hyper-creative but a bit scattered, you may decide to just capture your ideas (notes, audio recording, etc.), but not try to sculpt them into anything *in this moment*. Perhaps you'll decide to come back later – when you're feeling clearer and nutritionally fortified – to flesh out your ideas in a more linear fashion.

Having a basic knowledge of neurotransmitters can go a long way in making your life more manageable. It can give you something to grab hold of in times when you're scrambling to pull yourself back up again.

It's all about *effectiveness,* acquiring the information you'll need to construct a lifestyle that really works for you.

FOOD, EXERCISE, AND THE BRAIN

Now that we have a basic understanding of the effects that neurotransmitters (like dopamine) have on our ability to focus and stay motivated, let's explore how these "electrical circuits" are actually *manufactured* by our body.

If you're like me, and your high school biology lessons have long slipped out of your memory circuits – here's a little refresher course.

Any protein source you ingest, be it meats, eggs, beans, or seeds, are made up of *amino acids* – which are the building blocks of all living things. The first flickers of life in the primordial ooze at the dawn of time started with amino acids.

During digestion, your body breaks down proteins into their core components – amino acids – and distributes them where they are most needed. And *specific* amino acids are needed to build and maintain *specific* parts of the body.

In the case of dopamine production, the amino acid is *l-tyrosine*, while *l-tryptophan* is needed for the body to generate a proper supply of serotonin.

So, if your body is not getting an ample supply of good protein, it literally doesn't have the materials it needs to generate the neurotransmitters required for focus, motivation, and well-being.

But that's not the whole story.

There are foods that can severely *hamper* your body's ability to generate these much needed brain chemicals. Even if you *are* eating enough protein, you could still be markedly deficient in essential brain chemicals.

More about this in the Exercise, Diet, and Supplements chapter.

Our Ancient Hunter-Brain in the Modern World

Over the past three million years, the human brain has gradually evolved to optimize its growth and functioning, fueled by foods found in the local environment. It has, for example, established complex neural communication systems based on *enzymes*, derived from wild vegetables, plants, fruits, and nuts. And its very structure is built from proteins and fats – again, all derived from foods in our immediate surroundings.

Zoom ahead to the advent of agriculture – which introduced grains (carbohydrates) into the human diet – a mere 10,000 years ago. Its "recent" addition to the human diet may explain why grain-related food-allergies (gluten intolerance) are quite common. Ten thousand years, a seemingly vast stretch of time, apparently wasn't long enough for our bodies to fully adapt to this new food supply.

And it has only been in the past **50 years** or so that our human diet experienced the **most dramatic change it has ever gone through**.

Our modern diet is now *loaded* with refined sugars, trans-fats, and a host of man-made chemicals. Our body (and especially our brains) haven't had *nearly* enough time to adapt to this new diet.

It's no wonder that cancer, diabetes, severe depression, wild fluctuations in energy and focus, addiction, and a whole host of other chronic modern ailments, are the result. The intricate, finely-tuned, *sensitive* systems of the body were not meant for these kinds of foreign and exaggerated chemical inputs.

Our brain requires and *yearns* for the foods it has evolved to utilize through the many thousands of years we lived as hunter-gatherers.

The Long and Short of It

If your diet consists primarily of carbohydrates and sweets (like white breads, potato chips, pastries, french fries, etc.), you are most likely *starving* your body of the building materials it needs to create essential neurotransmitters like dopamine and serotonin. The result of which are magnified ADD/ADHD symptoms, depression, and a whole host of other psychological and physiological challenges.

Hunter-Types and Sensitivity to Food

By all accounts, we hunter-types are *far more sensitive* to diet than farmer-types. This means small alterations to our diet can have quite dramatic effects, in either the positive or the negative. We'll go into the specifics of this in the "Exercise, Diet, and Supplements" chapter.

Medications and Neurotransmitters

So, where do medications fit into all of this?

Most pharmaceuticals designed to treat ADD/ADHD and depression are geared directly at dopamine (ADD/ADHD) and serotonin (depression).

In fact, nearly *all* ADHD medications are stimulants of one kind or another. Although some find them helpful, there can be side effects. If you've been taking ADD/ADHD medications for any length of time you are probably familiar with some of them.

While pharmaceuticals may be effective for some people, they can mask the underlying nutrient deficiencies that may be intensifying ADD/ADHD symptoms.

Wrapping Up

You now have a general understanding of what makes our brain chemistry (as a hunter-type) unique. With this basic knowledge, you'll have greater insight into how the support systems – discussed in later chapters – actually work. Not only will you be targeting root causes, you'll most likely become healthier in the process.

You'll have multiple strategies at your disposal. It will be clear to you why regular cardio exercise, a high-protein/low-carbohydrate diet, and taking certain supplements, can positively affect your mood and ability to focus. You'll be able to construct a routine that's reliable, predictable, and integrates seamlessly with your lifestyle – without concerns of negative side effects or medications losing their effectiveness over time.

5

ADD/ADHD AND ADDICTION

Connection between ADD/ADHD and Addiction

According to recent studies, people diagnosed with ADD/ADHD are more likely to experience addiction. How likely? Researchers estimate 30 to 50% of people with ADD/ADHD use drugs and alcohol to self-medicate their ADHD symptoms.

"I have woven a parachute out of everything broken."
– William Stafford

That's a staggering statistic. Couple this with another study that suggests that close to 50% of the people currently in US prisons are ADD/ADHD, and a picture begins to emerge that we hunter-types were dealt some very clear challenges with addiction.

And it's not just drug abuse, addiction can take numerous forms: food addiction, gambling addiction, video game addiction, sex addiction – the list goes on and on.

Which begs the question, what exactly *is* addiction?

What Is Addiction?

The definition of addiction has changed over the years.

> *addiction*: the state of being enslaved to a habit or practice or to something that is psychologically or physically habit-forming, as narcotics, to such an extent that its cessation causes severe trauma.

Simply put, an addiction is any activity that:

1. You have an inability to stop yourself from doing.

2. Has consistent negative repercussions on your life (health, relationships, sense of well-being, etc.).

Addictions can be *either* substance *or* behavior-related.

The "American Society of Addiction Medicine" describes addiction as, "a primary, chronic disease of brain reward, motivation, memory and related circuitry."

And all forms of addiction seem to move in very predictable stages:

1. Binging

2. Withdrawal

3. Craving

4. Relapse

5. Sensitization – more needed to get the same effect.

UNDERSTANDING ADD/ADHD & ADDICTION

Why Are Hunter-Types More Prone to Addiction?

The big question is – why are hunter-types (people diagnosed with ADD/ADHD) more prone to addiction than the rest of the population?

Once again, all signs point to dopamine.

Although scientists have known for quite some time that dopamine was somehow related to addiction, it wasn't until recently that researchers began to name it as one of the *primary* components in nearly all types of addiction.

According to the "dopamine hypothesis," *any* substance or activity that stimulates the brain to release excessive amounts of dopamine has the potential for becoming an addiction.

However, this alone doesn't explain why certain people can participate in the *exact same* behaviors, ingest the *exact same* substances, and not acquire an addiction. What makes hunter-types more susceptible?

Lower Levels of Dopamine, Addiction, and the "Survival Brain"

As discussed in the previous chapter, hunter-types are genetically predisposed to lower levels of dopamine. This particular aspect of our biochemistry (which is likely responsible for our increased creative abilities), also leaves us vulnerable to addiction.

Above all else, the human brain is wired for survival. It has evolved very specific means for identifying those substances in the environment (and activities) that would most give us a "leg up" on our competition and help propagate the species.

DOPAMINE RELEASE GRAPH

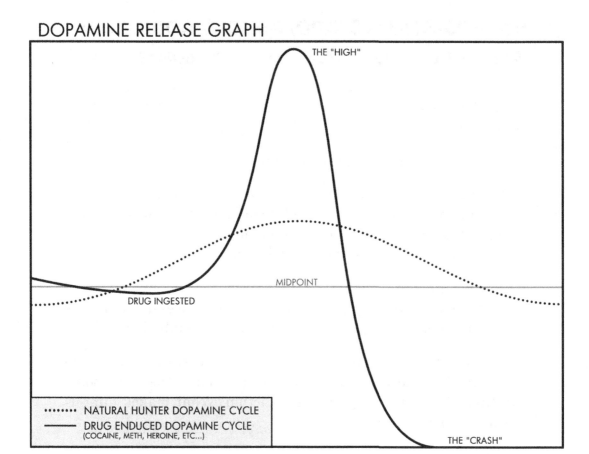

When a hunter-type ingests a substance that causes the brain to release very large amounts of dopamine, producing greater mental clarity, alertness, and energy, this survival mechanism kicks in and notes:

> "This substance is amazing! This clearly improves my functioning and potential for survival. This new substance is now *essential,* and must be found and ingested *regularly.*"

And thus, addiction begins. An association between the improved mental state and the substance (or activity) gets forged. Craving begins. And it's this craving that perpetuates the addiction.

In prehistoric times, this survival mechanism functioned brilliantly to make us the most dominant and adept species on the planet. However, in our modern world, it can be deadly.

An understanding of this primal biological process goes a long way to explain why people will completely destroy their lives to acquire substances they are addicted to. Their addiction is wired at the level of *survival*.

Take, for example, someone addicted to a methamphetamine like "crystal meth." Their brain has made the same association with it as it has with water or air. It believes it's *essential* for survival.

From the outside, we may look at this person and think they are just lacking in willpower – behaving completely irrationally. In fact, they are experiencing the same kind of urgency you would feel if someone denied you air or water. You would do *whatever it takes* to get them, because your life was on the line.

Self-Medicating through an Addiction

When dopamine levels are low, accomplishing mundane day-to-day tasks – maintaining focus for any length of time – can be extremely challenging.

"We, who control our feelings, who avoid conflicts at all costs, or seem to seek them – who are hypersensitive, self-critical, compulsive, workaholic, and above all, survivors. We're not that way from perversity, and we can not just *relax and let it go*. We've learned to cope in ways you never had to."
– Piers Anthony

By ingesting a chemical that induces dopamine (anything from alcohol, to cocaine, to crystal meth), a person can have a window of time where they *can* focus and be productive.

Unfortunately, this strategy is only a short-term solution, with very long-term consequences.

Low dopamine can also cause depression. Many hunter-types who abuse substances do so because, when they are high, they can feel "normal" for a time.

Addiction can be one of the deepest, darkest realms of human suffering. Having a clearer understanding of the underlying bio-mechanics can potentially assist the recovery process significantly.

Why Recovery Programs Often Fail for Hunter-Types

The "twelve step process" has helped countless thousands of people get sober since its founding in 1935 by Bill Wilson and Dr. Bob Smith. It is a shining example of what a clear program, focused on effective emotional support, can offer in terms of recovery.

Sadly, most recovery programs report a rather low recovery rate. Although studies differ, it usually hovers around 20%. That means at least 80% of the people in these recovery programs will relapse.

There are two factors that *may* play into this, as it relates to us hunter-types:

> 1. Most recovery programs don't take into account the "self-medicating" aspect of drugs and alcohol for people suffering ADD/ADHD symptoms.

> 2. There is little-to-no focus placed on nutrition and the underlying factors that made the person originally predisposed to the addiction in the first place.

One of the key motivations for writing this book came after speaking with a relative who has been struggling with alcoholism most of his adult life. After spending some time with him, it became very clear that he is a classic hunter-type with clearly defined ADHD challenges. He had been in and out of recovery programs for years, with no lasting effect.

An "a ha" moment came when he told me, "when I drink, I can think clearly. I can function. When I don't drink, my brain is fuzzy and can't seem to accomplish day-to-day tasks, or focus on what's in front of me. As soon as I drink, I'm a different person."

Once I heard this, it occurred to me that countless hunter-types must be experiencing the exact same thing – going in and out of rehab, to no avail. And, even if they *do* become sober, they are still left with a chronic need for support for their ADD/ADHD challenges, which recovery programs rarely (if ever) provide.

This led me on a quest to see if there were any recovery programs that addressed the *biochemical* aspects of addiction, and whether or not they had a higher success rate.

TREATMENT

Amino Acid Therapy and Nutritional Support in Recovery

While numerous recovery programs incorporate nutritional support, amino acid therapy in particular seems to address, most directly, the core deficiencies involved with "the addicted brain."

The premise of amino acid therapy is simple: replace the addictive substance (or behavior) with the nutritional support the brain needs to function optimally, ideally minimizing cravings and speeding up recovery time.

Julia Ross is a pioneer in the area of "nutritional psychology." With over 20 years experience utilizing amino acid therapy to treat addiction, she has thoroughly documented the beneficial effects of nutritional support in the recovery process. Her work illustrates that nutrition and proper supplementation are potentially the "missing links" in recovery programs.

In her book, "The Mood Cure," she outlines a very specific nutritional support plan, involving both a change in diet, and incorporating specific supplements that support brain health – supplements that can be purchased from any local vitamin or health food store.

The book is comprehensive, and I believe is invaluable reading for anyone in the recovery process. Much of the diet and supplement suggestions later in this book were based on Julia's work, because they target specific deficiencies common in ADD/ADHD.

The Role of Diet in Recovery

According to Julia, the role of proper nutrition during recovery can not be overstated. If you are not feeding your brain what it needs to function properly, it can only increase the craving for the addictive substance or behavior.

As will be discussed later in the "Exercise, Diet, and Supplements" chapter, there are two aspects of a daily eating plan that should be emphasized:

- Protein (amino acids)
- Essential Fatty Acids (omega-3)

In the case of alcoholism, stabilizing blood sugar is a primary component in reducing cravings. Supplements like chromium and glutamine are well known nutritional "assistants" during alcohol recovery.

Removing substances from your diet that deplete your brain of key neurotransmitters is equally important. In particular, refined sugars and white starches should be *completely* eliminated, especially during recovery. It's unfortunate that most 12-step meetings serve coffee and donuts, as these substances are at the very top of the "do not eat list."

A high-protein, low carbohydrate diet for anyone in recovery can be pivotal in providing the nutritional groundwork in reducing cravings, balancing blood sugar, and producing greater mental clarity.

A More Holistic Treatment Plan

Whatever the addiction, be it substance or behavioral, hunter-types require a specific support protocol. If provided, it may go a long way in making recovery more effective and less grueling.

An effective recovery program for hunter-types could look like:

- A clear understanding of our unique brain chemistry, especially our tendency to have lower dopamine levels (see previous chapter).

- Diet and supplement support for addressing underlying deficiencies and improving overall brain health.

- Specific support for dealing with day-to-day ADD/ADHD challenges.

One of my initial intentions for this book was to provide useful information for someone in recovery who *also* experiences ADD/ADHD related challenges. In addition to the "Exercise, Diet, and Supplements" chapter, the material contained in the "Navigating Emotions" chapter can be helpful in addressing some of the emotional challenges that may occur during recovery.

The "Life Visioning" chapter provides some practical tools for goal setting – potentially offering some much-needed inspiration during the recovery process.

The Importance of Recovery Programs

Recovery programs are *essential* in the process of rehabilitation. Most people, depending on the nature of the addiction, are literally incapable of overcoming the cravings on their own.

As discussed earlier, addiction gets woven into the part of our brain connected with survival. Often, there is no amount of willpower that can overcome the intense cravings because the core mechanism that controls motivation has been hijacked by the addictive substance or behavior.

A 12-step program, coupled with good nutritional and ADD/ADHD-specific support, can be a winning combination.

Moving Forward

Although hunter-types may be more prone to addiction – with a clear understanding of the biochemical dynamics at play behind the scenes – preventing addiction *and* lasting recovery are both possible.

I encourage you to further explore the ideas and materials mentioned, and share them with anyone you know who may benefit.

	Courses	Do Lat & Long in	Bearings & Dist at Noon
	East NE	63.48.N	Gorgona S S W
			Hor 3 Leagues
			Cape De Mila
27	W Vble NW	43.51.N	West 12 Leagues
			Maham
28	Vble SE Vble	42.16.N 78.2.E	Maham NbW N½W 2½ Leagues
Tuesday 29	NE Vble Calm	N½W 21 42.2½ N 7 42 E	Maham S4°W 4½ Leagues
Wednesday 30	Vble NE Vble	N½W 81 41.16.N E 42 E	Mahon S78W
31	Vble NbE		Mount NEN 8 or 9 Le
Saturday 1	NbE WbN North		Maho NNW Le or mile Single of
Sunday 2	Vble		Maho Cape NE
Monday 3	West Vble		6 or

6

LIFE VISIONING

Life visioning and goal-setting are big topics. This chapter is split up into two main sections. The first section deals with the meta-aspects of life visioning, while the second part provides specific, step-by-step exercises.

Finding Your "Fuel"

Making any kind of meaningful and lasting change in your life requires energy – the *fuel* to make it happen. For most of us, this motivation comes in one of two ways: *inspiration* for something we want to accomplish, or *reaction*, catalyzed by a situation that is causing us some kind of suffering or discomfort.

The *proactive* approach consists of harnessing the energy generated from an *inspired vision* – how you'd like your life to be. The *reactive* approach involves waiting until a major health issue or personal tragedy *forces* you to make changes. Both methods work, and both are effective.

However, only one of them offers *freedom of choice.*

Clearly, the "inspired vision" approach seems to have the most going for it. It has the potential for yielding *long-term* fuel. This, in contrast to usually short-lived energy produced from *reacting* to some momentary emergency, which usually dissipates once the initial crisis has passed.

I place this chapter early in the book because, without this kind of incentive – moving towards what you want – it's easy for the ideas discussed later to become "have to's" or *shoulds.*

> "I *should* eat better because I have ADD,
> and this is what they say will help."

This incentive only works when you're "on the program." As soon as you slip up, it's easy to feel guilty and frustrated.

Whereas, if your primary motivation is living a more fulfilling life – pursuing your dreams – then things like diet and exercise become part of the actions necessary to make this vision possible. They have the potential to become *meaningful* activities, versus just another weighty obligation.

A little backstory:

When I was in my early twenties, I started a multimedia company. It was 1995, right at the beginning of the internet boom. I realized quite early on, if I was to be successful, it was necessary for me to focus on eating a good diet, exercising properly, and in general becoming more self-aware. I needed to do this in order to sustain the energy necessary to follow the vision I had laid out for myself.

This prompted me to completely overhaul my diet, start running a few times a week, and make a host of other adjustments that resulted in much greater balance, energy, and mental clarity.

I'm highly doubtful I would have made these changes had I not had some kind of "inspired vision" in place. And it would have been even less likely that I would have sustained this lifestyle now into my forties, if it felt like a huge obligation.

Many people give up on their dreams. Through disappointments, lack of encouragement, and a whole host of personal or financial setbacks, many have settled with just making do. The result is often a life that is reactionary, lacking in energy, and often plagued with depression – underneath which is the sadness of not fully living.

A Whole-Systems Approach

On a more practical level, if you are engaged in work that doesn't take advantage of your innate skillset, and shoehorns you into a doing things that run counter to your natural tendencies, then the draw to medicate yourself in order to compensate for this will be immense.

A clear and thorough reviewing of your life, your skills, and your natural abilities can be truly eye-opening, and can make you aware of opportunities you had previously not considered. This is a good example of the Taoist expression "the watercourse way" – following the path of least resistance.

Having a Compelling Vision to Move You Forward

The path of "following your bliss" – as noted author and scholar Joseph Campbell puts it – requires a vision that you find *compelling,* and is clear enough to move you forward.

Equally as important is having a method by which you *regularly remind yourself of this vision,* to keep yourself inspired and on track. With all the complexities of modern life, it's far too easy to get lost in day-to-day challenges and distractions, and forget where you're going.

> "Strive not to be a success,
> but rather to be of value."
> ## – Albert Einstein

As I've studied the lives of individuals that have inspired me – those who appear to have achieved real happiness, fulfillment, and made a big difference in many people's lives – there's one common thread that keeps showing up. They didn't focus merely on making money or "being successful." They directed their energy towards honing and directing their skills to be, in some meaningful way, of service to others.

Based on this, I think of the following as a kind of "magic formula" for living a fulfilled life:

1. Uncover your unique gifts and talents.

2. Hone and refine them.

3. Use these gifts and talents to be of benefit to others.

If you are providing something that is truly useful to others, monetary wealth will follow as a natural bi-product. However, if you focus on financial wealth as your *primary* aim, there's a very good chance you'll burn out along the way.

Through asking yourself, "how can my life and plans benefit others?" – this question can cut through low self-esteem issues, because you are no longer doing it just for yourself. You recognize there is someone downstream that could directly benefit from this decision to follow your inner compass.

Overcoming Low Self-Esteem

It would have been wonderful if we all had grown up in a supportive and loving family environment, and had the opportunity to attend enlightened schools that valued our uniqueness. But, for the vast majority of us, this wasn't the case.

As a result, most of us have been left with a lot of unwanted mental baggage that tends to unconsciously rule our lives.

This often manifests as self-sabotage, inner criticism, chronically second guessing ourselves, and a seeming inability to achieve our most cherished goals.

At some point, it can be *extremely* useful to recognize: much of what has been weighing us down (both emotionally and mentally) was not of our creation. We, more than likely, picked up on the judgments, projections, and limiting thought patterns of family, friends, and society.

And this unwanted mental baggage, *in some very powerful ways,* is still governing our lives.

This is why, in the upcoming chapters, we'll discuss the nuts and bolts of consciously "re-programming" our thoughts. We'll explore ways to move more fluidly towards a life based far more on *choice* than unconscious behaviors.

Inspiration as Fuel

We hunter-types tend to be "inspirationally driven." This seems to be our natural fuel. We are not typically, by nature, driven by practicality. Instead, we are usually moved by what "lights us up."

The word "inspiration" comes from the latin, "spiritus", meaning *breath*. Words like *respiration* and *spiritual* also share this same root word. It refers to "the breath of life" – the life force itself.

For most of us in the modern world, this *core engine* (the life force), which directs our actions, gravitates us to certain experiences while pushing us away from others, is somewhat of a mystery to us.

It's like sitting in your house, staring out the window, watching the trees sway in the wind. You never actually see the wind, but you *do* see its effects.

In the same way, there is a force that animates our bodies, and the *entire world* around us, but we usually only see its effects. Most of us spend a lot of our time "in our heads" – in abstract thought. We perceive the world in a way that often has little to do with any *direct* connection with this life force energy. Because of this tendency, we're primarily motivated by concepts like "responsibility" and "societal obligation." We do things because *we have to* or *we should,* and not from this deeper place of connection.

The antidote to this, the way to get back in touch with this core life force inside us, begins by practicing awareness – becoming more present. It's about residing *in the now*, and not in future fears or past disappointments.

The next step involves regularly "checking in" – assessing whether the activities you are currently engaged in are *actually* contributing to your life, and to the lives of those around you. If they are, chances are you'll feel energized and *inspired*.

If not, it's time for a course correction.

The Power of Perspective – Knowing What Is Possible

Along with our unconscious mental baggage, another thing that tends to hold many of us back is – a lack of knowing what is possible.

If you're not aware of the options that are available to you, it's easy for your vision to become myopic – so entirely focused on what's right in front of you that you don't see the bigger picture.

This is where the process of "educating yourself" becomes *essential*. Whether it's becoming more aware of income possibilities, learning opportunities, or job options – research is essential.

The internet is one of the most valuable tools man has ever created. With it, we have access to seemingly unlimited resources. The world has truly become a global village. We're no longer limited by what's in our local area.

Seek out people who are doing what you want to do. Ask them how they got to where they're at. You'll be surprised by how many people are willing to offer you free advice. I find this is especially true of fellow hunter-types who've carved out their own niche in non-traditional ways.

This idea holds true for both someone just starting out, to people in mid-life looking to make some significant career shifts. Although this may sound like rather simplistic advice, it's a helpful reminder for just about everyone.

The point is, don't wait for the opportunities to present themselves to you. Go after them. Be willing to take risks. Risk-taking is a primary hunter-type trait, and can be maximized for your benefit. Here again, we're befriending "the giant." We're identifying a potentially self-destructive "ADD/ADHD" trait and using it to assist us in moving towards our intended destination.

Moving towards Mastery

The draw towards "mastery" is something that seems to be hard-wired into the hunter-type's DNA. In Thom Hartmann's book, "The Edison Gene," he notes that people with ADD/ADHD experience seemingly miraculous shifts in their lives once they've directed their ability to hyperfocus towards a skill they want to master.

This process of mastering something, in and of itself, can yield a tremendous amount of self-esteem. To me, if I'm not in the process of learning some new skill, my life feels flat. I've got no juice. I can easily get bored, lethargic, and possibly even depressed. I'm always looking for new opportunities to sharpen my existing skills, or develop new ones. As soon as I find these opportunities, I light right back up again. Oftentimes, the more challenging the task, the better I feel. I know this is true for many of the hunter-types I've worked with over the years.

In school, hunter-types are often labeled as "really smart but unmotivated." It's not that we're lazy, it's usually a case of not being *sufficiently challenged.*

Re-imagining Your "Work"

I have an issue with the concept of "my occupation." It implies that each of us only has *one* primary way of earning a living, and only *one* way in which to provide a service to others. It's a societal construct that is quite limiting, and yet most of us buy into it from a very young age.

There is an inherent instability to this idea. If you have only *one* means of bringing in money – and only *one* outlet for utilizing your talents – then, if something happens (like losing your job, or an injury that keeps you from doing this *one* thing), the results can be devastating.

It's the equivalent of putting all of your eggs into one basket.

Nature Thrives on Diversity

For a number of years now, I've studied the design science of *permaculture.* Essentially, it's the study of how to create sustainable/regenerative living systems.

Consider a forest. This meta-organism is a very densely connected web of interdependence, between plants, animals, weather patterns, soil, etc.

Forests existed long before us humans came onto the scene. And yet, surprisingly, they don't require us to continually truck in fertilizer, or water them, to keep them alive.

The more you study nature, the more you'll discover that nature thrives on *diversity* – it's a strategy that intrinsically produces balance and stability.

A tree doesn't rely on *just one* blossom in order to seed a new tree. It creates *thousands* of them. Perhaps only one will actually become a new tree, but the sheer volume of *seed options* ensures that new trees will come into being.

So too with your own life: the more options you have to make money, explore your creativity, and serve others, the more likely you'll be able to maintain balance, even if there's a challenge in one area of your life.

It can be immensely liberating to explore a whole host of ways of making money, even if you *do* have a stable well-paying job. Whether it's a consulting business on the side, an online storefront, some product you make for local shops, or selling something at your neighborhood farmer's market – knowing that you have *numerous* options of sustaining yourself *if you had to,* can do wonders for your sense of security in the world.

This sense of security can also be useful when making tough decisions about your *primary* occupation. It's easy to be taken advantage of if you have the sense that if you lose your job, you'd lose everything.

That's putting an *excessive* amount of power over your life in the hands of your employer.

✎

THE VISIONING PROCESS

In revisiting the title story of the book, your life vision *is* "the great mountain." It's your intended destination – the life you really want to be living. There are two questions we continually ask ourselves (whether or not we're conscious of it): *where* is this mountain located, and *how* do we get there?

There are countless books on goal setting, life visioning, and creative project development. I've listed a number of my favorites in the "Bibliography & Reference" section at the end of the book. Find a process that works best for you. If the methods shared in this chapter work for you, great. Stick with them. If not, explore other methods – mix and match them to fit you and your life.

The Essential Components of "Visioning"

Whether it's visioning for a creative project, a business, or your life, the basic principles involved are always the same.

Pure and simple, you "vision" to get clear about what you want to create. You are *envisioning* what it will look like when your ideas are in full form. If you're not clear on what you want, how can you possibly create it? You'll just move through the world with some vague idea of what you'd like to have, but it will most likely stay just that, *vague*.

No matter what specific process you use, visioning should accomplish the following:

- Provide clarity about what you *want* to create

- Clarify what you *don't want* to create

- Create a basic "road map" to work from

By going through a visioning process, many times it will reveal that, what you *thought* you wanted, isn't actually *it*. Therefore your primary objective is always *clarity*.

Visioning Step 1: Getting Clear about Your Talents and Skill-Sets

You may already have a clear inventory of what you're talented at, and the skills that you've honed over time. However, I find it's helpful, from time-to-time, to "take stock." A crucial idea may come to you through spending just a little time zooming out and examining the bigger picture of your life.

We all have *multiple* talents and abilities. There may be one or two that really stand out as "the primary ones," however there are most likely a handful of others that are either lying dormant, or perhaps have been swept aside, deemed "unimportant" or impractical.

TALENTS & ABILITIES

On a sheet of paper, or on your computer, write a list of all your talents and abilities. List as many as you can think of, anything from: "I'm good at chess" to "I'm a skilled graphic artist."

Use these questions to spur you on:

> What is it I do that, when I'm in the act of doing it, time flies by because I'm so engrossed in the activity?

> What have others told me I'm gifted at? This often relates to something that was of benefit to them in some way.

> What activities provide me with a sense of self-confidence?

That's a good start, however, most people have gifts and talents that are lying dormant, yet to be uncovered.

Take a moment, close your eyes, and ask yourself:

> If I could do anything in the world, and had an infinite amount of time and money, and had no obligations, what would I do?

That's a powerful question. Take a moment and let it sink in, then start writing.

You may find the first things that emerge center around travel, things you would buy, etc. Write all this out, and see if you can get to something that may indicate a specific skill or endeavor you'd like to pursue.

Next, spend some time reading back what you've written, perhaps refining it as you go. What did it reveal?

This exercise is immensely effective at delving into your subconscious, so you may want to revisit it a number of times over the next few days. Each time you do, you'll gain further inspiration and clarity.

Perhaps, as is often the case, a critical inner voice may show up saying something like, "this is silly and pointless!" Or, "you're just going to get your hopes up if your spend time doing this." Acknowledge these voices, and for the moment, set them aside and keep going.

The point of this exercise is to catalyze your creativity – getting you to the *core* of what you love and what inspires you. By doing this, you are tapping into that inner "fuel source" necessary to make meaningful changes in *all* areas of your life.

Both for myself and my coaching clients, this exercise has been quite effective at "untangling" – separating out core life passions from self-judgments, limiting belief systems, and expectations placed on us by others.

I've made several major life decisions based solely on the results of this exercise. Remember, there are no right or wrong answers – it's more about the process. Keep in mind your answers will most likely change over time.

Keep this list handy as you go though the other visioning exercises.

Visioning Step 2: Mining Your Day-Dreaming for Clues

We all fantasize about what our perfect life could look like. Perhaps, deep down, everyone knows what they're here to do. Our day-dreaming can often be a doorway into this wiser aspect of ourselves.

"The two most important days in your life
are the day you are born, and
the day you figure out why."
– Mark Twain

EXPLORING YOUR SUBCONSCIOUS

Take a moment, close your eyes, and recall what you've been day-dreaming about the past few months. As outlandish and seemingly unattainable as some of your dreams may be, write them out in as much detail as possible.

Now, look through what you've written. Can you detect a pattern? Is there a theme to the fantasies? Are they pointing you in a specific direction?

Many of them may be communications of unmet needs, like: companionship, respect, rest, etc. While others may directly relate to potential goals and activities to pursue.

Almost always, there's some useful material in there.

Make note of what your subconscious may be offering up to you, and use these insights as you move forward in the visioning exercises.

Visioning Step 3: Long-Term Goals in Specific Areas of Your Life

When it comes to life visioning and setting attainable goals, it can be helpful to work within specific categories. Otherwise, the process can be vague and overwhelming.

So, in order to provide context, here's a list of "life categories" I've adapted from Sonia Choquette's book, "Your Heart's Desire."

- Health and Body

- Work

- Relationships

- Creative Expression

- Finances

- Service

- Spirituality

- Home

- Travel / Adventure

- Possessions

WHERE I'D LIKE TO BE IN....

For each of the "life categories," write out a list of specific goals you would like to achieve in the next five years. Project yourself out five years from now. Where would you like to be? What does your life look like? Write whatever comes to you. It may be helpful to phrase each one in the form of: "I am now..." or, "I have..."

For example:

> (Work) I am now working four days a week out of my home and making $4500.00 a month.

> (Travel / Adventure) I have traveled extensively throughout Europe.

This list provides you with potential *long-term* goals. However, there may be a few others that didn't quite fit into any of these categories.

Take a moment and write out any other long-term goals you may have. When you're done, look through what you've written. Spend a little time refining your wording so that it clearly describes each intention.

Think of this list as a living document. It will grow and evolve over time. It is not stagnant. Continually revisit this list and refine it.

Visioning Step 4: From Long-Term Goals to Short-Term Goals

Now that you have a working list of long-term goals, the next step involves distilling each goal into a list of short-term goals. This step is essential, because it will provide you with the practical steps necessary to achieve each goal.

MAPPING SHORT-TERM GOALS

Choose a goal from the list you've created in the previous exercise. On a sheet of paper turned lengthwise (landscape), create a rough "map" for achieving it. Write out all the steps necessary in reaching your goal. You may want to go from beginning to end. Or it may be easier for you to work backwards, starting from the end result and listing each step that needs to happen in order to achieve the goal.

There's no right or wrong way to do this. You may want to place the goal on the lower right hand side of the page, and start listing steps from the upper left. Or make the lower left hand side the "start point" and move towards the upper right.

Don't worry about making it perfect. This is a creative process. If you've listed items out of order, take another sheet of paper and refine the original map once you have a rough map.

For example, if your long-term goal is "make a successful film seen by thousands of people," then your timeline may look something like this:

1. Study filmmaking in-depth (take classes, read books, etc.)

2. Make a few short films

3. Write a full-length screenplay

4. Find collaborators

5. Acquire the equipment

6. Shoot the film

7. Show film at festivals

8. Find a distributor

9. Successful screenings nationwide and abroad

The aim of this exercise is to help you get really clear on how the goal can *actually* be achieved – moving it out of "fantasy land" into something that feels doable.

This process will give you a list of potential short-term goals. Even though, "make a successful film seen by thousands of people" can feel overwhelming, "study filmmaking (take classes, read books, etc.)," is quite doable in the here-and-now. If you haven't arrived at a *realistic* short-term goal like this, keep refining until it feels doable.

Depending on the size of your long-term goals list, you may want to start with only a couple of the main ones. It's easy to get overwhelmed if you try to address too many goals in one sitting. Keep in mind, this is an *ongoing* process. Make it a habit of regularly revising and refining your life goals.

Visioning Step 5: From Short-Term Goals to Doable Actions

The next step is to take your short-term goals and turn them into doable actions that can be added to your action item list, and/or your weekly schedule.

I want to place special emphasis on the term "doable action."

For example, if your short-term goal is:

"Run a full-length marathon within a year."

And you presently don't engage in any kind of regular exercise routine – it may be unrealistic to start with with an action like:

> "Run everyday for 1 hour."

A more "doable" action would be something like:

> "Place a reminder on my calendar
> to jog twice a week for twenty minutes."

TURNING GOALS INTO ACTIONS

Starting with just the *first* short-term goal for each long-term goal, list a series of actions you can take *right away* to address this goal.

Revisiting our previous example, if your short-term goal is:

> "Study filmmaking (take classes, read books, etc.)"

Start listing a number of actions you can take *right away* to reach this goal.

It may look something like this:

- Research "filmmaking books" on the internet. Do a search for "best books on filmmaking", read reviews, and order books.

- Go to the local library and check out books on filmmaking.

- Watch filmmaking tutorial videos on the internet.

That's a good start, but you may want to carve out specific times in your schedule each week to address this short-term goal.

You may want to add to your list:

- Every Tuesday afternoon from 2pm - 4pm, study filmmaking. Write it on my calendar!

If you have a big list of actions, you may want to whittle it down a bit, prioritize, and get to a list of the most important (and potentially effective) actions to address this short-term goal.

In this way, go through each long-term goal, choose the first short-term goal, and repeat the process. Once you have your list of action items, the next step is to add them to your action-item list, and ideally onto your calendar.

We'll go into this process in more detail in the "Time Management" chapter.

How to Work with Goals and Action Items

Life isn't static. This process of setting and pursuing life goals should be dynamic and flexible. You may find, as time goes on, you'll adjust and update your methods of working with your goals. Avoid getting overly fixated on "the process." What you're aiming at is clarity, direction, purpose, and consistency.

Time specific goals can often bring disappointment because – if a goal isn't reached in the time-frame you've set for yourself, you may let the whole thing fall by the wayside. I've grappled with this many times. It's important to remember that we hunter-types are not usually predisposed to *accurately* assessing how long something will take to complete.

Your visioning and goal-setting processes should provide you with *ongoing* energy and inspiration. If they don't, revisit your methods to see how they can be made more enjoyable.

The Final Step: Visualizing Your Goals - Creating "The Map"

A *visual* representation of your goals can be extremely valuable. It's something you can look at every day that reminds you of the direction you'd like to move in.

In the past, if you were to sail to some distant land, knowing which direction to travel in wouldn't be enough to have a successful journey. You would need a map – something to continually reference along the way to ensure you're headed in the right direction. It's far too easy to get lost, or forget where you're headed.

There are numerous ways to visualize your goals. Here are two methods you may want to consider.

The Vision Board Process

A "Vision Board" is large poster board with pictures depicting your various goals. It's a simple concept, but it can be extremely effective in reminding you of your goals on a daily basis.

 VISIONBOARDING 101

1. Go to your local art supply store and pick up a poster board. 22" x 28" is a common size.

2. Assemble a list of images related to your goals.

This can be done in a number of ways. You can track down old magazines that contain photos related to your various goals. Check your local library for magazines they might be getting rid of, or visit sites like "StartSampling.com" to get free magazine samples sent to you.

You could also print out pictures downloaded from the internet. In this case, look for images that are high resolution. Google images (images.google.com) provides the option to search for images with specific resolutions. If possible, use high-gloss paper to get high quality prints. If you don't have a printer, your local office supply store or shipping center (like FedEx-Kinko's) can print from a disk, or from files uploaded to their website.

3. Review your images.

Once you've you've assembled your images, the next step is to find ones that are most inspirational, based on the goal it represents.

4. Create a caption for each image.

Write out a word or phrase that will appear next to each image to signify the goal. How you do this is up to you. You may want to write the goal in a sentence or two, or just a few key words. Affirmations also work well (e.g. "I am now building a successful and profitable business.") Again, your aim is to create something that inspires you to achieve this goal when you read it.

5. Assemble your images and captions.

Lay the poster board flat in the middle of your floor. Start assembling your images and captions. Find a good layout where each image and caption is clearly visible. You may need to crop some images so they will all fit on your poster board.

6. Glue your images to the poster board.

Using a glue stick, or a basic paper glue, glue your images to the board.

7. Place your vision board where you'll see it.

Once you've created your vision board, place it somewhere in your home where you'll see it every day.

If you are adept at using graphic design programs, you could design your entire vision board on the computer – at high-resolution – and have it printed on a poster board sized sheet at your local printers.

VISION BOARD

Create a "Vision Video"

For those a bit more adventurous, a "vision video" is another method of visualizing your goals. This process was made popular by an Australian named Malcolm Cohan.

The basic premise is – create a short video (3 - 5 minutes long) that depicts all of your major life goals, using music, photos, and videos to represent each of your goals.

MAKING A VISION VIDEO

1. Download images and video clips from the internet that represent each of your goals. You may want to choose *multiple* images and video clips for each goal. Free software is available online that allows you to download video (for personal use) from most of the popular video-sharing websites.

2. Choose a music score that really inspires you.

3. Review what you've assembled – pick the best video clips and photos that most inspire you to move towards each of your selected goals. You may want to create a separate folder for each goal to help you organize your material.

4. In your favorite video editing program, piece together images, video, and text that reflect each of your goals. Ideally, keep the entire video under (3) minutes.

5. Create a link to this video on the desktop of your computer (laptop, tablet, smart phone, etc.).

6. Commit to watching this video every couple of days to remind you of your goals. It may be helpful to create an email or smart phone reminder on your calendar to watch it.

7. If you have a regular life-coaching session, it can be helpful to watch this video prior to going through your session.

OVERCOMING BLOCKS & STAYING INSPIRED

Knowing What "Lights You Up"

Now that you have a clear map of your goals, there's one crucial element that often gets neglected, but is absolutely essential for achieving your goals: *staying inspired*.

Hunter-types are definitely "inspiration driven," and we often have a challenging time sticking with a project for longer periods of time. What typically happens: the initial inspiration for an idea or project wears off, and it becomes more and more challenging to summon the energy necessary to follow it through to completion.

If we revisit the hunter-farmer theory, this tendency makes sense. In prehistoric times, a hunter was primarily focused on short-term planning. The focus was on *this* moment – the immediacy of the hunt.

As opposed to the farmer, who's livelihood absolutely depended upon long-term thinking.

I can't stress how important it is to have a *practical* understanding of what keeps you inspired, so that you can consistently accomplish the goals and projects you begin.

To revisit one of the previous examples, if one of your long-term goals is:

> "Make a successful film seen by tens-of-thousands of people."

Then, you'll most likely have a long journey ahead of you. There will be, undoubtedly, numerous times in which you'll feel frustrated, disappointed, and tempted to give up. It's in these times that having a clear plan for *re-inspiring* yourself is essential.

Again, the best way to think about this is:

inspiration = fuel and energy

Although everyone is different, typically, inspiration comes from exposing yourself to media, people, and situations that reinvigorate you. Just as inspiring speeches and books have, throughout the ages, been the catalyst for world-altering movements, the same holds true on a personal level.

Whatever the goal or project, compiling a list of materials that will continually inspire you, is extremely helpful in achieving your goals.

Whenever I take on a new project, I *always* identify a list of things that will keep me lit and inspired throughout the process, because I *know* the energy can quickly dissipate if I don't. To me, this step isn't a luxury, it's essential.

STAYING INSPIRED

Choose one of your long-term goals. At the top of a sheet of paper, or in a text document on your computer, write out this goal.

Underneath, list all of the things you could do, read, listen to, watch, etc., that could inspire you to achieve this goal.

For example:

Goal: Learn German

- Watch German movies with English subtitles, online or on the internet.

- Take a "Speaking German" class at a local community college.

- Listen to a German music station on the internet.

- Watch German TV shows on the internet.

- Purchase a "Learn to Speak German CD" or track down a multimedia language course online.

- Plan a trip to Germany.

- Find someone locally who already speaks it, and start spending time with them.

Once you've made your list, review what you've written and add the simplest items to accomplish on your current action-items list, and/or onto your calendar.

In the next few weeks, commit to accomplishing at least *two* of these items.

Then, try doing this same exercise for other goals on your list. Over time, make note of which items are effective in keeping you inspired. Make these activities a regular part of your weekly/monthly schedule.

Dealing with Discouragement as You Are Re-Imagining Your Life

More than likely, as you work towards re-imagining your life, you will experience disappointment, self-doubt, distractions, criticism, and overwhelm.

> "If you get up one more time than you fall,
> you will make it through."
> **– Chinese Proverb**

You can have the most clearly defined goals, but if you aren't able to get yourself back up after some moment of discouragement, they won't matter much. Again, this is why knowing how to get yourself re-inspired is such an important skill to learn.

With all of the suggestions in the upcoming chapters, keep in mind that this is a life-long journey. Integrate what you can, celebrate your wins, and be accepting of yourself when you don't achieve your goals in the time you've set for yourself.

RE-IMAGINING HOW YOU "MAKE MONEY"

Money carries such a tremendous weight in our society. It connects deeply to needs like:

- Security

- Self-esteem

- Freedom

- Respect

It's no wonder it has such a charge to it. Learning how to bring money into your life in *many* different ways can be a big step in achieving greater stability and personal freedom.

In the "Bibliography & Resources" section, I've listed an audio series entitled "Prosperity Consciousness" by Fredric Lehrman. This program was fundamental for me in shifting my core beliefs around money, and I can't recommend it highly enough. Many of the following concepts to be discussed were derived from this audio series.

Getting to the Essence of Money

One of the primary reasons why many of us don't follow our dreams has to do with root-level fears about survival. Because money and survival (in our society) go hand-in-hand, many of us often settle for a job we don't like because it "pays the bills."

Feeling secure in the world is extremely important, but it shouldn't be the only factor that rules your decisions. Through consciously recognizing this deep connection between survival and money, you have the opportunity to move towards new ways of thinking. Otherwise, you can remain stuck in patterns that cause you suffering, unable to make important changes in your life because you're not dealing with this "fear of survival" directly.

As mentioned, re-programming your perception of how money comes to you is a good place to start. Through experimenting with numerous ways of making money, you can illustrate to yourself – *experientially* – the idea that money doesn't necessarily need to come from just one source (e.g. your primary job). In the "Tips and Practices" and "Creative Life" chapters, I'll go more in-depth into various ways of making money you may not have thought of.

Countless hunter-types have become successful entrepreneurs. We often thrive in an environment where we make our own schedule, and earn money based on our creative abilities. This lifestyle also requires self-learning, dedication, good time management skills, and a consistent ability to "vision" and accomplish our goals.

A famous yogi arrived in America from India with nothing but the clothes on his back. He soon amassed quite a large following who were struck by his deep wisdom and peaceful presence. One evening, he began sharing his plans for establishing meditation centers around the country.

His new followers grew increasingly concerned. One of them finally summoned the courage to ask,

"Baba, your vision is beautiful, but where on earth are we going to get the money for all of that?"

The yogi responded,

"From wherever it is now."

Money as Energy and Gratitude

Unless you live in the woods, forage for your food, and make your own clothing, you need money as part of your daily survival.

Let's take a moment to examine what money actually *is*, and how it works.

In its most basic form, money represents *energy*. Each of us has more energy than we need to manage our day-to-day lives. We offer this *excess* energy to others – often in the form of some service. With any job you've ever worked at, on a primary level, you were lending your excess energy to another person or organization, to assist them in some way.

In exchange, the gratitude for our service was expressed in the form of *money*.

Therefore:

$$Energy > Service > Gratitude > Money$$

This is an entirely different way of perceiving money than most of us were taught as children, which looked more like:

$$Job = Money$$

Seeing money from this broader perspective can unlock a whole host of hidden opportunities.

The question becomes, "How do I use my talents and abilities to help others in a way that truly provides value to them?"

If you go to a restaurant, and the waitress or waiter does a good job, you pay them a gratuity – money that expresses your *gratitude* for their service.

Let's take this further. There is a reason why famous artists, musicians, and entrepreneurs make so much money. There's a principle involved.

It's because they've connected their service, in some way, to reach large amounts of people. It's the same basic principle at work.

A successful film actor receives a big paycheck because what they are doing is reaching millions of people. People go to a movie theater and pay money for tickets because they are *grateful* for the experience the actor is providing them.

This is a major key to creating wealth:

> Once you've developed a way of providing value to others, the more you can *expand* this service to reach large numbers of people, the greater potential there will be for earning money.

Therefore, perceiving your work as "service" is probably the most profitable thing you can do. This may sound a bit lofty, but in essence, it's quite practical, and it's usually the difference between having work that really inspires you, and work that just earns you paycheck. Experientially, these are two entirely different planets.

Many Paths to Success

I was a straight C+ student throughout high school. For the most part, I found school boring and tedious. As a result, I typically did the minimum required. Had I known then what I know now about being a hunter-type, I would have done much better.

Once I got to college, I found the lack of structure to be extremely challenging. I felt lost, and dropped out after only a month.

Luckily, soon after, I stumbled onto something I really wanted to do: 3D computer animation. Once I realized this was a potential job option – that it was possible to do this *for a living* – I was hooked. I had my mission.

I obtained the necessary software, and devoted all of my free time to learning and perfecting my skills. My uncle was kind enough to loan me some money to purchase the equipment I needed.

I started by creating a "demo reel" – a video portfolio of my work – and shopped it around. Within just a few months, I was able to get a full-time job doing 3D animation for a video production house – allowing me to quit my nine-to-five job as an assistant manager at a music store.

It was a scary move. I didn't know if it was going to work out. But, I *did* know, deep down, this was what I wanted to do. And I was good at it.

Over the next few years, I refined my skills, cultivated a bit more self-discipline, and became quite proficient at the craft. This eventually led to work in television and film. Along the way, I was greatly assisted by my co-workers. They challenged me to continually improve my skills.

Since that time (1992), I've earned a living through utilizing my creative abilities. Along the way, there were countless disappointments, hand-wringing moments, and times when I wondered if I could pay my bills. As is often the case, freedom comes at a price, and you need to stay with it through the lean times. Here again, learning to diversify can really help create greater stability – something I didn't fully understand until much later.

I mention all this because, looking back, I *needed* to take a non-traditional route. I had to carve out a path of my own in order to maintain my sanity. I would have been miserable had I tried to force myself into the nine-to-five box. It took a long time and involved a lot of hard work. But, as a result, I now carry the confidence that, whatever I want to pursue, I *can* be successful. And, most importantly, I can do this in a way that honors my natural (hunter-type) tendencies.

My story is not unique. It's quite common for hunter-types to flourish once they realize they are not bound to societal expectations and traditional means of making a living.

I'm in no way saying this is the best path for you. And I'm definitely not discouraging you from acquiring the education necessary to pursue your passions. I merely want to illustrate that there are *numerous* ways of pursuing your dreams *while* making a good living. The broader your perspective, the more opportunities you'll see.

∽

Next Steps

Life visioning and goal-setting are essential for creating personal freedom. They are especially important for us hunter-types. These skills allow us the opportunity to carve out a life that is optimized for our unique gifts and tendencies.

I encourage you to revisit the exercises in this chapter regularly, especially when you're needing a little perspective. I also *highly* encourage you to integrate your goals list in with some kind of ongoing life coaching process. This will be discussed in the "Creating A Support System" chapter.

Once you have your goals list, try reading through the "Time Management" and "Tips and Practices" chapters. Both expand on the ideas just discussed, going into more of the ground-plane aspects of weekly and monthly planning.

As you continue through the book, use your life goals as the primary motivation for exploring things like nutrition, meditation, exercise, etc. See each of these as the means for creating a strong foundation for the life you envision.

7

NAVIGATING EMOTIONS

The Emotional Life of a Hunter-type

The inner life of a hunter-type can get pretty complex. Intense emotions can often be the norm. Confusion, frustration, overwhelm, depression, anger, and sometimes even rage, can often go hand-in-hand with classic ADD / ADHD symptoms.

Navigating this inner realm of emotions requires effective tools, as well as a general "getting the lay of the land." By having a clear map to work from, challenging emotions can be far more manageable. Even though hunter-types tend to experience emotions a bit more intensely than others, the basic principles that govern emotions are universal.

Biochemistry and Mood

Before launching into *psychological*-based techniques, it's important to reiterate the role brain chemistry has on our emotions. If you're deficient in the key nutrients your brain needs to regulate mood and focus, even if you have the best emotional tools, they're not going to be very effective.

As you read through this chapter, keep in mind that all these suggestions should go hand-in-hand with a well designed exercise, diet, and supplement plan, like the one mapped out in the "Exercise, Diet, and Supplements" chapter.

"Energy in Motion"

You may have heard the expression, "emotions are *energy in motion.*"

This gets pretty close to the truth. Emotions contain *energy.* When you experience a moment of intense joy, it's often felt as a buzzing inside all of your cells. The same holds true with anger. We're all familiar with that "fire in the belly" experience that occurs when our ire gets kicked up – that churning of energy in our solar plexus.

However, there's actually a force *underneath* our emotions that most people aren't aware of, that drives all of our decisions, whether we're aware of it or not.

Needs Are The Life Force Itself

From the dawn of time, all humans have been motivated by the same basic needs. Needs, in fact, are the *life force itself* – brushing up against us, moving us to take action in the world.

Needs are both primal and universal – they are every human's baseline operating system. No matter your race, belief system, or what language you speak, all humans share the same needs.

In relation to our emotional life, needs are the least common denominator. In a sense, they can be considered *atomic* (a Greek word meaning, "that which can not be divided into smaller pieces.")

Needs are the interface point between our emotions and the life force. And there's only a *finite* number of them. For example, the needs required for our basic survival are: water, shelter, food, and air. However, to live any kind of satisfying life, we *also* require a whole host of other needs, such as: peace, clarity, meaning, understanding, privacy, respect – to name just a few.

Our brains are hard-wired to meet needs. Unlike most other animals, who attempt to meet their basic needs (food, shelter, protection, etc.) *in the moment*, us humans have evolved the unique ability to *plan ahead* – strategizing ways to meet our needs sometime *in the future*. This ability to abstract our needs can be both a blessing and a curse.

When we were living in an environment where our survival absolutely depended on this strategy – it was a tremendous boon. We were able to predict when the herd would be in our area, and when the berries would be ripe enough to pick.

However, in our modern society, this same mechanism can turn *non* life-threatening situations – relationship issues, financial worries, or even the unintended slight by the guy at the grocery store – into an endless cascade of obsessive thoughts that bring stress to our bodies, and keep us in a constant low-level state of unrest.

Therefore, it can be *extremely useful* to understand the process by which our emotions are tied to needs – so that we can get to the root of what may be causing our current mental and emotional suffering.

My Personal Journey Into "Needs"

I was first introduced to the concept of needs through a process called Nonviolent Communication, developed by psychologist Dr. Marshall Rosenberg. Building upon the work of pioneers in the field of psychology, like Abraham Maslow and Carl Rogers, NVC (as it's often called) is now being used all over the world, from high-level diplomatic negotiations, to couples counseling – and is considered one of the most effective mediation and interpersonal communication tools available. And for good reason – it just plain works.

The further I've gone into the process, witnessing its consistent effectiveness, it's clear that Dr. Rosenberg has really "cracked the code" on how our emotions and thought-patterns function – getting to the very fabric of both our individual and collective emotional selves.

The Connection between Our Feelings and Our Needs

Dr. Rosenberg has one of the most useful analogies about feelings I've ever heard:

Feelings are like the lights on a dashboard, letting us know whether a need is met or unmet.

I highly recommend memorizing this. It provides a very accurate description of what our feelings *actually* do for us.

For example:

If you're driving on the freeway, and someone cuts you off – almost hitting you – your initial *emotional* reaction would most likely be an upwelling of both fear and anger.

A cascade of negative thoughts towards the person driving in the other vehicle would typically follow.

Depending on your personal temperament, you may even roll down your window, yell at them, or make an obscene gesture.

But what is actually triggering these feelings and gut-level responses?

Looking at the chart on the following page, most likely the "triggered" needs are:

- Safety
- Care
- Awareness
- Respect

NEEDS LIST

Safety / Security	Spontaneity	Focus
Health / Physical Well-Being	Celebration	Consistency
Relaxation	Friendship	Order
Rest / Sleep	Companionship	Simplicity
Affection / Touch	Belonging	Ease
Nurturing	Community	Harmony
Exercise	Acceptance	Peace
Movement	Support	Effectiveness
Privacy	Respect	Awareness
Space	Appreciation	Presence
Choice	Understanding	Accomplishment
Freedom	Listening	Self-Esteem
Autonomy	Empathy	Self-Confidence
Meaning	To be seen and heard	Growth
Purpose	Trust	Challenge
Inspiration	Authenticity	Learning
Hope / Reassurance	Creativity	Discovery
Play	Self-Expression	Competence
Joy	Clarity	Skill

Chart based on Center for Nonviolent Communication "Needs Inventory" - www.cnvc.org

"Safety" is one of our most primal needs. When our safety is threatened, are bodies are "wired" to sound the alarm bells. In this example, the "alarm bells" are *anger* and *fear*.

Here's the trick. If you have the presence of mind during (or soon after) the experience to name what needs are alive, you're far less likely to take an action you'd later regret.

Your inner response in this particular situation could be:

> "That JERK!!! OK... breathe... I notice I'm feeling really angry right now. And I'm also feeling shaky and scared because I really have needs for *safety* and *awareness*. I want to remind myself that the danger has passed. I'm going to take a few deep breaths and try to relax myself."

Just that simple inner dialog, which connects you directly with what's happening internally, can bring you back to center surprisingly quickly. You've 1) brought your awareness to exactly what triggered you, 2) named the needs underneath your feelings, and finally 3) identified a simple action to diffuse some of the energy. In a sense, you've told your emotional self, "The danger has passed. You can turn the alarm bells off now."

In "non-awareness mode," you may continue to scream at that driver for the next two hours, *in your head*, with your whole body clenched with tension. This doesn't do anything to them, and *definitely* doesn't do anything positive for you. The danger has passed and there's no need to carry the emotion and tension with you.

Most people can relate to this example of getting cut-off on the freeway. However, we typically carry around a whole host of uncomfortable, unresolved, emotions that may not be as intense, or easily identified. Nevertheless, they stay with us and cause low-level but *consistent* stress, because our conscious mind hasn't resolved them yet.

Through bringing more awareness to your emotions – *naming* the underlying needs – you can untie yourself from a great deal of emotional baggage.

FINDING "THE NEED"

Here's a simple exercise to illustrate how needs are at work in *all* areas of your life, whether or not you're aware of it.

Think of a recent experience that really triggered you. Recall it as vividly as you can. Once you have it clear in your mind, look at the "needs list" chart earlier in the chapter and identify which needs were involved in this particular situation.

As you scan through them you will probably notice that, once you get to a need associated with this particular incident, you'll feel a release of tension in your body. That's an indicator that you've touched on a key need. This is not an intellectual process. Trust your gut-level reaction.

For example, if you recently got into an argument with your spouse, it may have been the need for *understanding* that wasn't met. When you read the word "understanding" – your gut-level reaction maybe: *"Understanding!* Yes! That's what I was really needing in that moment."

Once you've completed analyzing this one incident, try this process a few times with other instances in your past.

Why It's Important to "Name The Need"

You may find this discussion of feelings and needs just a lot of psychological mumbo-jumbo, but there is a very *practical* reason why learning to "name the need" is so important.

Needs tell you what you are *really* wanting at the core of your being. So much time can be wasted in pursuing actions that *in no way* meet the underlying needs we have.

For example:

You might really want to buy a new sports car, and you're prepared to put yourself into debt in order to obtain it. If you're not aware of what's actually driving this purchase – unmet needs for *respect* and *self-esteem* – you could waste a lot of time and energy taking an action that really won't meet these needs in any substantial way.

So, not only will you be dissatisfied with the purchase, you'll have to deal with the hassle of paying it off. And debt *often* creates suffering, because it challenges our ability to meet another important need – *freedom*. Therefore, the strategy of buying a nice sports car and putting yourself in debt could be a lose-lose proposition.

It's far more practical to "get to the core." An awareness of needs can be liberating because it gives you access to what is *really* motivating you in the first place.

In the above example, with a little awareness, you may be able to list a whole host of other actions that could also meet your needs for respect and self-esteem, *without* having to go into debt.

What's Happening in the Brain?

For another perspective, let's look at what's actually happening in your brain during the process of naming feelings and needs.

The amygdala is the part of our brain that handles "fight-or-flight" situations. We are all alive today because, many generations ago, our ancestors evolved this brain region to tell us to be *fearful* and *cautious* in situations that could potentially be life-threatening. If we *didn't* have this part of our brain, we wouldn't know to be cautious when in the presence of a wild animal, such as a lion. We would be oblivious to the potential threat, and would, most likely, get eaten.

When the amygdala perceives something that is a potential threat in the immediate environment, it literally shuts down our "rational" brain – the neocortex – and focuses our energy towards fight-or-flight. This is what author Daniel Goldman has coined, "the amygdala hijack." Our amygdala hijacks our normal consciousness, overriding the controls, and pushes us into "fight-or-flight" mode.

However, in our modern world, which is often flooded with stimuli, this part of our brain often becomes triggered by *non*

life-threatening situations, creating a lot of undue stress.
Here's where the process of naming feelings and needs comes in.

Through adopting a practice of naming emotions, you are actually speeding up this entire process, getting your rational brain back "online" much more quickly.

Recent brain studies conducted by Dr. Mathew Lieberman of UCLA confirm this. It was discovered that, when a research subject *names* their feelings, their amygdala (according to brain scans) calms down much quicker than if they just allowed their emotions to take their course.

In fact, by bringing more awareness to your emotions, you are actually *re-patterning* your brain – training your neocortex to keep the amygdala from completing "taking the controls" when you are emotionally triggered. In a sense you are, "claiming more brain territory for consciousness," as Sarah Payton (a teacher of Nonviolent Communication) puts it.

It is well documented that Buddhist monks (who dedicate their entire lives to present-moment awareness practices) are less likely to be startled by loud noises than the rest of the population. They have, in a sense, *re-wired* their brains to be far more calm and "in control," even in potentially life-threatening situations.

Effective Actions to Meet Needs

Once feelings and needs are identified, the next step involves getting clear about what *specific* actions can meet these needs.

Coming back to the drummer story, this is part of "facing the giant" – getting it to carry you where *you* want to go. Heavy emotions and mood swings can be gigantic energies that probably have crushed you over and over again. Identifying specific actions to meet unmet needs is one method of transforming this "energy" into something positive.

FINDING A PATTERN OF UNMET NEEDS

Make a list of notable "melt downs" and challenging moments you've experienced in the last few years. Try to use one sentence to describe each one.

For example:

- "Got angry at my girlfriend on New Year's" incident.

- Felt devastated when I found out I didn't get the promotion at work.

- Feeling deeply depressed for two weeks a few months back.

- Felt miserable after failing to get my mid-term paper done on time.

- Constantly feeling angry at my boss for belittling me (numerous occasions).

Whatever they are, list as many challenging moments as you can remember. Pay special attention to the ones that seem to happen over and over again.

Then, look at the "needs list" earlier in the chapter. Next to each incident, identify which needs were alive in that instance.

For example:

> Felt devastated when I found out I didn't get the promotion.
>
> Needs: *respect, security, hope*
>
> Frustrated that I was able to get the paper done on time.
>
> Needs: *competence, effectiveness, self-esteem*

More than likely, there will be a *few* needs associated with each instance, but you'll probably find one or two that are most pertinent. As with the previous exercise, pay attention to your body as you read through the list. It usually will give you some cues – the most common being a release of tension in your body.

Once you've completed your list, look it over. See if you can spot any patterns. Are there certain unmet needs that show up over and over again? Make special note of these.

With this list of "regularly unmet needs," you now have an idea where to place your attention. Refer to this list as you go through the rest of this chapter.

Needs Are Like Vitamins

Here's another way of looking at needs.

When our body is deficient in key nutrients (like a particular vitamin) for long periods of time, it can easily become diseased. Likewise, when a person becomes chronically deficient in key *needs*, emotional challenges are usually the result.

For example:

If I'm working on a creative project, I have the tendency to seclude myself. The needs that motivate this dersire to socially withdraw are: *focus* and *ease*. If I'm constantly interacting with people, I tend to feel diffused and scattered. Depending on the nature of the project, I usually do better work when I can shut off the outer world for a bit and just *focus*.

But I'm only good for a week or so. Then, the need for *connection* will come roaring in – demanding to be met. If this is below the surface, and I'm not consciously aware of it, I'll find myself feeling mildly depressed. If I allow this need to go unmet for longer periods of time, I've watched it turn into depression and feelings of hopelessness.

However, as soon as I bring this up to my conscious mind, and realize, "Oh, that's probably why I'm in a funk. I really have a need for *connection* that I haven't been addressing..." — I'll feel re-invigorated because I have a clear object to place my focus on to relieve the uncomfortable emotional state. There's also a sense of *relief* that comes from meeting my need for *clarity*.

The remedy – the clear doable action – could be as simple as calling up a friend on the phone, planning to have lunch, or going somewhere I know I'll be able to see friends.

Granted, this is a very basic example of unmet needs triggering emotional challenges. Usually there are *many* layers of unmet needs lying below the surface. However, the path is always the same:

1. Identify the unmet needs.

2. Identify actions that have (or could potentially) meet these needs.

The "Needs-Actions" List

For your entire life, your actions have been motivated by needs. Through getting clear on what *specific* actions have, in the past, met certain needs – you'll have a map to work with.

A "needs-actions" list is like a menu. It's a list of possible actions to meet certain needs.

> "If you don't know what you are aiming at,
> you're just shooting arrows into the dark."
> **– Fredric Lehrman**

The goal is to have a trusted list of actions you'll repeat on a weekly/monthly basis that are effective in creating *overall* balance in your life. As these activities become habits, you'll minimize those times when needs go chronically unmet for long periods of time, which *always* leads to emotional suffering of some kind.

Survival needs like food, shelter, and water, aside – here's a list of needs that *we all* require to be met on a regular basis:

- Rest

- Sleep

- Connection

- Play

- Movement

- Listening

- Being seen and heard

- Understanding

- Belonging

- Stability

- Support

Let's explore a couple of these:

listening, being seen/being heard, understanding

Perhaps, in the past, these needs were met by talking to an old friend. When you got off the phone, you felt lighter. Life didn't feel so dark, and the next few days went really well. This was a clear indication these key needs were abundantly met by this one activity.

Learning to identify effective actions to meet unmet needs is *essential* in achieving emotional balance.

What Is a "Doable" Action?

It's important to make a distinction between a doable and *non*-doable action.

A *doable* action:

> 1. Is specific.
>
> 2. Does *not* involve an indefinite commitment.
>
> 3. Can ideally be undertaken in the moment, or in the very near future.
>
> 4. Can be accomplished within the means you currently have available to you. (money, time, etc.)

All this takes a bit of self-honesty.

For example, your challenge may be:

> "I am constantly spending money on things I don't really need. I wish I didn't do this. It causes me so much suffering. It often happens when I'm out with friends. They want to go to expensive restaurants. I get caught up in it, and spend more than I intend to. I want more awareness around how I spend money."

Needs: *awareness, security, clarity*

Non-doable action:

> "I will meticulously save and review all of my receipts once a week *from now on*."

One possible *doable* action:

> "I will set up a reminder for myself on my computer calendar that says "think before spending!" to pop-up on my phone every Friday afternoon, *before* I go out with friends.

As you can see from the above example, the *doable* action is present-moment focused. It doesn't involve an indefinite commitment, unlike the first example. It's a simple action that can be taken *right now*. Because of this, it has a good chance of actually meeting the need(s).

Whether or not the action is actually effective should be tracked. If it didn't work – if it didn't meet the needs – try something else. If you stay with doable actions, eventually you'll lock in on something that does work.

However, if you start with a non-doable action, odds are it won't work *and* you'll probably get down on yourself because you "failed" to make it happen. In a sense, you set yourself up for defeat before you even started.

If you stay with this practice of coming up with doable actions, your overall effectiveness in *many* areas of your life will increase.

Identifying Multiple Ways to Meet a Need

It's best to have a few different ways of meeting a specific need – otherwise you're putting all your eggs into one basket.

For example:

If your only means of meeting your need for "connection" involves spending time with your girlfriend, then, when she isn't available, you'll probably feel pretty miserable, and perhaps even resentful. (This is a common occurrence in relationships.)

The remedy to this is to ensure you have a *list* of activities in your week that meet your need for connection:

- Go to the movies with friends

- Take a karate class

- Go to the local club to listen to live music

This may sound extremely simplistic, but I've seen again-and-again in my life coaching practice how this basic awareness of "multiple actions to meet a need" can make a huge difference in a person's life.

CREATING A NEEDS-ACTIONS LIST

Now that you have a bit more clarity in regards to the unmet needs in your life, the next step is to create a list of actions to potentially meet each need.

On a sheet of paper, or on your computer, create two columns. Label the first one "Needs", and the other label "Actions."

Start by writing your unmet needs in the "Needs" column. Leave some space below each one. Next to each need, in the "Actions" column, make a list of doable actions that have (or may) meet this need.

Spend some time on this. Continue to refine it until you've gotten to some actions that feel both doable and potentially effective at meeting each need.

Consider this list a starting point. This list will change over time, as you move through your life. When you're feeling "off" or "triggered," review this list. See if you can identify some actions that would help you meet the needs that are currently alive. The goal – as with all the other exercises in this book – is *effectiveness*. If this specific process doesn't quite work for you, adjust it to best suit you.

If nothing else, by going through this process of making a needs-actions list, you'll most likely stumble upon a few insights that could make your life a bit more enjoyable. In the "Creating a Support System" chapter, I'll discuss specific ways to use this list as part of a regular life coaching routine.

Where to Place Your Needs-Actions List

Place your needs-actions list where it will be seen on a daily basis. Post it on your bathroom mirror, or place it on your computer calendar as a "recurring event," so it gets emailed to you every couple of days. Get creative.

Schedule Actions with Reminders

Once you have a needs-actions list, the next step is to turn these actions into regular habits. Placing them on your calendar, combined with some method of reminding yourself, are crucial steps to ensure you will actually do them. Even if you have a great list, filled with well thought-out strategies, life happens. It's easy to forget to do them.

By placing key activities on your schedule, *combined with* methods of reminding yourself to do them, you are greatly increasing the likelihood you're going to make them happen on an ongoing basis.

In the "Time Management" chapter, we'll go further into this.

Going from Doable Actions to Habits

Over time, as you keep returning to your needs-actions list – scheduling these activities into your life on a consistent basis – these actions will eventually become habits. You'll start doing them regularly without even thinking about it. *That's the goal.*

When you have habits in place that consistently meet essential needs, your life will naturally become more balanced and manageable. It's that simple, and *it will always work*, because you are addressing the core building blocks of your psyche – needs.

Again, when needs go unmet for any length of time, you're much more prone to challenging emotions. Through utilizing this needs-actions exercise, you are (in a sense) "heading them off at the pass" – handling the needs *before* the uncomfortable emotions get triggered.

The Chronic Unmet Needs of Hunter-Types

For us hunter-types, there are a few specific needs that are more likely to go unmet because of how our brain is wired. Needs like:

- Consistency

- Order

- Self-esteem

- Self-confidence

- Clarity

- Perspective

- Stability

Make no mistake, these needs are *essential* for your well being. When they're unmet, just like any other need, they can trigger heavy emotions, like: frustration, anger, sadness, even hopelessness.

As with all other needs, the process is the same:

1. Recognize the needs that go unmet

2. Brainstorm on actions that can meet theses needs

3. Make these actions a part of your regular routine.

As will be discussed in the "Creating A Support System" chapter, a regular life coaching practice can be a very effective tool for addressing needs for *consistency* and *support*.

༄

Understanding Anger and Rage

Often, anger and rage occur when needs go chronically unmet for long periods of time. You have ignored them and now they are *demanding* to be heard and addressed.

For example, if your need for "respect" hasn't been met in *numerous* situations recently, this can build up a lot of energy. We *all* have a need for respect. Typically, our unconscious doesn't just "let things go." It knows, "I have a right to be respected, just like everyone else. This need *should* be met." It's actually watching out for you. And it will tell you, *in the moment*, when this need isn't being met with clear emotional cues.

Perhaps your boss said something to you recently that you interpreted as a put down, and you never addressed it with him out of a fear of getting fired. Your unconscious registers that. Then, a few days later, a friend makes a joke at your expense, which really angered you. But again, you didn't pull him aside and let him know. You just smiled, pretending it didn't hurt. That also registered as "a lack of respect," and your unconscious notes it.

You can see where this is going. A few days later, your wife says something to you, in a playful way, and you completely blow up on her – totally out of proportion to what was said. This clearly was your need for *respect* voicing itself. Because you continually ignored that need, your unconscious took over. At that point, you're out of control.

Had you spoken up in those previous two situations, it wouldn't have gotten to this place. Here again it's about *awareness*. The more you understand the workings of your inner life, the more you can prevent out of control emotional out-bursts.

To get some support with this "awareness training," you may consider taking an anger management class, and/or join a "nonviolent communication" study group in your area. If you have a recurring issue with anger, be proactive in getting support. Don't wait for it to turn into a crisis.

The Breath and Emotions

The breath is a powerful and trusted doorway into shifting unpleasant states of consciousness. When we're anxious or stressed, we tend to breathe more shallow.

Conversely, our bodies are wired to associate deep breathes with ease and relaxation. At the end of a long day, when you return home and plop down on your bed or couch, you'll likely take a deep breath and let out a long, "ahhhhhhhhhh."

When you find yourself locked into an unpleasant mental state, try using your breath to bring you back to center. Take a long, slow, deep breath in, then let it out slowly. Breathe into your belly first, allowing the breath to then fill your lungs. Make your out-breath twice as long as your in-breath.

"I'm such an incredibly, stupidly, sensitive person... everything that happens to me, I experience it really intensely. I feel everything very deeply. And when you feel things deeply, you think about things a lot. And, when you think about how you feel, you learn a lot about yourself. And when you know yourself, you know life."
— Fiona Apple

You may also want to bring your awareness to your belly as you breathe in and out. Typically, stress and anxiety manifest as mental talk and imagery. Through simply bringing your attention to your belly as you breathe, your thoughts naturally will begin to quiet down. You'll start to feel more "in your body."

Remember, your body is *always* in the present moment, whereas your mind is constantly banking around from thinking about the future (anxiety), to ruminating about the past (regret, anger, etc.).

When your awareness is in the present moment, you're far more likely to experience a sense of peace. From this place, you'll be able to handle your current situation with greater ease and clarity. You can waste a lot of energy trying to tackle a problem from a stressed-out state.

Wrapping Up with "Needs Awareness"

As you continue to work with needs, your inner life will become more and more decoded. You'll have a clearer understanding of what triggers uncomfortable feelings, and gain the ability to create supportive actions that address chronically unmet needs. Freedom isn't just about doing whatever you want, whenever you want. True freedom comes from an ability to understand your inner life with a certain degree of precision and predictability.

"Needs awareness" is a theme we'll return to again-and-again throughout the book. As with all learning, this material takes time and practice in order to master. I encourage you to read through this section a few times to gain a thorough understanding of the basic concepts. I also encourage you to research the "nonviolent communication" process, and the work of Dr. Marshall Rosenberg. Most likely, there's a study group in your area. Check cnvc.org for more information.

DEVELOPING A CONSCIOUS INNER DIALOG

"Start Talking to Yourself"

Most of us were taught from an early age that you're a little "crazy" if you talk to yourself.

However, we *all* talk to ourselves *all the time*. But, it's usually an unconscious dialog – meaning, it's just *happening*, versus being intentionally directed by our conscious mind.

It turns out, having a conscious inner dialog can make a huge difference in your overall emotional well-being. It can provide you with a kind of rudder to steer the boat of your inner life. Interestingly, "talking to yourself" has quite an impressive lineage that connects with many ancient spiritual practices, such as prayer (in the west), and chanting mantras (in the east).

Through a conscious inner dialog, you are stepping into that endless mental stream of thoughts, shifting its flow to move in the direction you would like your thoughts to go in. A conscious inner dialog can also act as a doorway into your emotions – calming you down, inspiring you, and carving out gullies for more nourishing thoughts to flow through.

As discussed previously, feelings are triggered by needs. The problem is, if we don't have some midway point – some buffer zone in which to *stop* and bring to consciousness what's happening internally, we can easily be swept away by emotions and reactions – instead of *consciously* making decisions. This is where an inner dialog practice comes in very handy.

An Inner Dialog Example

Earlier in this chapter, we covered one example of an inner dialog in the "getting cut-off on the freeway" scenario.

Here's another example:

> You just received a very challenging work assignment. It's potentially a "make or break" moment in your career (at least that's how it feels.) And you *definitely* don't feel up to it.
>
> Initial Reaction (feelings): overwhelm and confusion.
>
> Body sensations: Biting nails, pacing, shortness of breath.
>
> Your inner dialog: "I can't do this! How am I going to do this? I'm going get fired, I know it. I hate this job! And I think the boss is just doing this to mess with my head. He knows I'm not the right person for this. What was he thinking?!!! Man! I can't think straight, I'm so stressed out!"
>
> Possible *conscious* dialog: "Wow. I'm really overwhelmed (feeling) right now. I'm totally confused (feeling) and I'm desperately wanting some *clarity* (need) on how to make this happen, and I'm also wanting some reassurance (need) that this is going to turn out well."
>
> "OK.... breathe... All right, here's the plan: let's call Scott. He's pretty sharp. I'll ask him for some advice."
>
> Listening to the inner response: "I'm still *really* overwhelmed. I can't even handle talking about this right now. I'm famished and kind of light-headed!"
>
> Conscious inner dialog: "OK. Here's the plan. Let's go to the store, grab a snack, chill out for a bit, then call Scott."
>
> Watching for the body's reaction: shoulders relax, long sigh. A sense of relief.

In this example, the first step was to listen to the internal dialog, identifying the feelings and needs associated with the current situation.

In this case, the feelings were:

overwhelm and *confusion.*

The needs were:

clarity and *reassurance.*

The action suggested to meet the needs:

"talk with Scott and ask for advice."

The body and emotional responses were:

too overwhelmed, needing to eat.

Response and suggested action:

address the overwhelm by taking a break
and getting something to eat.

Action that could help meet the need for *clarity*:

talk with Scott.

Confirmation that this suggestion connected:

shoulders relax, long sigh. A sense of relief.

Inner Dialog Essentials

As illustrated above, when working with challenging emotions, try the following steps:

1. Listen to your inner talk *first*, with total acceptance. Don't judge yourself. Just accept what's there.

2. Do your best to identify feelings and needs present.

3. Acknowledge your feelings and needs in your inner dialog.

4. Propose an action (or actions) to meet the needs that are alive.

5. Listen to your body and emotional response to the proposed strategy.

6. Keep going until you get a clear indicator from your body and emotions that you've "connected."

That may seem like a lot to remember, but as you keep doing it, it will become second nature.

And think of the benefit. From now on, no matter *what* life throws at you, you'll have a technique to calm yourself down enough to make a clear decision, even in intense situations. It's quite a useful tool to have in your toolbox.

The Importance of Self-Empathy

Many of us hunter-types had a rough time growing up, and there still may be some deep emotional scars left over from people who didn't appreciate our uniqueness – people who expected us to "be like everyone else."

As a result, many of us have adopted a very harsh, self-critical, inner dialog that mirrors what others have told us in the past:

"I'm so lazy! I'm a failure at everything!"

"I am *truly* a psycho. I wish I could be more normal."

"I'm just an unfocused slacker. I'll never amount to anything if I stay like this."

Here's where a *conscious* inner dialog practice can make powerful in-roads into having a more compassionate connection with yourself – lifting your self-esteem and giving you a greater ability to pick yourself up after disappointments.

You may catch yourself looping on the thought:

> "I'm just an unfocused slacker. I'm never going to amount to anything if I stay like this."

Becoming aware of this thought, you may want to note the needs underneath it: *focus* and *self-esteem*.

You then could step into the stream of this looping negative thought and say to yourself:

> "I'm feeling miserable right now because it *so* matters to me that I can focus when I need to. And I'm *desperate* for some self-esteem right now!"

Already, you're much further down the road. Instead of just a loop, you're clear about what's creating the negative thoughts. You can then start thinking of ways to get these needs met *in the present moment*, or at least takes steps towards meeting them in the immediate future.

For example, if you're a good guitar player, you may want to take a break and play some music. You *know* this activity brings you a sense of self-esteem. And you also know it took a tremendous amount of *focus* to get you where you are now.

All of this is a kind of mental aikido. It's emotional alchemy. You're transforming one kind of energy – the negative self-talk – into activities that will actually nourish you.

"Don't Get Full of Yourself"

Most of us received some variation of this phrase growing up, usually from parents and family members. However, there's a *big* difference between arrogance – thinking you are inherently *better* than someone else – and having a healthy sense of self-esteem.

Unfortunately, this idea of "don't get full of yourself", at a young age, can get internalized as, "If I'm self-confident, and proud of my achievements, people will judge me."

However, if you want to be successful *at anything* you absolutely require self-confidence. It is the prerequisite for success. If you pay attention to people who've attained success in their field, the one thing most of them have in common is: *a strong belief in themselves.*

Life can be challenging. Attaining your goals can often be like sending a rocket into orbit. You need to have enough momentum and fuel to break free of earth's gravity.

A positive internal dialog, coupled with a deep appreciation of who and what you are, create the rocket boosters necessary to break free from the gravity of life's challenges. They are *how* you maintain self-confidence.

Waiting for someone to approve of you is a disempowering strategy. It places your well being in the hands of someone else. Learn to be your own cheerleader – both inwardly and outwardly.

You may say things like:

> "I'm so proud of the work I've done on this. It's some of my best work!"

> "I have a real talent for this."

> "This came out fantastic!"

If you find yourself having a negative reaction to those above examples, it's a good sign that you've adopted the thought form "If I celebrate my good qualities, I won't be loved and accepted."

If so, you now have a clue where to put some energy and attention.

Transforming the "Inner Critic" – a Misdirected Need for Excellence

Hunter-types often have a very loud "inner critic." This continuous barrage of self-critical thoughts can be especially challenging when attempting to pursue new creative endeavors, or make crucial changes in your life.

> ## "My inner tyrant plays dress-up in the form of other people."
> ## – Alli Brook

You may assume that nothing beneficial can come from self-critical thoughts. The perception most people have is, "I'm just messed up in the head," or, "there's something evil inside me that wants me fail. It's *self-sabotage.*"

However, as I've examined my own inner critic, I've come to recognize that it's merely a misdirected need for *excellence.* Excellence is a beautiful need. It's connected with offering something of value to the world.

For example, if I record a song and play it back, a thought may come:

> "That sounds like crap! I just suck!"

If I go inside of this self-judging thought, there's something deeper:

> "I really want to be *excellent* at what I do. I'm so grateful for those artists that have inspired me in the past, and they clearly had a need for excellence that guided them to refine their craft."

The key word when working with the inner-critic is: *refinement.* Many critical thoughts are simply a yearning to *refine* who you are and what you do. This clearly relates with the hunter-type tendency to move towards the mastering of a specific skill.

Unfortunately, the actual communication of this unmet need gets distorted, and these critical thoughts can be devastating, actually *hindering* us from moving in the direction they're pointing at.

So, the process becomes *re-training* this part of our psyche to communicate in ways that are supportive – that guide us to refine what we do, *without* sapping us of the very life force and self-confidence needed to make it happen.

The process of transforming your inner-critic begins with bringing an awareness to these self-critical thoughts as they arise. When the thought, "Man, I really suck at this!" appears, you can take a moment and connect in with what's underneath it.

Perhaps it's –

> *"I really want to be successful, and I wish I*
> *could have done a better job. I really want to be*
> *excellent at what I do."*

Just bringing this kind of awareness to the self-critical thought can transform your whole experience. Most likely, you'll experience a release of tension, and feel far more motivated to refine what you're working on. Once you touch that deeper need for excellence, it may be easier for you to get to the place of,

> *"OK, I really want to put more energy into this."*

Here again, consciousness is the key.

It's about keeping this part of your psyche in check. It should be an adviser, not the ruler of the land. While it can be a tyrannically leader, it can also be a helpful and trustworthy confidant.

Bringing awareness to your inner-critic is another great example of how to transform your "giant" into something that will carry you forward on your life's path.

JOURNALING

Journaling goes hand-in-hand with the "conscious inner dialog" practice, and can be one of the most effective tools in the hunter-type's tool kit. There are countless benefits to having a regular journaling practice. Here's just a few of them:

- Helps get worries out of your head and into a form you can "look" at.

- Tool for fleshing out creative ideas.

- Helps build the muscle of contemplation, offering perspective before taking action.

- Planning your day.

- Decision-making.

- Creates a clear feedback loop between your conscious mind and your emotional self.

- Offers a method of consciously creating your life (self actualization), by setting aside time each day to assess, intend, and refine your activities to align with your goals.

- Supports freedom and emotional autonomy through an activity you do *by yourself.* You no longer *require* someone else to occupy the role of listener. You become your own day-to-day life coach.

Many of us were introduced to journaling in school. But few of us learned a method that could be useful in our day-to-day lives as adults. This was the case for me. In the eighth grade, journaling was a "homework assignment." I found it a rather pointless activity. I would just write down what happened to me that day, maybe doodle a bit in the margins, and that was it. It didn't seem very practical or engaging.

It wasn't until I was in my early twenties – when I started exploring personal growth work – that I discovered the many hidden benefits journaling could provide.

Specifically, there are two key benefits I continuously derive from journaling:

> 1. *Clarity.* It gets the ideas, concerns, and issues that are constantly bouncing around in my head onto paper (or computer) where I can "look" at them, and work through them.

> 2. *Emotional autonomy.* It provides me with a regular process of reflecting on my day, especially as a way of looking at challenges. It gives me a method to vent my frustrations, really seeing what's going on with my emotions and what may be triggering them. This allows me to get to constructive solutions much quicker.

The Journaling Process, Step-by-Step

1. Choose a method of journaling that best suits you.

If you use a laptop, a desktop computer, or a tablet on a daily basis and are fairly proficient at typing, I recommend using this as your primary mode of journaling.

If you are more comfortable writing by hand, pick up a blank journal at any book or stationary store. If you already use a paper-based planner, you may want to simply add some blank pages and use *it* as your journal, because you already carry it around with you.

2. Always date your entries.

This will make it easier to go back and reference what you've written, track your process, and sort through loose sheets that may have come out of your journal/planner.

3. Journal in a way that feels natural and "connected."

I've found the most effective method of journaling is to *write as if you are having an in-the-moment conversation with yourself.*

The tendency many people have is to journal as if you're writing a book – as if you're documenting your life for someone else to read sometime in the future.

> "Today is Thursday. It's sunny. Yesterday I went to see my friend..."

Avoid this. This method of journaling tends towards the conceptual crafting of words – and is usually ineffective at making a strong connection with yourself.

Focus on what's happening for you *right now.*

In the beginning, many people will journal only when they're feeling triggered. That's a good start. It may look something like:

> 2–21–14
>
> I AM SO ANGRY!!! I can't believe Krista said that to me!....

This can be immensely helpful. It can take that amorphous flood of emotions you may be feeling, and put it into a more concrete form that can be looked at and worked with.

Because we all walk around with a continual conversation going on in our heads, this "mental talk" is *actively* affecting our mood, whether we like it or not. If you can project that conversation out onto your journal, you have the opportunity to look at it, assess it, and at the very least, get clarity on what's triggering your feelings.

Journaling for Planning and Problem Solving

That's a good start, but we can take this process a step further by utilizing it as a means of planning and problem solving:

> OK, here's what's going on. I've got the following things on my plate today:
>
>> Contact charlie about the new job
>>
>> Work out how to get the car fixed
>>
>> Pay bills and do my finances
>
> Reading this list, I'm *feeling* really <u>overwhelmed</u>. OK, let's break this down. I think I'm most overwhelmed about how to get the car fixed. I'm freaked out it's going to cost me a lot of money. But the "not knowing" is worse than just dealing with it. Perhaps I should call Dave and see if he has any suggestions.
>
> YES! That's really helpful. I'm feeling much clearer. Those two other things should be much easier to tackle now.

After going through this process, you may want to add a few actions to your action-items list, perhaps also placing them onto your calendar, with a specific time, to better your odds of completing them.

Journaling on Your Computer

I prefer journaling on the computer because I can type faster than I can write by hand, and it feels a bit more private. It's easier for me to just "spill my guts."

Someone else may have the exact opposite experience. Choose a method that works best for you.

How to Organize Your Journal on a Computer

I've been using the same journaling system for many years now. I have a folder simply named "Journal." In it, I have a different text file for each day. The contents of the folder looks like this:

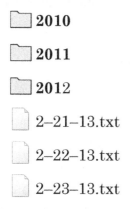

At the end of each year, I'll create a folder inside the main journal folder. Then, I'll move all the journal files from the previous year into it.

Another reason why I like journaling on the computer – it allows me to use the "search" function to find something I may have written about in the past – *quickly.*

If you have a tablet, there are numerous apps available for journaling. Just be sure to pick one that allows you to export and backup your journals, in case you upgrade your tablet at some point and need to move them to a new one.

Journaling Tip #1: Make It Enjoyable

As with all the other tools mentioned in this book, the key with journaling is – create a positive association with it *in the beginning.* Avoid making it into a "should" or a "have-to." "Shoulds" don't last, but they *do* create an immense amount of guilt and self-judgment. Make it into something you *get* to do because you enjoy the positive effects it brings.

Don't get down on yourself if you don't do it every single day. If it's helpful *and* enjoyable, you'll just do it. I often have days when I don't journal. Then I'll go through spurts where I'll journal *multiple* times a day. Stay flexible.

Journaling Tip #2: Don't Worry about Spelling or Grammar

Remember, this isn't a homework assignment. But, you may have that kind of association with it at first. It may feel like there's a grade-school teacher standing over your shoulder, constantly watching your every word, ready to correct your grammar. That feeling will go away on its own the more you journal.

Don't worry about spelling or grammar. Focus on keeping the process as free-flowing as possible. Keeping focused on making the process more enjoyable will increase your odds of it becoming a regular habit.

Journaling Tip #3: Be Mindful of Privacy

If you're concerned about someone reading your journal, and you use a computer, you can always "password protect" your journal folders. Most operating systems (mac, pc, linux, etc.) offer this option. Check the internet for specific instructions. This may give you a greater sense of privacy, allowing you to write more freely.

Be wise. If you have nosy siblings, or spouses, take the necessary precautions.

Journaling Tip #4: Have Your Journal with You at All Times

Ideally, you should have access to your journal wherever you are. Obviously, laptops are better than desktop computers for journaling. If you have it in your planner, keep the planner with you at all times.

You may even find your smart phone does the trick, if you've mastered the art of typing with your thumbs.

When to Journal

This is up to you. I find journaling in the morning, before I get out of bed, can be extremely helpful. Or, you could journal just before leaving your house for work, making it the last step in your morning routine.

Journaling in the morning, before the minutia of life starts pulling on you, can be useful in planning out your day. You can assess your actions, identify potential blind-spots, and get clear on the best ways to navigate your day.

In this way, journaling becomes an amazing tool for self-actualization – providing you the opportunity to *consciously* create your life. You're utilizing a method by which you are reflecting, then *consciously deciding* on how you would like your day to go, instead of just being dragged along by habits, and reactions to perceived urgencies.

"Expectation Is the Mother of Frustration"

Hunter-types tend to have a flexible perception of time. Tasks often take longer than we expect. Our minds naturally move fast, but the physical world tends to move much slower. Because of this, it's easy to get into a situation where we become bored, frustrated, and/or overwhelmed by the enormity of a task, stopping before completing it.

This pattern is definitely a byproduct of our unique brain chemistry (as discussed the "Hunter-type Brain" chapter). It has to do with stimulation, dopamine, and focus. This is yet another area of life where support from others really comes in handy. Through regular life coaching sessions, with someone who is an ongoing observer of your life, you can can attain valuable insights on patterns you've been looping on for a long time. This process can also offer much needed encouragement when you find projects are taking longer than expected, and you're beginning to lose steam.

When faced with the situation of "things taking longer than expected," journaling can be quite helpful. You may write something like:

> "MAN! This project is taking <u>so much</u> longer than I expected. I'm really in deep. I feel overwhelmed and frustrated. There are so many other things I want to be doing, and this is taking up all my time. It's really stressing me out."

> "OK, I want to remind myself that it's my tendency to have challenges with time frames, but that doesn't mean I should quit now. I want to get into the habit of completion. How can I get support to finish this? How do I make this easier on me?"

As mentioned in the above dialog, this process connects directly with building a "habit of completion." The reason why many of us hunter-types have a problem with completing tasks is because we often have the expectation it will take less time.

Therefore, it can be helpful to be mindful of this tendency *prior* to embarking on a new project. If you find yourself in a situation where things have taken longer than expected, you've already mentally prepared yourself for it ahead of time. Ideally, you'll simply need to rearrange your schedule a bit. You also may need to seek out support from someone else, or rethink your goal to make it more manageable – possibly trimming it down a bit so it can be completed in a more doable time frame.

Again, life is messy. The more you accept this, and accept your own shortcomings, the quicker you'll be able to right yourself again and keep moving.

The Work of "Emotional Integration"

Inner conflict is like the friction inside an engine. Without the oil of self-acceptance, you will eventually burn out – or at the very least, not function at your highest capacity.

When you become more at peace with yourself, you'll naturally have more energy to focus on creating the life you want. The tools discussed – *needs awareness*, *conscious inner dialog*, and *journaling* – all actively address this goal, and can, in a relatively short period of time, make a huge difference. I encourage you to test them out and make them part of your daily routines.

TRANSFORMING DEPRESSION

Unfortunately, depression can be a constant companion for many of us hunter-types. ADD/ADHD and depression often go hand-in-hand. There are numerous reasons why this may be so.

> "Whatever divinity we can lay claim to,
> is hidden in the core of our humanity."
> **– Bruce Springsteen**

For one, we typically have a more sensitive brain chemistry, easily thrown off by poor dietary choices, nutrient deficiencies, and exposure to chemicals in processed foods. A depressive state can also manifest as a "come down" from a creative high, or a time of feeling really "up." Extreme examples of this can be seen in a condition called manic depression – now referred to as bi-polar. In a sense, the brain uses up its reserves of feel-good chemicals (dopamine, serotonin, endorphins, etc.), and needs time to refill its reservoirs. This in-between time can be experienced as depression.

Simply put, there are two main components to depression. One is *chemical*, the other is *psychological*.

The Biochemical Link

When dealing with depression, good nutrition should always be step one. You can rearrange your thinking all you like, but if you're fighting against something like low serotonin levels, or vitamin deficiencies brought on by a less-than-ideal diet, you probably won't get very far.

You may want to schedule an appointment with your physician to get a blood test that checks for vitamin and mineral deficiencies. Deficiencies in both vitamin B12 and vitamin D are well known to induce depressive states. If you are currently without medical insurance, there are labs in just about every city that, for a nominal fee, will do a blood work-up that includes checks for vitamin deficiencies.

I'd also highly recommend picking up the book "The Mood Cure" by Julia Ross. In it, she describes a very specific diet and supplement plan to re-balance brain chemistry in treating depression.

The Psychological Component of Depression

Depression rates in westernized first world nations are statistically higher than in most developing nations. This has been known for quite some time. You'd think it would be the opposite. If you have money and access to resources, you should be happier, right?

However, if you dig a little below the surface, these statistics make sense. In poorer countries, people are forced to live in community out of necessity. Family and communal bonds are typically stronger. For the bulk of human history, this was how we lived. This is the social fabric that humans have existed in for tens of thousands of years, and our nervous system evolved out of this environment.

In the west, because we can have our basic survival needs met *without* living in community with others, we tend to seclude ourselves. And this isolation is often one of the key ingredients of depression. Although the Western world is *technologically* advanced, in relation to understanding how to meet our emotional needs, we are still quite immature. Our higher rates of depression reflect this.

In a recent talk for the annual TED Conference, Dr. Neel Burton posed the question, "Can Depression Be Good For Us?" What adaptive advantage could depression give us, and why do all humans have this built-in emotional mechanism?

To summarize his talk, depression may be telling us: "The way you are living your life *right now* isn't getting you anywhere. A shift needs to happen. You need to reconnect to yourself, to your purpose, and what you uniquely have to share with the world." We are not islands. We live inside the collective organism of mankind. The perception that we are separate, and can exist entirely independent of the world around us, is both inaccurate and potentially destructive.

A Disconnection from One's Needs

Revisiting the earlier quote from Dr. Marshall Rosenberg, "feelings are the needs on the dashboard that let you know whether a need is met or unmet..." Depression, in many cases, can be a state of being almost *completely disconnected from one's needs*, and therefore from your very life force. You just can't see how certain needs will ever get met.

To take a very common example – if you're feeling depressed because you've been out of relationship for a long time, and have the sense you'll never find someone, this could easily throw you into a depression.

Underneath this is probably the thought, "I will *only* get my needs for companionship, affection, support, and touch met by being in an intimate relationship. This is the *only* strategy to do this." Isn't that what we've all been taught from a young age?

Again, it's helpful to recognize that many of us have been brought up in an emotionally immature culture, and we've adopted habits of thinking that are quite dysfunctional.

Taking this example, if the unmet needs are: companionship, affection, support, and touch, how else could these be met? Clearly, going out and engaging socially with other human beings is a good first step. Being open to the possibility of having good friends of both sexes could be another shift in your thinking – getting your needs for affection and support met *without* the inference of "relationship" could also be helpful.

If you're aware of the needs, but not the specific actions, at least you have a starting place. You're no longer completely lost. Sit with these needs. Once you're aware of what's triggering the depression, you'll at least have a general direction to move in.

I don't want to, in any way, make light of how immensely challenging and all-encompassing depression can be. It can be a soul-crushing experience, and it can color all of your thinking. But, if you're not getting to the core of it, or just looking to a pill to make you feel better, eventually you'll be right back where you started from. Pills don't yield personal insights, but self-reflection absolutely does.

Creativity as Medicine

If you have no outlet for your creativity, you're missing out on one of the most powerful antidepressants there is. If you can summon the energy to channel your depression into something creative, you're on a well-trodden road walked by countless artists throughout history.

Some of the greatest works of art were a response to depression. It's fertile ground, and having a capacity to go into the darker realms of your psyche in order to bring forth treasures is part of the work of an artist.

To paraphrase Carl Jung, "Enlightenment comes, not from the ability to hold onto bright things. It comes from a capacity to enter the darkness." With all its beauty, our world can be an ugly and disturbing place to live. It's often hard to find flickers of hope.

Moving *into* your sadness, and not pushing away from it, can be cathartic. It's truly "facing your giant."

FINDING THE NEEDS UNDERNEATH

Often, a depressed mood is marked by tunnel vision. All of life is colored by the depression, and potential ways out can feel very distant. This exercise is designed to broaden your perspective on your life.

Start by letting yourself fantasize about what could potentially make you feel good again. Allow yourself to freely daydream.

Then, just write. Don't edit. If you find your thoughts saying, "this is childish" or, "that will never happen", just allow those thoughts to be present, but continue on with the exercise.

Allow yourself to be as far-fetched and dreamy as you want. You may be surprised by what comes through. Or you may find you write out those exact fantasies that have been looping through your head for many months. These fantasies are often your brain's way of devising how you can get your needs met. And, just as often, it has placed these strategies sometime in the future – not in doable actions in the here and now.

Now, read through what you've written. Using the "needs list" chart (found earlier in this chapter), identify the specific needs each fantasy is attempting to meet.

For each need you've listed, ask yourself, "what doable action can I take *now* – or very soon – that will meet this need?" You now have a potential map for getting yourself out of your depressed state. Choose at least *one action* from the list and do it right away.

Place this list where you'll see it, and refer to it regularly over the next few days. Just one or two of these actions can be your doorway out of your current depression.

Suicidal Thoughts

Chronic depression often leads to suicidal thoughts. Here again, these could be the result of brain chemical imbalances, or triggered by the psychological issues just discussed. Most likely, when the roots of the depression are unearthed and addressed, the suicidal thoughts will disperse.

Having suicidal thoughts, especially in our modern culture, is very common. You'd most likely be surprised by how many people you know have had suicidal thoughts – thoughts they've kept hidden for fear of judgment by others. Or, potentially worse, the aggressive and unwanted intrusion from family members. Since most of us were kids, we received the message, "if you are feeling suicidal, seek out help immediately!"

What prevents most people from doing this is their fear of getting locked up in an asylum, placed on strong mind-altering drugs, and/or getting labeled as a "really messed up individual." No wonder you'd be reluctant to "seek help."

The idea of "ending your life" seems to be a strategy our brain devises to meet a need for "relief." Because the emotions are so crushing, the brain runs through its bank of possibilities and says, "we *could* do this."

However, there's a big difference between having the occasional suicidal thought, and a true willingness to take action. If you are constantly obsessing on suicidal thoughts, *seek out support*. It's such a cliché, but you really aren't alone in this. So many of the people that work for suicide hotlines, and lead support groups, have been where you're at, and can relate to what you're going through. You'll probably not be able to shift the inner tide on your own. You'll need some support.

I've listed a few resources in the "Bibliography & Resources" section in the back of the book – all of which allow you to remain completely anonymous.

WORKING WITH OVERWHELM

Most hunter-types experience overwhelm *regularly*. It definitely can be a "giant" of epic proportions.

Overwhelm tends to happen when:

- The pressure of mundane details and "have-tos" of daily life pile up.

- We are faced with numerous challenges simultaneously.

- Our body requires rest or sleep.

- We haven't exercised enough.

- We've been eating poorly.

We all respond to overwhelm differently. Some people just shut-down, while others get angry and "blow up" on others. Some look to intoxicants to "take the edge off," while others do a combination of all of these. They are all coping mechanisms.

Why Are We Prone to Overwhelm?

If you read the chapter on "The Hunter-type Brain," you should have a pretty clear understanding as to why us hunter-types can easily become overwhelmed. When our dopamine levels are low – focus and prioritizing tasks can be *very* challenging.

If you hit a pinball machine too hard, it goes into tilt, and the game shuts down. Being forced into a situation where we have to focus when we're somewhat "chemically incapacitated" sets us on tilt. That's overwhelm.

Here again, in order to increase our ability to handle what life throws at us, a proper diet and regular exercise are essential. Creating good habits and setting boundaries can go a long way in preventing overwhelm from occurring in the first place.

However, there are a few specific tools – methods of "digging yourself out of the ditch" – that may be helpful when you find yourself on tilt.

Overwhelm Tip #1: Map Things Out

Overwhelm is often connected with feeling confused – a need for clarity. Usually, there's a number of "urgent" items bouncing around in your head, making it challenging to pick just one to focus on.

A helpful first step is *journaling* – writing it all out. A friend of mine calls this "vomiting it all out onto paper." Just sit down and start writing.

"There's no difference between Twitter, the emails, the letters that come to me, my relationship with my girlfriend, my relationship with my cat, with my parents... Everything is operating at the same emotional intensity, and it's all happening at once!"
– Marc Maron

It may just be a list:

> Taxes are due.
>
> Haven't bought my wife a gift for her birthday.
>
> My work report is due in three days and I have no idea how to get it done on time.
>
> I'm concerned about the mole on my left arm.
>
> The trash still needs to get taken out.

Whatever it is that's causing the overwhelm, get it onto paper, or into a text document on your computer.

Then, one-by-one, write out potential actions to remedy each item:

> Taxes are due
>
> > * File an extension
> > * Ask my wife to handle it
> > * Plan to sit down this evening and do them online
>
> My work report is due in three days and I have no idea how to get it done in time
>
> > * Schedule a meeting with Mitch and see if he's open to going through it with me
> >
> > * Call Donna and see if that's a hard deadline, or can it be moved to next week

You'll notice that, as you get things out of your head and into a form you can "look at" – your tension will most likely ease up, and you'll feel less overwhelmed.

A few questions you may want to ask yourself when looking at a particular item:

- What are the *exact* steps I need to take to address this?

- Can this be delegated?

- Who can help me with this?

You may also want to prioritize the list based on what is most urgent – what needs to be handled within the next day or two – and what can be set aside for a later time.

Overwhelm Tip #2: Talk Things Through

Talking things through with someone else is another effective method for dealing with overwhelm. Every hunter-type should have a list of people they can call on when they need to "process out loud."

Often, the most helpful request is:

> *"Would you be willing to just listen*
> *for few minutes while I work this out?"*

Here again, just start listing what's on your "overwhelm list." You then may want to request the other person help you brainstorm on some specific items. It's ideal to have some way of taking notes, so you can make a list of what actions you'll need to take based on the conversation.

Through speaking things out loud, they become far more manageable. You can "look at them" and work out what to do. You have the added benefit of someone outside the situation offering perspective and advice, so the burden doesn't feel like it's all on your shoulders.

Overwhelm Tip #3: Get Some Rest

Overwhelm also tends to rear its ugly head when there's a chronic need for rest. If you've been pushing really hard, and haven't appropriately scheduled in rest, you'll be far more prone to overwhelm.

Many of us hunter-types have a pattern of pushing really hard, then crashing. The "crash," in these cases, is overwhelm caused by your body telling you, "I need to rest *now!*" Ultimately, the body always wins that argument, so it's best to learn how to work with it proactively.

Anger and Overwhelm

Just about everyone, hunter-type or not, has had the experience of "snapping" at someone when we're feeling overwhelmed. It happens when we're in "urgent" mode, and our subconscious is seeking to minimize external distractions. It's a "don't mess with me right now, my plate is already full!" reaction.

Many hunter-types are quite familiar with the pattern of:

1. Snap at someone when feeling overwhelmed.

2. Saying something we regret.

3. Having to apologize later.

Depending on how big the trigger, and how overwhelmed we are in that moment – once we're "in it" (in the state of angry reaction), it's almost impossible to stop. Therefore, it's essential to catch it on the ramp-up, *before* the explosion.

In extreme cases, this same space of being triggered when you're already feeling overwhelmed can result in physical violence. As mentioned earlier, if you have a big challenge with anger, *make it a priority* to work on it, and seek out support.

If you find yourself *really* triggered, and close to really "laying into somebody," try one or more of the following:

Remove yourself from the situation.

Give yourself a few minutes to "cool down," so you can avoid saying something you may regret later.

Get in your car and shout. This is a great "release valve" for tension.

Name the feeling and identify the needs that are alive. As mentioned before, merely naming the emotion "I'm really feeling angry right now" tends to calm the part of the brain that is connected with "fight-or-flight."

Call someone. Talk to a neutral party. Again, just by "getting it out" you'll most likely feel better, and have a clearer perspective on what actions to take.

Rest. Lack of rest and overwhelm are the breeding ground for angry outbursts. If you can, get away from the situation and take a short nap. Chances are, you'll feel a lot better because you'll have a clearer head.

Feeling "Pressured" by Someone

Many times, angry outbursts can occur when someone is pressuring you to make a decision when you're already feeling overwhelmed. If someone is trying to rush you – or talk to you while you're trying to work things out in your head – it can be *extremely* frustrating.

An effective strategy in this situation is *articulating clearly what you're wanting*:

"I'm feeling a bit overwhelmed right now. Would you be willing to give me two minutes in silence so I can work this out? Then I'll be able to be more present with you."

That's a very doable request – it gives the other person something *specific* they can do to to assist you in gaining clarity. *Don't assume other people know what you need* – that's a guaranteed recipe for not getting what you want.

Remember, it's *your* responsibility to know what you are needing. Get clear on what *specific actions* you would like from another person to meet your needs. The clearer you can be about your requests – the easier your life will become.

Life Coaching: An Effective Long-Term Solution for Overwhelm

Through regularly speaking about your life with someone you trust – in a focused and organized way – you can circumvent *many* issues that could lead to overwhelm. There's also a great sense of peace that comes from knowing that – even if you're feeling challenged by a situation in *this* moment – at least you'll have the opportunity to work on it with someone else in the very near future.

More about this in the "Creating a Support System" chapter.

THE WEATHER PATTERNS OF HUNTER-TYPES

We hunter-types can be a bit more cyclical in our energy patterns compared to other folk. We tend to have very distinct "up" times, and "down" times.

What goes up, must come down. Typically, if you've gone through a time of really feeling "up," there may be a day or two of lower energy and mental fuzziness that follow. Also, hunter-types tend to work best in short bursts. A great deal of mental suffering and self-judgment can be averted through recognizing and working with this pattern.

The Down Day

Undoubtedly, no matter how well you care for your body, there will be down days. You can think of this as part of the hunter's "resting time" after the hunt.

You may wake up feeling mentally fuzzy or exhausted, virtually *incapable* of doing your exercise routine, accomplishing certain daily tasks, or even going to work. It's like an old dog that lies down in the middle of the road and refuses to move – even though a driver is yelling and honking their horn.

When you have one of these days, see if there's a way to rearrange your schedule to allow yourself some "down time." Much of the internal suffering on these days comes from our inner critic saying, "You're lazy! Why can't you keep up and function like everyone else!" But, this experience can be *completely different* when you truly understand (and have compassion for) yourself. Your inner dialog *could* sound like this:

> "Oh man! I feel *so* crappy today. I don't want to do anything. *I can't do anything*. OK, here's the plan... I'll go to work, but I'll do my best to rest on my breaks and not push too hard."

Undoubtedly, as I've recommended this to my life coaching clients, it really transforms their day. They can actually *enjoy* the "blah" days because they're not putting a big *should* on themselves. Typically, if I have a blah day, and allow myself just to chill out – go see a movie, or just do *nothing* – I'll bounce right back the following day.

If I fight it, it may take *a few days* to get back on course again.

What Chills You Out

Understanding *specifically* what calms your emotions down is essential information to have. Some time in the future you will undoubtedly be faced with a situation when you'll feel overwhelmed. Knowing what *specific* actions to take that will successfully calm you down – getting you to a place of thinking clearly again – is key knowledge.

"CHILL TIME" ACTIVITIES

Write out as many activities you can think of that, from experience, effectively "chill you out." Don't edit. Include both the healthy ones, and the ones you perceive as "not-so-healthy."

The next step is identifying which of these strategies are most sustainable and effective *in the long-term*. Only you can determine what these are. Put a star next to these on your list.

Next, write out some other possibilities that *may* be effective, but you've never personally experienced. Again, think in terms of calming and rejuvenating activities. Here are a few ideas:

- Take a nap in the afternoon

- Go for a walk around the lake at your local park

- Watch some stand-up comedy on the internet

- Call a friend

- Spend time in a hot tub / take a warm bath

- Go to a "restorative yoga" class

- Get a massage

Then, review your full list of actions. Pick the ones that look most appealing, then place them on your action-items list, and/or onto your calendar, to be acted on in the next two weeks.

Tracking Successful Strategies

Over the next few weeks, assess – make note of which actions were actually effective in bringing you back to center.

Avoid getting attached to a particular strategy. But, if a strategy works, *do your best to make it part of your weekly schedule.*

Transforming Procrastination

One of the most common tendencies for hunter-types is procrastination.

> *"I always wait until the last minute..."*

You continually postpone a task until it absolutely *must* get done. Then, it *does* get accomplished, but it's usually wrapped up with a lot of stress, anxiety, and self-loathing.

Once again, it goes back to dopamine. Dopamine is necessary for motivation and focus. Because we're a bit low in dopamine to begin with, it can often be difficult to motivate ourselves to accomplish tasks that don't stimulate us. *Non*-stimulating / mundane tasks often fail to cue the necessary release of dopamine to accomplish the task, whereas more exciting and stimulating tasks can. So, on one level, when we're faced with a mundane task, we're doing battle against our own physiology.

Here's the key: *some part of you knows this.* When a task becomes urgent enough (i.e. the term paper is due tomorrow, the electricity will get cut off in two days if you don't pay the bill, etc.) this sense of urgency triggers a dopamine release in your brain, along with some adrenaline. You are now able to focus on the task and complete it. However, that's a hard way to live.

Diet, exercise, and good supplementation (designed to keep your dopamine levels up), can be major components in transforming procrastination.

Having clarity on what time of day you're best able to handle certain tasks, is another key.

For me, I always handle things like finances and mundane tasks *in the morning*, after I've had some natural stimulant like yerba mate. I never schedule these activities in the afternoon or evening because I know I won't be able to muster the focus to accomplish them.

Here's a list of suggestions for transforming procrastination:

1. Maintain a good diet and health regime so that your dopamine levels are more even.

2. Figure out ways to make mundane or overwhelming tasks interesting in some way. Get creative.

3. Ask for support (from a friend or family member) in handling difficult tasks. Don't assume you have to do them on your own.

4. Delegate as many mundane tasks as possible. Hire a housekeeper, a bookkeeping service, or a personal/virtual assistant. This is probably less expensive than you realize, and can make your life so much easier.

5. Use your regular life coaching sessions to help you prepare for upcoming tasks *before* they turn into emergencies.

Procrastination is definitely a "giant." It's more about being crafty than trying to will yourself through it.

HUNTER-TYPES IN RELATIONSHIPS

Intimate Relationship Challenges

Just about everyone, at one time or another, experiences problems in intimate relationships. We hunter-types have our own specific set of issues that are common. In looking at the "challenges" list in chapter 3 – just about every one of these can have a corresponding "relationship challenge."

For example, when we are having a hard time being "consistent," this may trigger challenges with our finances, putting a strain on our relationship.

Issues with "focus" may create challenges with listening to our significant other. We may get complaints that we interrupt, or don't listen when they are talking to us. However, if this person could live inside our brain, they'd have greater insight into just how challenging it can be to listen at certain times.

Our need for "stimulation" can create all sorts of problems in relationship. We may *unconsciously* attempt to "liven things up" through creating some relationship drama.

The list goes on and on. Many of these challenges can be reduced *dramatically* when there's a firm grasp of common hunter-type tendencies. When clear strategies are in place, and a greater self-awareness has been established, many of these challenges can be worked with and diffused to a significant degree.

If you're aware of what's happening, you can do something about it.

Relationship Drama Spikes Dopamine

Because hunter-types can go through cycles of low dopamine, this can create an *unconscious* desire to create drama in relationship. Drama and intensity can induce a dopamine release in the brain – giving us both the ability to focus, and a feeling of *aliveness*. As mentioned in the "Addiction" chapter, any substance or behavior that can trigger dopamine can *also* create an addiction.

The same tendencies that make hunter-types susceptible to addiction, are the same tendencies that can create unconscious drama in our relationships. Because this behavior is *unconscious*, it can take a bit of time to tease it apart from the challenges common in every relationship. This often takes a heroic level of self-honesty.

Once again, the first step is to bring the behavior *up to the conscious mind*.

> "Why did I just say that?"

> "Is my reaction 'over the top' from what triggered it?"

> "Am I unnecessarily aggravated in this situation, instead of moving towards some kind of balanced resolution?"

The next step is to catch yourself *before* the situation escalates. *Journaling* and *inner dialogs* (mentioned earlier in the chapter) are both extremely useful tools in catching the escalation early on.

Undoubtedly, you will slip up numerous times during the process of becoming more conscious of your habits. *Have patience with yourself*. Recognize that this re-patterning takes time. Just because you are aware of your tendencies, doesn't mean they will change overnight.

You may want to adopt a simple strategy like:

> "When I feel the energy coming on during an argument – the need to direct my anger or 'punish' the other person – I will take a deep breath and leave the room."

Then, you can take moment, identify the needs underneath the feelings, and see if you can diffuse the trigger enough to talk more calmly.

Depending on the severity of the challenge, it can be helpful to find a good counselor. If you have medical insurance, start by first interviewing a few therapists. Try to find someone you feel comfortable talking to – especially someone who has a good understanding of ADD/ADHD. Avoid blindly going to the first person on the list. This can often lead to frustration. Be sure you feel a sense of trust with the person before unburdening yourself.

I would advise looking for a psychologist / therapist, versus a *psychiatrist*. Unfortunately, many psychiatrists are more likely to prescribe medication as a first tactic, instead of as a last resort.

Making Someone Else Responsible for Meeting Your Needs

Making someone else responsible for *your* feelings is a common mistake in relations, hunter-type or not. You may find yourself saying:

> "It's all *their* fault. If they would just..."

> "He's so judgmental!"

> "She should just *know* how to make me happy."

By doing this, you've given away your free will. In your thinking, you've placed the responsibility for *your* well being in the hands of someone else. Doing so, you'll *only* be happy if *they* meet *your* needs. This unconscious habit is often at the root of codependent relationships.

However, most of us do this – to one degree or another – all the time.

Culturally, we've been spoon fed a diet of emotionally unhealthy examples, through movies and sit-coms, as well as inheriting bad habits passed down from generation to generation.

Hunter-types may be especially vulnerable to codependent patterns because we often have challenges meeting our needs for self-care and consistency. We may be drawn to a mate who will handle these needs for us. An unconscious agreement gets forged:

> "I'll love you as long as you meet these needs for me. But as soon as you don't, you'll pay."

This could be more overt (anger and verbal abuse), or it may be passive (withdrawing love, distancing, etc.).

It's important to look for strategies that support emotional autonomy. This starts by identifying what feelings are being triggered for you "in the situation." Then, identify the underlying needs. From there, you can examine the situation objectively and ask yourself:

> "What can *I* do to meet these needs?"

Another question you can ask yourself is:

> "Have I placed the responsibility of meeting these needs exclusively on this *one* person?"

Making Clear Requests

The ability to make clear, doable requests is an art form. It can be one of the most effective skills you can develop. Not only is it helpful in relationships, it's also a helpful skill in business.

For example, if you have a need for *listening* – to just "talk something through" without interruptions, or unwanted feedback, you could phrase your request in this way:

"Would you be willing to spend 15 minutes just listening to me, without interrupting, while I sort this out?"

The phrase "would you be willing to..." is extremely useful. It gives the other person a sense of choice. They'll be more able to offer you what you're wanting because they are *choosing* to assist you, versus getting roped into something they may not have wanted to do in that moment.

Most people appreciate clear requests, and will feel more at ease knowing *specifically* what you are requesting of them. Many disagreements are born out of vague requests, or assuming the other person knows what you want, without telling them. *Clear requests lead to greater harmony.*

SOCIAL SITUATIONS

Challenges in Social Situations – Sensitivity to Sound and Noise

Back in the Paleolithic, sensitivity to sound and to our immediate environment would have been traits *essential* for being a successful hunter. However, in modern social situations, this same trait can be immensely burdensome. Being in a loud room, with a lot of people talking all at once, can be really disorienting.

For some people, it may just be an annoyance, while it may lead others towards a tendency to seclude themselves. Being socially withdrawn is a coping strategy that can keep us from getting key needs met, like community, connection, and companionship.

Here again, the first step is bringing this tendency up to our conscious mind. Ask yourself, "do I find it challenging to be in social situations because they feel overwhelming to me?"

If so, recognize that not all social situations have to be loud and unfocused. Quiet dinner parties, talks, and discussion groups are a few options you may want to explore.

You may also find, as you explore diet, exercise, and the other points covered in the "Exercise, Diet, and Supplements" chapter, you're naturally more comfortable in unfocused social situations. Perhaps you're better with them at particular times of day (i.e. after exercising or taking certain supplements that help boost dopamine levels).

Here again, the key is – *experiment and track what works.* Recognize this sensitivity is common to many hunter-types and can be greatly minimized with a little effort.

Learning to Navigate

Being a hunter-type can sometimes be an emotional roller coaster, and the process of becoming more conscious of our inner life takes time. Having good tools is essential. Through exploring the exercises and suggestions in this chapter, you'll undoubtedly experience ever-increasing amounts of joy and fulfillment. You'll be able to navigate your emotions with far more ease, transforming your inner life into something you'll feel much greater control over.

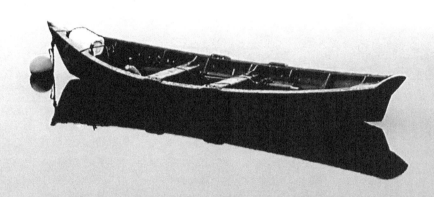

8

SPIRITUALITY

The term *spiritual* comes from the Latin word *spiritus,* meaning "breath." Spirituality, in its broadest sense, refers to an interaction with "that which can not be seen, but the effects of which *can* be seen." You can't see the wind, but you can *feel* it, and you can witness its influence as swaying trees and drifting clouds in the sky.

It's quite absurd to believe that we primates, through our limited sense receptors of eyes, ears, taste, touch, and smell, could possibly perceive the depth of what is really happening all around us. We know for certain that we are unable to see things like x-rays and atomic particles – and yet we know they exist. So, it only makes sense to assume that many *other* aspects of the universe also exist, that just can't be perceived from our vantage point.

I would be remiss if I didn't include a chapter on spirituality for a number of reasons. First off, from my observations, hunter-types tend to be seekers. And oftentimes, it's not in the strictly religious sense. In fact, it could simply be a deep respect for the mysterious aspects of the creative process – an acknowledgment that something else is happening "behind the scenes" that is beyond the confines of our rational mind.

> "Tug on anything at all and you'll find it connected to everything else in the universe."
> **– John Muir**

And secondly, spirituality has been a *vital* aspect of my own journey. It would be disingenuous for me to write *any* book on personal growth and not give credit where credit is due.

This chapter is about the broadest definition of spirituality. And I believe all of the practices mentioned are accessible to anyone, regardless of your religious beliefs.

MEDITATION

Many years ago, when I first became interested in meditation, I recall reading lots of books on the subject. I found a vast and confusing array of practices and reasons for doing them. Over time, it's become clear to me that meditation is about strengthening one's ability to focus – to be more fully present in the here and now. In a sense,

> *focus* and *presence* are muscles, and meditation is a very effective means of strengthening them.

All hunter-types can benefit from some form of regular meditation practice. It can slow us down, calm our nerves, improve our overall health, and increase our ability to focus for longer periods of time. In fact, studies have shown that meditation can actually increase dopamine levels.

Additionally, meditation is about cultivating "awareness." We all have choice, in every moment, as to whether we're in "the driver's seat" of our life, or just a passenger to cause and effect.

If we're lacking in awareness, we're much more prone to unconscious reactions and behaviors, which often lead to suffering – both for ourselves, and for those around us. Meditation strengthens this muscle of awareness to help us stay in the driver's seat.

The Essence of Meditation

Just about every meditation practice contains one basic directive: rest your attention on a single object, and keep it there for an extended period of time. Whether it's a repeating phrase (prayer, mantra, chant, etc.), or focusing on a physical sensation (like your breath), meditation begins and ends with single-pointed awareness.

> "Barn's burnt down,
> now, I can see the moon."
> **– Masahide**

"Watching Your Breath" Meditation

One of the most common (and yet extremely powerful) meditation practices consists of simply watching your breath.

Sitting comfortably, on the floor, or in a chair, rest your attention on the tip of your nose, just at the point where your breath is entering and exiting your body. Keep your attention on the breath, continually bringing your focus back to the tip of your nose if you find yourself getting distracted.

Ajahn Brahmavamso, a Buddhist monk, also encourages his meditation students to consider the phrase "the beautiful breath," as if your breath is the most wonderful thing you could possibly observe. With this slight shift in perspective, your meditation can often go much deeper.

That's the basic practice, and the further you go with it, the more subtle the mind states you'll experience. It can be both calming, and rejuvenating. As with any meditation practice, it's helpful to determine how long you would like to meditate before starting. You may want to start with a five or ten minute meditation period. Then, over time, extend it to a half hour or longer, ideally making it into a daily practice.

A timer of some kind, that makes a sound when your meditation period is complete, can be helpful. Most smart phones have "meditation timer" apps available for them.

B.I.T. Meditation Practice

The "Body, Image, Talk" practice – or simply BIT – is taught by a meditation teacher named Shinzen Young. It's based on traditional Buddhist meditation techniques that go back centuries. I've found this particular practice extremely beneficial, and it can be a good starting point for beginning meditators.

If, like myself, you were raised Christian (12 years of Catholic schooling), and concerned about adopting a practice from another religion, let me assure you that this meditation technique carries no religious connotations. It's merely a method for focusing the mind. Just as lifting weights, jogging, or riding a bike, are not "religious" activities, neither is this.

The Basics

There are three primary "sense gates" that will be focused on during this meditation:

Body: All physical sensations.

Image: Imagery arising from thoughts.

Talk: Internal "talk" and chatter.

#1 Sukasana (easy pose)

#2 Seiza-style

This meditation involves resting your attention on each of these, one at a time.

Here's the basic practice:

Find a quiet place, either in your house, or out in nature – somewhere you won't be disturbed. Sit comfortably. You may want to sit on the floor, either cross-legged [illustration #1], sitting knees bent [illustration #2], or in a chair.

Do your best to keep your spine straight, and allow your head to relax – either facing forward, or tilted down slightly. Get comfortable.

Close your eyes, and take three slow, deep breathes. On the exhale of each breath, allow all the muscles in your body to relax. So, by the third breath, your body should feel noticeably less tense.

Body

With either your left or right hand, touch your thumb to your *index/pointing* finger. Say to yourself, "body." Gently holding

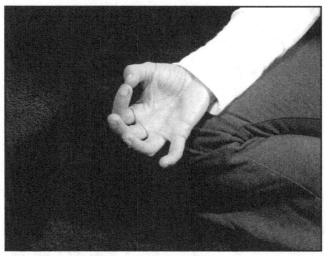

"Body" : Thumb touching index finger

your thumb to your index finger, pick one specific spot on your body to place your attention on. The point where your thumb and index finger are touching is a good place to start. But, it can be anywhere on your body.

For at least the next three breathes, allow your entire focus to rest on this one place. If your mind wanders, gently bring it back to this location. All that exists in the universe is this one location on your body.

You may notice your mind starting to discuss, label, or comment on, this location. There may be a running commentary about the entire meditation process. Again, just keep coming back to resting your attention on the *physical* sensation of this place on your body.

After three breathes, release your fingers, then breathe in and out for at least three breaths.

Then, repeat the process. Touch your thumb to your index finger and pick another location on your body. Do this a total of *three* times.

Image

Next, touch your thumb to your *middle* finger and say to yourself "image." Bring your awareness to the *thought imagery* that is appearing in your mind's eye, as if you were watching a movie screen. Rest your attention there. Whether the thought images are pleasant, annoying, disturbing, or nonexistent, just keep your focus on this "screen" – without following or

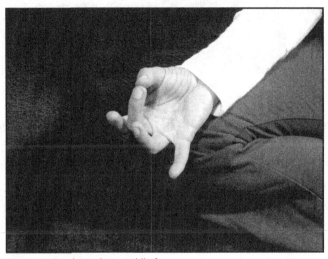

"Image": Thumb touching middle finger

commenting on any of the images. Just become the observer. Do this for at least three breathes.

Then, relax your attention, release your thumb and middle finger, and take three breathes.

Then resume. Touch your thumb to your middle finger, and again rest your attention on the movie screen of your thoughts. Do this for a total of three rounds.

Talk

Next, touch your thumb to your *ring* finger, and say the word "talk." Bring your awareness to the space between your ears.

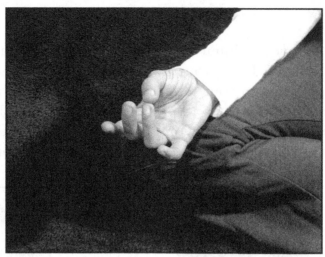

"Talk": Thumb touching ring finger

Rest your attention on the talk and chatter that is going on in your mind. Don't follow it, just become a passive listener. It's not about making note of what is being said, just become aware of it. If your mind wanders into body sensations, or imagery in your mind's eye, bring your attention back to awareness of the "talk" that is happening in your mind. Do this for at least three breathes.

Then, relax your attention, release your thumb and ring finger, and take three breathes. Again, repeat this two more times, for a total of three rounds.

Noting Your Experience

What was your experience? You may have found, as you brought your attention to these various "sense gates," they became louder, and/or more uncomfortable. That's normal. However, you may have found just the opposite. As you placed your awareness on a particular sense gate (body, image, or talk), it quieted down.

This process highlights one very interesting point:

> If you are able to *observe* your thoughts, some part of you is *not* your thinking mind. Some part of you is awareness itself.

I've found no other practice that can so succinctly and *experientially* illustrate this.

Through doing this practice regularly, you are (in a sense) installing three buttons "programmed" to shift your consciousness. For example, if throughout your day, you consciously touch your thumb to one of the three finger combinations, it can literally *boot up* the experience from your meditations. They become "anchor points" that get infused with a specific mind state. This is especially useful in times when you're feeling stressed or anxious.

For me, if I have lots of chatter going on in my head (perhaps I'm worried about something), merely touching my thumb to my ring finger, and quietly saying the word "talk," *almost instantly* quiets my mind.

Other Notes on the Process

Starting with "body," it's common to experience pains and itches as soon as you start meditating. Work with them, instead of against them. Try resting your attention, as precisely as possible, on the point of discomfort. You may find it dissipates. The same holds true with heavy emotions. If you are experiencing a strong emotion, try finding the place on your body where it's emanating from, and rest your attention there.

In relation to "image," as you bring your attention to this "viewing screen," the images may begin to fade. What's left is just what your eyes are actually experiencing – namely, flickers of light and patterns that come from the act of keeping your eyes closed. I would take this as a good sign. It means that, in effect, you've shut off your thinking/visualizing mind, and are left with just what your eyes are taking in.

Regarding "talk," as you bring your attention to this sense gate, you may find the chatter completely stops, and you are left with just the sounds of the environment around you. As this happens, you may want to allow your awareness to shift to just what is coming through your ears in that moment. Experiencing "sound," free of inner commentary, can be a deeply profound and subtle mental state.

When to Do This and for How Long?

I recommend starting with *15 minutes* every day, for at least *three days in a row*. This will give you a taste of what meditation can bring to your daily life. After this, consider making this meditation practice part of your regular routine. You may want to experiment with making your sessions 30 minutes or longer – perhaps starting with the BIT meditation, then moving into the "watching your breath" meditation mentioned earlier. Combining these two can produce very deep and subtle states of awareness.

This practice can be done at any time of the day. A good rule of thumb is: *pick a time when you can most enjoy the process*. This may be in the morning, before work, or perhaps in the evening, just before bed.

OUR THOUGHTS CREATE OUR REALITY

As I've studied spiritual practices from the east, the west, and indigenous cultures, there are two common recurring themes.

The first one is:

> *Your inner life – your thoughts and beliefs –*
> *<u>do</u> have an influence on the external world.*

I've road tested this idea for over 15 years now, and I know it to be true. It boils down to:

1. You *do* have a choice about what you think about.

2. Your thoughts (and specifically your "intentions"), can catalyze events in the external world.

A second common theme can be summed up by the phrase:

Self-discipline creates greater personal freedom.

Any spiritual practice, be it prayer or meditation, is an act of self-discipline. Like physical exercise, any practice of self-discipline strengthens your *will,* giving you a greater ability to focus. The result is being more effective at dictating the course of your life.

INTENTIONS

The Intentioning Process

All long-term goals are made up of countless day-to-day, moment-to-moment intentions. Essentially, intentioning (as I refer to it) is an internal goal-setting process. It brings to your conscious mind what *specifically* you are wanting to experience.

Because we all have a tendency to get distracted and forget our goals, the practice of day-to-day intentioning can be quite helpful in reminding us to *choose* our reality, instead of being just dragged along by life. Especially for us hunter-types, any regular practice of *mental clarification* can be helpful in digging us out of those brain fog – "thoughts all blending together" – states we're prone to.

There's also a hidden bonus to this practice that denotes its inclusion in this chapter on spirituality. From my experience, the more you are clear *internally* on what you are wanting, the *external* may just follow suit in some surprising ways. You may draw to you those experiences, resources, and people, that reflect your inner intentions.

After having taken a skeptical, almost scientific, approach to intentioning, I've concluded that our thoughts *do* affect our external reality. The unlikely strings of coincidences, and statistical improbability of events occurring that were directly related to my intentions, forced me to conclude that my internal clarity was at least a partial catalyst for them.

In fact, we're doing this all the time, whether or not we're aware of it. Sometimes, it's easier to see this mechanism at work when we draw negative experiences to us. We're all familiar with the "having a bad day" syndrome, when everything that could possibly go wrong, does.

This all can be summed up in two phrases:

     1. "What we think about expands."
     2. "Energy flows where attention flows."

My rational explanation of this phenomenon is – at an unseen level – we are *all* connected. As science has journeyed ever deeper into quantum physics, word has gotten back that everything is essentially energy. It is an illusion that I am separate from the world and the people around me. We are constantly exchanging atoms. Perceiving myself as something separate is just a trick of perception.

Keeping this in mind, you can be more open to the possibility that the thoughts arising in *your* brain, and the intentions you set, can somehow be linked to everyone else.

But, don't take my word for it. Try it out. Give it some time, and draw your own conclusions.

"Therefore I say to you, all things for which you pray and ask, believe that you have received them, and they will be granted you."
– Jesus
Mark 11:24

There are countless books on intentioning, however there are a few agreed upon rules of thumb:

> 1. Envision the end result of what you are intending. Get very clear on what it looks like, feels like, etc.

> 2. Imagine what it feels like to *already* have what you are wanting. Make it as real as possible in your imagination.

> 3. Express gratitude for it as if it has already come to pass. Thank the universe, God, that bigger consciousness – whatever you want to call It – for bringing it to you.

GRATITUDE

The Practice of "Being Grateful"

A "gratitude practice" consists of simply naming all the things in your life you're grateful for. Why on earth would you ever want to do this? It turns out, this is quite a sophisticated psychological process.

Through the act of calling to mind everything you're grateful for, you are – quite literally – eliminating the mental state of "desire." Desire always wants something more. Experiencing desire implies you are lacking in something. When you are constantly focusing on what you *don't* have, you're undoubtedly suffering in some way. However, the mind state of gratitude directly connects with "satisfaction" – the experience that affirms, "this *right now* is enough."

Science has started to take note of this concept. Emmons Lab, at UC Davis, led by Dr. Robert A. Emmons, is now conducting a study on the effects of gratitude on well-being. Their findings have already demonstrated that a gratitude practice can increase overall happiness by up to 25%. Participants in the study, after using gratitude as a regular routine, were overall more optimistic about their future, and felt better about their lives. They even exercised more!

THE GRATITUDE PROCESS

Write out a list of all the things you are grateful for in your life. You may find this an easy process. But, if you get stuck, here are some things to consider:

> I am grateful I have enough food to eat
>
> I am grateful for my health
>
> I am grateful for fresh air to breathe
>
> I am grateful that I have a place to live
>
> I am grateful for my friends
>
> I am grateful for my family, spouse, girlfriend, etc..
>
> I am grateful that I have enough personal freedom to take the time to do this exercise

If it's helpful, call to mind how much worse things *could* be. Recognize that you are probably among the most fortunate people on the planet because of your access to shelter, clean drinking water, and personal freedoms.

When you feel complete, pay attention to your state of mind. How do you feel? Did you notice any releases of tension in your body? Was it easy or challenging to write this list?

If you started off in a bad mood, it make take a little effort to create this list. However, after a few times, you may find it gets easier to write.

Consider making a commitment to do this exercise once a day for the next week. There is a cumulative effect to doing this process every day.

Try doing this exercise during your break at work, or just before leaving your house in the morning.

If you start seeing the benefits of this exercise, make it part of your daily routine. It has the potential to significantly alter your perception of your world, and yield ever-deepening states of satisfaction and well-being.

Meals as Spiritual Practice

For many of us, eating is almost a completely unconscious behavior. We're constantly munching throughout the day, while *simultaneously* watching TV, driving, reading a book, et cetera.

"Believe in the holy contour of life."
– Jack Kerouac

Most people are familiar with the idea of prayer before meals. This is a common practice in just about every culture throughout the world. There are actually numerous benefits to this you may not have considered – especially if you were raised in a religious household, and were just doing it just because you were "supposed to."

1. *It's a meditation.* It has the ability to bring you into *this* moment. If you analyze your day, you'll probably find you are *very rarely* in the present moment. You're constantly thinking about the past or the future. A mindfulness practice before meals can be a means of bringing you *fully* into the here and now. *"I am now preparing to eat. I am completely present in this moment."*

2. *It's a gratitude practice.* As mentioned earlier, when you are in the state of gratitude for what you *already* have, you're no longer trapped in the uncomfortable feeling of "wanting." Gratitude and "enjoying life" are synonymous.

3. *It's an intentioning process.* Depending on the wording you use, you are intending that this food will be nourishing to your body.

4. *You'll enjoy your food more.* If you're just plowing through the eating process unconsciously, you're not really appreciating the meal — the tastes and the smells. When you're mindful, you allow yourself to fully take in the experience.

5. *Being mindful as you eat may help you lose weight.* When we eat unconsciously, it's easy to overeat. Mindfulness, once again, shines a light on what's happening, and offers you more choice in the situation.

Consider using the acronym MPG as a mnemonic device to remind you of the process: Mindfulness, Prayer (intentions), Gratitude. Through making at least one meal a day into a conscious spiritual practice, you're bringing together *all* of the previously mentioned techniques in this chapter.

MEANINGFUL RITES OF PASSAGE

In our modern world, most people are severely lacking in meaningful rites of passage. If you live in America, the only ones you're likely to experience are: getting your driver's license at 16, voting at 18, being able to drink and gamble at 21, getting married, and retirement.

A rite of passage marks a transition from one phase of life to another. Without these kinds of bookends, most of us never truly let go of our old ways of being. One life experience bleeds into the next, without definition or reflection. A rite of passage, when done properly, is like diving into a cold but pristine river. It should be both intense and revitalizing.

I believe us humans are hard-wired for ritual. Every religion that has survived for any length of time has specific rites and initiations associated with them. This is the *glue* that binds these communities together. Unfortunately, even religious rituals can be just a "going through the motions" experience – not necessarily getting to the core of what we're actually needing for our emotional and psychological sustenance in that moment.

A ritual should be custom-made for the person being initiated. It should be relevant to their life, in this world, *here and now*. A rite of passage should meet the participant's need for *closure* – marking the end of one phase of life and ushering in the next.

Most indigenous cultures have *multiple* rites of passage – for different stages of life. It's also common in these cultures for someone to change their name in order to make a complete break from past associations. It denotes you are now a new being – free from who you were in the past.

When I first moved to Hawaii in my mid-twenties, I met all sorts of people that had changed their name. I recall names like Harmony, River, even "Jedi." To some people this may sound pretentious, but I think there's something deeper, more primal, at work. These people, either consciously or unconsciously, were making a clear break from their past – perhaps drawing upon a deeper knowing that we're all much bigger than the name we were given at birth.

Unconscious Rites of Passage

Without *conscious* rites of passages, many of us will do it *un*consciously, and oftentimes, destructively. Maladoma Somé, author of the book "Of Water and the Spirit" was born and raised tribally in the West African country of Burkina Faso. In observing people in the west, he noted that divorce is most likely our way of creating a rite of passage. Think about it, if you get divorced, you typically change your surroundings through moving to a new location, and shift countless other things about your life.

However, there's a lot of suffering associated with this. In a more extreme form, someone may end up in jail, or in the hospital, due to extreme behavior. This can definitely usher in a major life shift, creating a clean break from the past.

Intentional Rites of Passage

The alternative is to create a *conscious* rite of passage. This may simply look like pulling some friends together and sharing what you're wanting to let go of, then stating your intentions for the next phase of your life. This "being witnessed by the tribe" ritual is very common amongst indigenous societies. Whatever it looks like, do your best to make it a meaningful experience. It's about drawing a clear line in the sand, denoting that *this is a new phase of your life.*

In my late 20s, I climbed to the top of a mountain at sunset, spent the night up there in the cold and the rain, and burned a list of things I wanted to let go of. I also cut off my long hair and burned it in my campfire. It was a deeply meaningful experience. As I look back, that was the precursor to a very successful stage of my life.

A Ritual of "Letting Go"

None of us are what our parents or family expected. Good or bad, we are unique expressions of the life force. At one point or another, it can be a valuable experience to consciously let go of any painful aspects of our past that we find ourselves constantly dwelling on. Part of our life force can get sucked into these memories. And the energy invested in replaying those tapes over and over again never gets focused on moving us forward.

A "letting go" ritual is one way of reclaiming some of this energy. There are countless ways of doing this.

"LETTING GO" RITUAL

Set aside a morning or an afternoon – ideally on a day when you don't have any major commitments. On a sheet of paper, write down all of the things you'd like to let go of. These could be:

- Unpleasant memories

- Self judgments

- Limiting thoughts or perceptions of yourself

- Ideas of who you *should* be, and what you *should* be doing (given to you by society, family, friends, etc.) – that don't match up with what you believe and value

It may be helpful to start from the present moment and move backwards, to as far back as you remember. As you write, you may touch on some sadness or anger. It's ideal to do this process in a place where you won't be disturbed, so you can fully *feel* what comes up for you.

Anger and tears are often our body's way of releasing stuck energy. You'll see this in certain animals. A deer, for example, after it's gone through some traumatic experience will start to shake and vibrate. It's an unusual phenomenon if you've ever witnessed it. It's their body's way of releasing trauma.

However, many of us were taught from a young age not to cry or show emotion. In a sense, we've been trained to disconnect ourselves from the natural energy flows of our biological organism. Because of this, trauma and negative emotions tend to get "stuck" in our body. Massage therapists often report their clients experiencing strong upwellings of emotion during deep-tissue body work.

Through tears, or *safely* releasing anger, we can get this stuck energy moving again. You may even experience rage. A good way to move rage is to get in your car, roll up the windows, and shout at the top of your lungs. Yelling into a pillow is a method often encouraged by therapists.

Important: Be mindful not to direct your emotions at others. If anger or grief arises, talk to a friend, or someone *not* involved with the issue. Request that they simply listen as you share. Even though you may want to confront the person involved with the anger or sadness, this may just create more challenges for yourself.

The next step in the process is to destroy the list you've just made. You may say to yourself:

> "I am no longer ruled by the items on this list. From this moment on, I intend this energy be used only for my highest good and for the benefit of those around me."

Then, destroy the piece of paper (burn it, shred it, tear it, throw it into the ocean, etc.)

On another sheet of paper, write out all of those things you *do* want in your life – what you choose to create and experience –

and place this where you'll see it on a daily basis. In fact, this could be a good time to go through all the exercises in the "Life Visioning" chapter.

Even though all this may feel a bit like "make believe" – your psyche registers *all of it*. Through creating a powerful experience of release and renewal, you are actually reprogramming your subconscious – instructing it that you wish to move in a new and different direction with your life.

⸎

Living More Consciously

We hunter-types are a unique breed. We're risk-takers and adventurers, both inwardly and outwardly. We often seek out new and challenging experiences for growth and learning. Focusing some of this energy in the direction of spiritual growth can be a deeply rewarding enterprise, potentially improving all areas your life.

9

EXERCISE, DIET, AND SUPPLEMENTS

Let's face it, your physical health affects everything else in your life, whether you like it or not. You can be extremely well organized, have boundless talent and creativity, but if your physical body isn't functioning properly, all of that won't matter much.

Your body is at the base of the pyramid – no matter what changes you want to make in your life, if you don't start with your body, you'll be working against yourself. If neglected, it's just a matter of time before *it* takes the controls, and a "crash" of some kind becomes inevitable. If you don't take care of your body, it has the power to override all of your other plans.

This chapter contains a whole-systems approach to transforming your *overall* physical health, targeting ADD/ADHD-specific challenges with exercise, diet, and supplementation. We'll also discuss specific health problems common to hunter-types, including sleep issues and depression.

Putting It into Practice

There's a big difference between knowing something and putting it into practice. Along with identifying the "essentials" in the areas of exercise, diet, and supplementation, I'll also provide hunter-type friendly methods for creating stable daily routines. It's often difficult for us to consistently maintain good habits, so this piece is crucial.

As you read, I encourage you to take notes (on paper, on your laptop, etc.), and jot down those points that really jump out at you. This will begin the process of "grounding" this information into your life. Later, we'll discuss specific methods for creating reminders, tracking your progress, and getting support for meeting your health goals.

Why Try the Natural Approach First?

ADD/ADHD medication, while sometimes effective in the short-term, often masks the root physiological issues causing our difficulties with focus and hyperactivity. Vitamin deficiencies, poor diet, and lack of exercise, all can *greatly* exasperate ADD/ADHD-related symptoms. This has been well-documented.

The fact is, there are countless hunter-types who wouldn't label themselves "ADD/ADHD." They, early on, developed good health habits which kept their issues with focus and hyperactivity from impacting the rest of their life. As discussed in the "Hunter-type Brain" chapter, we hunter-types have a very specific brain chemistry, which – when understood properly – can be effectively addressed through proper diet, exercise, and supplementation.

Sadly, it is *rare* for medical doctors or psychiatrists to check for nutrient deficiencies prior to prescribing medication. Because these core deficiencies are never addressed, medication becomes a band-aid solution – not providing any real nutrition for the body. Going the "medication first" route, you lose the opportunity to educate yourself and explore the numerous other options available to you.

Many of you have been taking ADD/ADHD medication since you were children and are, most likely, interested in methods that don't involve popping pills. A natural approach can potentially be more effective than pharmaceuticals (especially in the long-term), and you'll gain the added benefit of your *overall* health improving. A win-win.

Everyone Is Different

Everyone's body is unique. It's up to you to explore and refine the practices mentioned in this chapter to be optimized for *your* life and *your* body.

This is why "tracking" is so important. Through consistently checking-in to see *what's working*, and *what isn't*, you'll be able to fine-tune habits that are truly effective.

A High-Performance Sports Car

Hunter-types are a bit like a high-performance sports car (to borrow an analogy from Dr. Edward Hallowell, author of numerous books on ADD/ADHD). We have a very *specialized* vehicle. We're definitely not economy cars. Our brains, when functioning optimally, are capable of *immense* creativity and ingenious ideas. Hunter-types are often the visionaries in a society.

Our challenge is, just like any expensive sports car, we require a *higher grade* of fuel. Think about it, you wouldn't put low-grade, or contaminated, gasoline into a Ferrari. It would wreck the engine, and you'd experience dramatic reductions in performance (we require a *healthy diet*).

These cars also need special fuel additives to ensure the engine is functioning at its optimal state (certain *nutritional supplements* can really help us).

To carry this analogy further, whereas an economy car is designed to be driven at slower speeds, a Ferrari is capable of quick acceleration, and much higher speeds. Driving one demands far more focus, sensitivity, and awareness when steering it (*meditation and awareness practices* can be extremely beneficial).

Also, if you just drive around town, it won't be good for the engine. Our vehicle was designed to be driven *fast* (*cardio exercise* is essential).

My Health Journey

Like many of us who grew up in the suburbs of America during the 1980's, my diet consisted primarily of fast food, soft drinks, and sugary snack foods. As I think back on that time in my life, I existed in a kind of perpetual haze. I felt like a flashlight with really low batteries. Somehow, I was able to eek out a 2.5 grade-point average in high school, but I found school to be extremely boring and tedious. I *often* fell asleep in class.

At 19, I began having heart palpitations. When I laid down to sleep at night, my heart felt like it was going to beat itself out of my chest. I was also experiencing greater and greater levels of anxiety. I finally got up the courage to go to the doctor to get checked out. He went through a series of tests, looked at some x-rays of my heart, and mumbled something to the effect of "hmmm... it looks like there could be something there. I'll have to run some more tests."

That was all I needed. I was officially *freaked out*. My thought was, "I'm 19 years old, and I'm going to die in six months!" That's how I translated his remark. I decided to do some research on my own. After a few hours at the library (this was in the stone-age, *before* the internet), I came across a medical text that mentioned *caffeine* could cause heart palpitations and anxiety – something the doctor had failed to mention to me. In fact, he didn't ask me *anything* about my diet whatsoever.

At the time I was overweight and was drinking about three to four sodas a day. Clearly, they were the prime suspects. (It wasn't until much later that I discovered there are healthier forms of caffeine, like yerba maté and green tea, that don't induce this kind of anxiety.)

I made the decision, right there in the library, to drastically change my diet. I cut out *all* soft drinks, and started jogging at the beach. Within a few months, I felt like an entirely different person. I had lost 25 pounds, and I felt vibrant and self-confident. The shift in my consciousness was dramatic. It was as if I had been living in a perpetual fog most of my life, and it had finally lifted. It wasn't until years later, while I was writing this book, that I fully comprehended *why* this lifestyle change eliminated so many of my ADD/ADHD challenges.

This entire experience taught me some extremely valuable lessons:

> 1. Diet and exercise can have *profound* effects on consciousness, emotions, energy, the ability to focus, and self-esteem.

> 2. My health is *my responsibility*. I shouldn't entirely rely on someone else to know what's wrong with me. I can gather information and opinions, but it's up to *me* to "test it out" to see how effective they are. *It's up to me to become an expert on my own body*.

> 3. Positive changes in health *are possible* in a relatively short period of time. And they can be sustained.

However, this was only the first step in my health journey. It has taken me many years to fine-tune my daily practices. I'm keenly aware that "my health" is a lifelong journey of discovery and refinement.

PART 1: EXERCISE

The Hunter-Farmer Theory as It Relates to Exercise

Going back to the earlier chapter on the "Hunter-Farmer Theory," our ancient hunter ancestors were involved in mission-critical rigorous exercise while on the hunt. Life cycled through bursts of high energy, followed by rest.

Hunter-types need to move. We think clearer when we're in motion, and we tend to feel better.

Why Exercise?

Exercise is the "perfect drug." Just look at the cocktail of beneficial brain chemicals that get produced during (and after) a good cardio workout:

- Dopamine (focus and motivation)

- Serotonin (feelings of well being)

- Endorphins (natural pain killers)

- Epinephrine (needed for handling stressful situations)

Once again, I want to note dopamine in particular, as it's deficiency is often the prime culprit of our ADD/ADHD challenges. During a cardio workout (like running, or rigorous sports activities) our brain literally gets *flooded* with dopamine. This explains why the day or two *after* this kind of exercise we typically experience greater focus, self-confidence, and increased mental clarity.

Over the past few years, just before going to sleep, I've documented the following aspects of my day:

- energy level
- mood

- ability to focus
- productivity

- what I ate
- exercise

The results really surprised me.

After a medium-paced 35 minute run on one day, I could *noticeably* track the effects of this, both the following day *and* the second day after the run. In fact, it was this *second* day that most surprised me. Consistently, this was my "peak day" when I went back and charted out my results.

In those rare weeks when I didn't exercise, the effect was definitely noticeable – greater emotional challenges, low productivity, and overall mental fuzziness were often the result. I found myself much more prone to obsessing on small things, or getting "caught" in external stimuli (like watching TV for hours at a time, even when I didn't really want to). I now know these are clear indicators of "low dopamine."

Designing Your Optimum Exercise Program

There are a few essential points to consider when designing your exercise program. Let's start with looking at the results you'll probably want to achieve:

- It must create greater mental clarity, and increase your ability to focus.

- It should produce stable energy levels.

- It should increase your overall sense of well being.

- It's fun and enjoyable, not something you'll need to *force* yourself to do.

This last point is crucial. If you don't enjoy your exercise program, the odds of keeping with it are quite low.

For us hunter-types, an exercise program should include:

- A cardio workout of some sort (to get your heart pumping).

- Lasts for at least 30 minutes.

- Ideally outdoors (gets more fresh oxygen into your body, especially your brain).

- You do it at least (3) times a week.

Cardio Workout Ideas

Because an *outdoor* cardio workout is ideal, here are a few ideas (for both men and women) to consider:

Jogging/running at a beach, around a lake, or at a local park

Hiking a scenic area near where you live

Rebounding (mini-trampoline)

Tennis / racquetball with a friend

Join a local softball team

Swimming

Hooping

Biking / mountain biking

Join a rowing team

Go kayaking with a friend or group

Outdoor aerobics

Parkour or capoeira (google 'em)

Field hockey

Jump rope

Soccer

Volleyball

Rollerblading

Jumping Jacks

Dance

Obviously this list is far from complete. It's merely to get you thinking about exercise ideas you may not have thought of, that you'd enjoy doing on a regular basis.

Finding What Works for You

For me, jogging barefoot on the beach has been my main exercise routine for the past 20 years. I get to the beach about two hours before sunset. At that time, it's not too hot (I live in southern California, so heat can sometimes be an issue). Usually, it's not very crowded, except on the weekends, or in the middle of summer.

There are few things I enjoy more than being at the beach at sunset, standing next to this vast stretch of water teaming with life. Often, I'll see dolphins jumping, a whale breaching, or a flock of pelicans flying in perfect formation, hovering just a foot or two above the waves.

Typically, I'll jog for 30 to 40 minutes. If I'm up for it, during the last 5 minutes, I'll really push. Then, I walk back. It's on this walk back that I usually have some of my most valuable insights – business ideas, solutions to problems I might be facing, spiritual insights, etc. It's truly a meditation. In fact, many successful ideas (creative and business-related) have come to me during this time after a run.

However, I just really enjoy it. I rarely have to force myself to exercise. Because of this, my running practice is very stable.

Finding Your Exercise Routine

So, that's my exercise routine. Yours will most likely be different, based on your surroundings. Just remember:

1. Experiment

2. Make it fun

3. Assess

4. Turn it into a habit

BUILDING AN EXERCISE ROUTINE

Write out a list of exercise ideas you've enjoyed in the past. List as many as you can think of, even if you only did them once.

Now, look over the "cardio workout ideas" list a few pages back. See if anything jumps out at you. Perhaps you'll be inspired to write out a few others to explore.

Next, assess which of these are most doable, given where you live, your schedule, and the financial investment required.

Using this list, place a few of them on your schedule for the next few weeks. Identify the ones, that you really enjoy, that can be turned into a regular routine. You may want to pick two or three you go back and forth with, just to keep things interesting.

Remember, the goal is to have some cardio exercise on your schedule, a few times a week.

Assessing an Existing Exercise Routine

Perhaps you already have a solid exercise program. If so, you may want to assess it to see if it's optimally serving you. Here are a few criteria to look at:

1. Do you enjoy doing it, or does it feel like a chore — something you *have* to do?

2. Are you spending time outdoors (getting fresh air) while doing it?

3. Do you experience greater mental clarity and balance the following day or two after your routine?

If not, it may be a good time to reassess your routine. Shift it up a bit with some other types of exercise, and track which ones make you feel the best, consistently.

Running and Jogging

Running and jogging are some of the simplest, yet most effective, support exercises for us hunter-types. They can be done just about anywhere, and directly mimic the kind of hunter activity that our brain seems to be be hard-wired for.

Running or jogging *at least* three times a week, for 30 minutes at a time, is ideal. From my experience, the run doesn't have to last more than a half hour to get the full benefits of clarity and focus. Running "a marathon" every three days isn't necessary.

Secrets Held in Fresh Air

Exercising in nature reduces tension and boosts mood more effectively than exercising indoors. This is the finding of a recent study by the University of Essex, conducted by Dr. Jo Barton and Professor Jules Pretty.

> ## "Man's heart away from nature becomes hard."
> ## – Standing Bear
> *Ponca Tribal Chief (1834-1908)*

Trees give off oxygen, and in a stuffy unventilated room, oxygen levels may be significantly lower than outside air. And "forest air" contains higher levels of oxygen than "city air" (*minus* the higher levels of pollutants). Most everyone has experienced that increased sense of well-being that comes from breathing in the air of a forest, or by the ocean – compared to breathing stale indoor air. It feels more like "living air."

Many of us spend the bulk of our lives indoors. This is sometimes due to climate. If you live in a particularly cold section of the globe, or in a city that is significantly polluted, it may be a bit more difficult to track down areas where you *actually* get fresh air.

However, just about all of us live within driving distance of nature areas – whether it's a park, a beach, or a hiking trail.

The fact is, we *all* need the kind of nourishment only nature can provide. Don't relegate nature to just the occasional vacation or camping trip. Make it an ongoing part of your routine.

Putting Exercise on Your Schedule

Some people find a good cardio workout *in the morning* can really brighten up their whole day. Others find exercise *in the evening* works best for them.

The key is – *experiment.*

SCHEDULING EXERCISE

Continuing on from the previous exercise...

Once you've identified a few types of exercise you really enjoy, the next step is to test them out at different times of the day. Assess how you feel – before, during, and after (including the couple of days following).

In order to create a stable exercise routine that really contributes to your ability to focus and be more productive:

> 1. Schedule in exercise at least 3 times a week (using your calendar software, or your physical planner). Schedule it on *specific days*, not just a general note.

2. Create other reminders for yourself (post-it notes, smart phone pop-up reminders, etc.).

You may occasionally need to shift the time you exercise, but you should get reminders to exercise *every day* (see the "reminders" section of the "Time Management" chapter for more details on this).

It's ideal to pick the same days (and times) to exercise every week. This makes it simple. If you have to vary your exercise times, remember to stick with a minimum of *three times a week*.

Exercising with Others

If you find it difficult to stay consistent with a "three times a week" program, try scheduling your exercise with someone else. That's often the simplest and most effective solution.

When you incorporate someone else in with your exercise routine, you're far more likely to stay consistent with it. It creates accountability. Also, exercising with someone else (a friend, a family member, a group, etc.) can make your whole exercise experience much more fun. And if that person falls off, or becomes inconsistent, just find someone else.

The point is, *do what it takes* to make your exercise routine as consistent and pleasurable as possible.

Exercising If You're Not Currently in Shape

It's important, if you haven't been exercising much, to *ease into* a new exercise routine. You want to give your body a chance to warm up to the new activity. It may feel intimidating, or perhaps you have some physical challenge that keeps you from doing a harder cardio workout, like jogging or running, but you have plenty of other options available to you.

Here again, develop a routine that works best for you, *as you are right now.*

Here's are a few low-impact exercise ideas you can start with:

- Walking (start with one or two miles, then gradually increase)

- Rebounding (mini-trampoline)

- Hiking (easier hiking trails)

- Walking up and down stairs

- Stationary bike (spinning)

- Dancing

- Step aerobics

- Rollerblading

Breathing Exercises While Working Out

As you work out, spend at least a couple of minutes focused on taking deeper breaths. Consciously fill your belly and lungs with air.

Our brain needs oxygen to function properly, and most us are in the habit of shallow breathing. By setting aside a little time (even a minute or so) during your routine to focus on your breathing, the more likely this habit will show up in your day-to-day life. This is a key part of optimizing your workout routine to ensure you're getting as many benefits from it as possible.

Exercise in Cold Environments

If it's 30-below and snowing, a five-mile run may not sound very appealing. Winters can be the bane of us hunter-types, because they can cut into a usually stable exercise routine.

If you find yourself in this situation, obviously you'll have to adapt your exercise routine to be indoors, unless you really enjoy braving the cold. Consider adding some simple indoor cardio exercises (like jumping jacks) into your schedule. Check out local gyms, or explore indoor sports like basketball or racquetball.

However, it's still important you're getting enough fresh air. Frequent "fresh air breaks" are essential. Crack open a window occasionally. Take short walks outside, if possible. Do whatever it takes to ensure you're filling your lungs with *fresh air* a number of times a day, regardless of the weather.

Dealing with Seasonal Affective Disorder (SAD)

Lack of sunlight can also be a problem, depending on where you live. We need at least 15 minutes of sunlight per day to generate brain chemicals like serotonin and melotonin (both of which affect sleep and overall well-being). It's easy to become depressed in rainy/cold climates. Seattle has one of the highest suicide rates in the country because of this.

However, the fix is fairly simple – *purchase a full-spectrum light.*

Full-spectrum lights mimic the light spectrum of the sun's rays. Exposure to them has the same basic biochemical effect as being out in the sun. They are available over the internet, and in many hardware stores.

If you live in a sunlight-deprived environment, *make the investment*. It will only cost you a few dollars. Because of our more sensitive brain chemistry, it can be an essential purchase for a hunter-type. Make it a priority to get one *before* winter rolls around. In the midst of brain fog or depression, it can be difficult to handle a task like "track down a full-spectrum bulb." Be proactive.

Yoga

Yoga, as an exercise routine, has so many benefits. It should seriously be considered as a part of your ongoing exercise routine. Yoga:

- *Improves focus concentration.*

- *Promotes breath awareness, re-patterning poor breathing habits.*

- *Is a full-body workout.*

- *Can be done with a group (an added support element), or by yourself.*

- *Classes can be found just about anywhere.*

- *Is community-oriented.* People who do yoga tend to be a bit more focused on their health, so they can often be a good overall support system for your health.

- *Is also a meditation practice, helping strengthen focus and concentration.*

- *Promotes self-empowerment and self-discipline.*

- *Can be done by anyone, no matter what your religion or belief system.*

That's a lot of benefits in one activity.

If you enjoy a classroom atmosphere, look up classes in your area. Chances are, you'll find a *number* of them. Experiment. Each style and teacher is different. Find one that best suits you.

You can also pick up a yoga DVD – check out online videos, or pick up a book. Consider setting aside a half hour every day to do a few yoga postures, focus on your breathing, and end with a few minutes of silent meditation.

"Track" Your Exercise Routine

Tracking the results of your exercise routine – especially noting your mood, productivity and ability to focus – provides clear feedback on what *is* working and what isn't. This is vital information. Later in this chapter, I'll discuss a simple, yet powerful, method of tracking. Over time, you'll be able look back and see, quite clearly, the effects of your exercise program.

⁓

Wrapping Up: Exercise as Medicine

Exercise is an essential part of a natural ADD/ADHD support plan. To recap:

- Exercise (3) times a week for at least 30 minutes per session.

- Make your exercise routine a cardio workout.

- Exercise outside, in nature, whenever possible.

- Find exercise activities you really enjoy.

- Keep to the same days and times every week.

- Incorporate breathing exercises in with your routine.

- Track your progress at the end of each day.

If you follow these basic steps, I'm confident you'll see a noticeable improvement in your ADD/ADHD symptoms within a relatively short period of time. Just as important, you'll be adopting habits that will have *overall* health benefits, potentially lasting you the rest of your life.

PART 2: DIET & NUTRITION

An eating plan optimized for our hunter-type brain (and nervous system) is the second main component to a natural ADD/ADHD treatment plan. What you eat is *already* greatly impacting your ability to focus and energy levels, whether or not you're aware of it. Proper nutrition (as I can personally attest to) can have *dramatic* positive results on your entire life. Simply put, if you're wanting more consistency, productivity, and an increased ability to maintain focus, *optimize your diet*.

As discussed in previous chapters, hunter-types seem to have a more sensitive brain chemistry. It's no surprise then that we're *far more* affected by what we eat than those around us. And it's important to remember this. It's easy to compare ourselves with others, not taking into account we're "wired" quite differently than they are.

On the plus side of this sensitivity, a little goes a long way. A few minor adjustments to your diet plan can have significant results in the positive direction.

"Realistic" Means Sustainable

There are countless books on eating healthy, including a few specifically for ADD/ADHD. I've found nearly *all* of them leave out one very important piece of information – how to actually transition your diet *in the real world,* taking into account:

- Emotional attachments to food.

- Where to shop and eat that are both affordable and satisfying.

- Addressing overwhelm due to the complexity of some meal plans.

With this in mind, I'd like to offer you a simple but effective eating plan, and a hunter-type friendly system for implementing it.

A Hunter-type Friendly Food Plan

As will be discussed, the basic plan for optimizing your diet to be "hunter-type friendly" consists of the following steps:

1. Avoid foods that tend to aggravate ADD/ADHD symptoms.

2. Integrate more optimal hunter-type foods.

3. Find satisfying "replacement foods."

4. Form enjoyable and *doable* eating habits.

5. Adopt an effective support system that includes regular reminders to keep you on track.

Why Natural?

One of the main themes of this book is – how to treat the symptoms of ADD/ADHD *naturally,* without the use of medications.

As this relates to food, the strategy is simple:

1. Eat foods that are optimal for your brain chemistry.

2. Eat foods that are free of artificial colors, flavoring, and/or preservatives.

To make it even more simple:

Put into your body what it
was meant to use as fuel.

Going back to the sports car analogy in the previous section – hunter-types, when we're functioning optimally, are high performance, high energy people. But, we require special *fuel* to achieve best results. However, there are a number of unseen advantages to eating a healthier diet as a method for managing ADD/ADHD symptoms.

Not only can you experience:

More energy.

Greater mental focus.

Improved sense of well-being.

You will most likely experience:

Improved overall health.

Get sick less often. If you eat a poor diet, chances are you catch a cold or the flu a few times a year – and most people think this is "normal." That's what I thought for many years. However, once I improved my diet, I got sick far less often. And when I did come down with something, my body was able to knock it out quickly. For us hunter-types, getting sick is pretty much a "shutdown" experience. Brain fog is a common by-product of having the cold or the flu. And, during this time, ADD/ADHD symptoms typically get magnified.

Decreased risk of cancer. Countless studies have shown that a healthier diet decreases your risks of getting cancer, not to mention other ailments like heart disease and diabetes.

Greater self-esteem. Eating better usually increases your self-esteem. You're more self-disciplined, you can think clearer, and you'll probably have quite a bit more energy. All of these make you a more attractive person.

You're a model of healthier living for others. This may sound pretentious, but I've had numerous people tell me that I was a source of inspiration for them in eating better – just by observing the foods I ate. Through your own perseverance and willingness to make shifts in your diet, you impact other people in ways you may not have imagined.

Less body fat. If you're looking to loose a few pounds, eating a healthy diet can increase your metabolism. This gives you more energy and the added benefit of loosing excess fat.

The Powerful Effects of Food on Brain Chemistry

The foods you eat affect your brain chemistry, just as much as any drug can. Each item of food you put into your body is made up of countless elements (amino acids, vitamins, minerals, chemical additives, etc.). If you were to take all the food you eat in one day into a lab, the result would be *pages* of information.

More importantly, certain foods alter the key brain chemicals that most affect hunter-types, namely *dopamine* and *serotonin*. If you're eating a diet that is depleting your store of these two essential brain chemicals, the most common results are:

Low dopamine:

> Mental fuzziness, distractibility, hyperactivity, a challenge maintaining consistency, and an increased susceptibility to addictive behaviors (those chemicals or behaviors that induce a dopamine release).

Low serotonin:

> Moodiness, depression, obsessive behaviors, being socially withdrawn, and increased anxiety.

This is why eating a healthy diet is so mission-critical. **Most of us are constantly eating foods that exaggerate our ADD/ADHD symptoms.** We think our diet is "normal," not realizing it's actually making life far more challenging for us. We're constantly swimming upstream.

When you eat in a way that nourishes your body, and supports the creation of these two essential brain chemicals, you're most likely addressing the root cause of many of your ADD/ADHD problems.

The "Modern" Diet

In order to put "food and ADD/ADHD" into proper context, it's important to take a brief look at "the history of food" to understand why the phenomenon of ADD/ADHD has become such an major issue in the last 20 years.

In the 1950s, after World War II, America was in the process of retooling industries involved in supporting the war effort. Specifically, the war brought about numerous discoveries in the area of chemistry.

During this time, numerous companies decided to experiment with how this "new chemistry" could be applied to the food industry. "Better living through chemistry" was the motto, and a whole host of new products flooded our grocery store shelves, laden with artificial flavors, chemical food dyes, and preservatives (designed to give food a surprisingly long shelf-life.) They were bright, shiny, multi-colored, and everyone loved them.

At the same time, chemical-based fertilizers hit the farm industry, touting "increased yields" and lower costs to farmers.

Unfortunately, what they didn't take into account – **our bodies had not evolved to digest and process these new chemicals that had abruptly entered into our collective diet**.

If you consult an evolutionary biologist, they will tell you it usually takes *many generations* of a species to adapt to dramatic shifts in its diet. And this process usually involves a good percentage of the species dying off. The time we've been consuming these chemically-laden "new foods" is only a blip on the human evolutionary map. Sixty years, in the great scheme of things isn't *nearly* long enough for our bodies to evolve the mechanisms necessary to process these new chemicals.

Not only that, but they failed to consider the long-lasting impact chemical-based fertilizers would have on our farmlands. Over the span of less than one generation, once fertile land became less and less productive, requiring ever higher amounts of these chemical fertilizers to maintain the same yield. Because most farms also adopted mono-cropping strategies (planting a single crop over a large tract of land), pests increasingly became a problem.

In a diverse ecosystem, insects rarely become "pests" because they have a diverse diet of plants to eat from. In fact, what we often label as "weeds", are commonly pest-deterrent species. When these plants are eliminated, they decrease biodiversity. Once again, the chemical industry came to the rescue, repurposing their stores of chemical agents (once used as nerve gas, in some cases), to be touted as "new and effective pest control."

So, not only did our food supply now contain these artificial flavorings and preservatives we hadn't adapted to, we added to this mix – *chemicals used in modern warfare*. That's quite the cocktail for our bodies to process on a daily basis!

The Rise of the "Health Food" Movement

Zooming ahead a few years...

It wasn't until the mid-1970s that some people started to recognize there may be a correlation between these new chemicals in our diet, and the host of chronic diseases, and physical/psychological challenges that were on the rise (cancer, diabetes, manic-depression, heart disease, etc.).

A new movement began, focused on eliminating artificial ingredients, replacing them with whole, natural foods, not sprayed with chemicals, or "tampered with" in any way. Shocking reports started coming back of people "healing" themselves of all kinds of diseases – without the use of pharmaceuticals.

A new wave of health food proponents were born, and the health food industry was on the rise. Some farmers began to grow foods "organically" without the use of chemical fertilizers or pesticides.

The exponential growth of the health food industry, with only a fraction of the marketing dollars used by the mainstream food industry, is a testimony to the word-of-mouth health benefits of eating a cleaner, healthier diet.

No One to Blame

Although in the beginning, profit was clearly a prime motivator in introducing these new chemically-laden foods onto the market, I don't believe there was any malicious intent – *they just didn't know any better*, and could not have predicted the adverse affects these new food products would have on the public health.

Unfortunately, huge industries have been built on the corner-stone of chemical additives and preservatives. It wouldn't be an easy task to restructure the way they've been doing business. And because they have lots of money, and one of the loudest voices in the main-stream market place (and in politics), they've maintained their foothold on the food industry to this day. This is why it's still difficult to locate foods that aren't chock-full of chemicals at your local grocery store.

What This All Means to You

It boils down to this – if you've been eating the "Standard American Diet (SAD)," it's highly probable:

- You've been *intensifying* your ADD/ADHD symptoms.

- *Overtaxing* your body.

- You're *deficient* in critical vitamins and minerals.

- You'll most likely see a major improvement in your *energy and focus* by addressing just this one aspect of your life – your diet.

The film "Supersize Me" clearly demonstrates what happens when an otherwise healthy individual (Morgan Spurlock) increases their intake of fast food during the span of 30 days. Before even reaching day 30, his doctors advised him to stop the experiment because they were concerned it could start to damage a number of his organs. He felt sick, extremely low in energy, and mentally fuzzy.

The further I go, and the more people I work with, I feel confident in saying that changing your diet is probably the most effective way to improve all aspects of your life. And if you're a hunter-type, what you eat can make the difference between "being successful" at what you do, and a life of chronic distraction, hyperactivity, and possibly even addiction.

The Emotional Component of Food

Most of us have a challenging time shifting to a healthier diet because of our strong *emotional* attachment to the foods we eat. Food brings us joy, relief, calm, and satisfaction. Eating certain kinds of foods (comfort foods) help us soothe emotional pain. To pretend we don't do this, or to get down on ourselves for doing it, is absurd. We all have this tendency, and we need to accept it... then work *with* it.

Any long-term shifts in your diet *must* take into account (and work with) the emotional components of food, in order to be successful. If we don't, the most common result is *backslide*. You'll get really excited about changing your life, make a sudden shift to a healthier diet, and you'll feel great... for a few weeks. Then, the stresses of life beat against you, and to cope, you return back to old eating habits in order to ease life's pain.

Learn to work with your emotional attachments to food, finding healthy *and* satisfying replacement comfort foods, so that you can have a more even and long-term shift in your eating habits.

Designed to Be Addictive

Fast foods, processed foods, and sugary sweets are "designed" to be addictive. Companies want lasting customers, and they go to great lengths in the lab to create just the right blends of chemicals that will keep you coming back for more.

I grew up eating fast food. I *loved* fast food. I drank at least three sodas a day, and lived for Big Macs, and bacon double cheeseburgers. Once I shifted my diet, I felt great. However, two years in, I had a particular stressful day and decided I would break with my routine and go to one of my favorite fast food restaurants. I remember, quite clearly, I ate a bacon cheeseburger, fries, and a shake.

Two hours later I was doubled up in pain – literally laying on the floor in my hallway. I stayed there all night. I was miserable, and I couldn't even get up. The message my body was sending to me was clear, "I can't process this junk anymore! Stop eating it!" That was the last of the fast food for me, and I was grateful for the intense negative reinforcement my body provided me.

THE BASICS

Now that we've covered "the big picture," it's time to explore the basics of a hunter-type food and nutrition program.

WHAT TO EAT	WHAT TO AVOID	WHAT TO ADDRESS
<ul><li>A high protein / low carbohydrate diet 20 grams of a "complete" protein per meal</li><li>"Brain Foods" such as berries, and foods high in omega-3 fatty acids (fish, flax)</li><li>A diversity of fresh vegetables and fruits (to ensure you are getting a wide variety of vitamins, minerals, and micronutrients)</li></ul>	<ul><li>Foods containing artificial ingredients or chemical preservatives</li><li>Refined sugar (appears on food labels as just "sugar")</li><li>High-fructose corn syrup</li><li>Partially-hydrogenated oils</li><li>Minimize alcohol consumption</li></ul>	<ul><li>Identify and address food allergies (especially the more subtle ones that may be affecting your mood and energy levels)</li><li>Identify and address nutrient deficiencies (especially key vitamin deficiencies known to intensify ADD/ADHD symptoms)</li></ul>

What to Avoid

In many ways, eliminating those foods that are intensifying your ADD/ADHD symptoms, can be the most important step you can take in transforming your diet. Simply by eliminating some key food items, without any other supplementation, can result in noticeable results in energy and focus levels. By all accounts, hunter-types are more affected by the foods we eat, compared to the rest of the population. Revisiting the earlier analogy – if you put poor fuel into a sports car, it's likely to wreck the engine, and it will *most definitely* decrease performance.

Foreign Chemicals Take Energy to Process

Digesting foreign chemicals (substances our bodies didn't evolve to process) takes energy. The less energy your body needs for digestion, the more energy it will have for thinking, repairing damaged tissue, and a whole host of other tasks.

For many of us, our body is working overtime just to deal with the toxins we're ingesting. In fact, our digestive process often resembles what happens when we're attempting to fight off a virus. Our white cell count increases, and the organs that filter out toxins (such as our liver and kidneys) have to work overtime. Our body never gets a break.

Through eating foods that are easier to digest, and nutrient-rich, we're giving our body what it needs to "streamline operations." The obvious results are more even energy, and overall improved brain functioning.

Refined Sugar

Refined sugar is in just about every processed food available. Not only in "sweets," it's ubiquitous in items such as potato chips, salad dressings, soups, and ketchup, to name just a few. Consumption of sweets has increased over 400% in the last 150 years – running nearly parallel with the staggering growth in both diabetes and cancer.

On a product ingredients list, refined sugar is listed simply as "sugar." If not preceded by words like "organic" or "cane" – sugar when by itself on a label always means *refined* sugar.

As the name implies, this is not sugar in its natural form, as it comes from the sugar cane. In fact, most refined sugar is derived from sugar beets. It's heavily processed using a whole host of chemicals. During refinement, nearly all of the nutrients that *were* in the sugar cane (or sugar beet) get extracted. Blackstrap molasses, one of the derivatives of the process, is actually an excellent source of calcium, magnesium, potassium, and iron. One tablespoon provides up to 20% of the daily value of each of those nutrients. In fact, blackstrap molasses has been sold as a health supplement for many years.

What's left over, *after* the refining process, is a super concentrated, ultra-sweet substance, that resembles something more like cocaine (another highly concentrated plant material) than a food substance. This is why refined sugar can be so addictive.

OK, that's all fine and good, but what harm is it really doing to you, and how does this relate to ADD/ADHD?

Here's what happens in your body when you drink a typical can of soda, which contains (on average) at least 10 teaspoons of refined sugar. If it were something like a super-sized drink from a fast food restaurant, that number would be much higher.

To start with, your body recognizes that a massive amount of glucose (sugar) has been dumped into your body that now needs to be processed. Your pancreas frantically starts pumping out insulin to manage this new influx of glucose. This partially explains why so many people develop diabetes (at ever-younger ages). Their pancreas just can't keep up with this extreme day-in, day-out glucose intake.

During this time of glucose processing, your immune system also becomes compromised. Studies have shown that our immune system is lowered for literally *hours* after having some food or drink that contains high amounts of refined sugar – leaving you wide open for any viruses that may be floating around in the air, or ones that are already in your body, that your immune system has been keeping at bay.

This explains why, when people remove refined sugar from their diet, they commonly find they get sick far less frequently. Their body is no longer being continually shocked by this highly concentrated substance on a regular basis.

Your brain is also affected. The digesting of large amounts of refined sugars tends to deplete key brain chemicals, such as serotonin and endorphins. In fact, author Julia Ross in her book, "The Mood Cure" names refined sugar as the top "bad mood food," because of its ability to deplete brain chemicals needed to regulate mood.

OK, but here's the kicker. In recent studies at the University of Bordeaux, France, a scientist named Serge Ahmed demonstrated that refined sugar *surpasses cocaine* in its addictive qualities, even in drug-sensitized individuals. In experiments done on lab rats, the rats consistently chose refined sugar over cocaine, thus making refined sugar one of the most addictive substances available on the market.

What Goes Up Must Come Down

We're all familiar with the high we get from eating something particularly sweet. We're also aware of what the "crash" feels like when we eventually come down. We often feel dull, fuzzy, and sleepy. Then the sugar cravings kick in again, moving you to seek out another sugary "hit."

Many of us cycle through this same routine five or six times a day, if not more. And every time we do, we're taxing our body and our brain chemistry – significantly aggravating our ADD/ADHD challenges.

White Flour Starches and High-fructose Corn Syrup

High-fructose corn syrup and white flour products are nearly identical to refined sugar when it comes to their effect on the body. These products also convert to glucose rapidly and are not in a form our bodies have evolved to process.

"White flour" is used in many products including: cookies, breads, cakes, crackers, and cereal. These are a double-dose of "the bads," because they often contain lots of refined sugar as well. The good news is, you can find versions of all of these foods that contain more wholesome ingredients. More about this a bit later.

The "Artificials" – Colorings, Flavorings, and Preservatives

To continue on with the theme of "not putting into your body what it didn't evolve to process," there's a whole host of chemicals in our modern diet that are most likely "bringing us down" on a daily basis.

In regards to food dyes, a 2004 double-blind study conducted by researchers Boris and Mandel, at North Shore Hospital-Cornell Medical Center, New York, found:

> Children with ADHD had marked reactions to foods with artificial colorings and preservatives. After removing these from their diet, there was a significant diminishing of their ADHD symptoms.

According to Michael F. Jacobson, the executive director of Center For Science In the Public Interest (CSPI):

> "These synthetic chemicals do absolutely nothing to improve the nutritional quality or safety of foods, but trigger behavior problems in children and, possibly, cancer in anybody."

James Huff, an associate at the National Toxicology Program, further confirms this statement,

> "Some dyes have caused cancers in animals, contain cancer-causing contaminants, or have been inadequately tested for cancer or other problems. Their continued use presents unnecessary risks to humans, especially young children. It's disappointing that the [U.S. Food and Drug Administration] has not addressed the toxic threat posed by food dyes."

Identifying "The Artificials"

Identifying these substances on product labels is fairly simple. Start by looking for anything with the prefix "artificial" in the ingredients list. Food dyes are usually listed with a number: (yellow no. 5, red #40, etc.).

With regard to artificial flavorings and preservatives (also common in processed foods) – these may be a little harder to identify. Most artificial flavorings are derived from petroleum (yes, oil – the same substance you put in your car).

Sodium benzoate, one of the most common preservatives, is now documented as increasing hyperactivity in ADHD children according to a recent study by Dr. Jim Stevenson, and his team of researchers, from the University of Southampton, United Kingdom.

What To Eat

Now that we've explored what *not* to eat, let's examine what an optimum diet for us hunter-types looks like. Again, everyone's body is different, but there are a few universal dietary recommendations that seem to be effective across-the-board for us hunter-types.

The ideal hunter-type diet consists of the following:

- Higher protein (20g per meal).

- Lower carbohydrates.

- Omega-3 fatty acids (fresh fish).

- Healthy fats and oils.

- A mix of live greens, vegetables, and fresh fruits.

Higher Protein / Lower Carb

"Higher protein, lower carb", that's the magic formula. We hunter-types function at our best when we have a higher protein / low carbohydrate diet. And there's a very clear-cut reason why this is so.

Protein is made up of amino acids, which, as you may recall from your high school biology class, are the essential building blocks of life. In fact, the word *protein* is Greek for "of primary importance." Without adequate amounts of protein, our body can't produce the vital brain chemicals required for sustained focus, motivation, and well being. Once again, it comes back to those two primary neurotransmitters, *dopamine* and *serotonin*.

Paleolithic Diet - "A Hunter's Diet"

A high protein / low carbohydrate diet would have been the typical diet of our ancient hunter ancestors. In studying hunter-gatherer tribes still existing in remote regions of the world today, their diet is typically high in protein, followed by fresh harvested vegetables of some kind, and much lower amounts of sugars (fruits) and possibly some grains (carbs).

This was the diet practiced by humans for millennia. It only makes sense that when hunter-types adopt this way of eating, we can think clearer and have more energy. Genetically, we're wired for it. This diet is commonly referred to as "the paleolithic diet" (or simply, "the paleo diet," if you're researching it online).

Not All Proteins Are Created Equal

Although there are many sources of protein, a few stand out as being more ideal than others. In fact, our body isn't actually looking for "protein," per se, it's looking for *amino acids*. And certain proteins have a more robust "amino acid profile" than others.

If you're of an omnivorous bent, these would include:

- Fish
- Eggs
- Goat
- Poultry (chicken, turkey, etc.)
- Select dairy products from cows, goats, and sheep (provided you are not lactose intolerant)

For my fellow vegetarians, it's important to look for "complete proteins" – foods that contain all 22 essential amino acids:

- *Combinations* of either *seeds and legumes*, or *grains and legumes*, such as hummus, or rice and beans. Combining dairy with any vegetable protein source usually makes a "complete protein" as well.

- Quinoa (the Peruvian "super grain", is a complete protein on its own).

- Nuts: black walnuts, brazil nuts, cashews, macadamia nuts, hickory nuts, almonds, pecans, and pistachios.

- Seeds (pumpkin, sunflower, sesame, etc.).

- Nutritional yeast.

- Cottage cheese (one of the most concentrated complete proteins a vegetarian can eat).

- Protein powders made of rice, peas, and/or whey (one of the simplest means of ensuring you're getting enough protein, especially at breakfast).

Why Organic, Free-Range, and Grass-Fed Are So Important

When assembling the protein part of your diet, it's important to include only those protein sources that are "clean" – devoid of the "extra chemicals" issue discussed earlier. Having a little background into "the modern history of meat" can be helpful in making informed decisions.

Over the past 60 years, the commercial meat industry has gone from mostly family-owned farms, to being dominated by commercial farms. This, in large part, is due to the demand of the fast food industry, which has grown exponentially since the 1950s. These commercial farms utilize the same assembly-line mentality used in the manufacturing of automobiles – applying these same methods to animals. Apart from the atrocious living conditions these animals face on a daily basis, there are some serious *societal* health risks involved as well.

Because these animals are packed and stacked like pallets in a warehouse, they're far more prone to disease. To address this issue, commercial farms adopted the practice of pumping into each animal a steady stream of *antibiotics*. When you eat this antibiotic laden-meat on a regular basis, *you* are now ingesting these antibiotics, slowly building up your tolerance to them. When you *do* need to use antibiotics, you may require ever higher doses to attain the same effect.

The *big* concern about this practice (that has global health organizations increasingly worried) – the conditions in these factory farms are the *perfect* breeding grounds for super strains of viruses that have built up an immunity to our antibiotics. These "super viruses" have the potential to create a pandemic. There are numerous examples over the past few decades of health epidemics being traced back to factory farms.

But wait, there's more...

The livestock in factory farms are typically fed the absolute minimal diet to keep them alive. You may be shocked to hear what was fed to the animal you ate for lunch. Common "feed" in commercial farms may consist of gelatin (from hooves of cattle and other species), rendered horse meat, and fats, oils, grease, and tallow from cattle and other species.

According to James A. Riddle, Endowed Chair in Agricultural Systems, University of Minnesota,

> "It is totally unnatural to feed them [livestock] animal by-products and manure, but that is exactly what high output industrial factory farms, especially dairy farms, are doing, since these are cheap sources of protein."

As you can imagine, poor quality input, yields poor quality output. So, even though you *are* eating potentially good sources of protein, they may be far from ideal.

What's the answer to this dilemma?

Simple. When shopping for your meat products, look for labels that say "organic," "free range," or "grass-fed." These are usually sourced from smaller farms that typically don't use antibiotics. And these farms usually place a much higher emphasis on humane animal treatment, ensuring their livestock is properly nourished.

The nutrient quality of this meat is typically higher, and you're supporting companies that are actually contributing to the overall health of society.

Dangers of Too Much Protein

Is there a danger of eating too much protein? This depends a great deal on the source of the protein. It's well known that eating a diet consisting primarily of red meat increases your risk of heart disease quite dramatically. This is why "red meat" is not on the list as a recommended protein sources. Also, certain fish contain high amounts of mercury, depending on where it came from.

Once again, the key is – *educate yourself*. Ideally, only eat fish three times a week, and pay attention to where it comes from (wild Alaskan salmon, for example, is known to have very low amounts mercury). Also, purchasing your meat from a trusted source (like a local health food store, or a brand known for its attention to food quality) can simplify your entire shopping process. They've already done the groundwork for you.

So, What's the Problem with Carbohydrates?

To understand why high amounts of carbohydrates in your diet can compound ADD/ADHD symptoms, there's one basic thing to remember:

carbohydrates convert to sugar.

To your body, carbs are sugar. So, the same basic principles discussed earlier with regard to refined sugar, often apply to carbohydrates. Our body turns carbs into sugars, requiring insulin production. Then, it *stores the excess "energy" on your body in the form of fat.* It's not "fat" that's making most of us fat, carbs and sugars are the usual culprits.

Fast Carbs vs Slow Carbs

However, our body *does* need carbohydrates, and our brain, in particular, requires good sources of carbohydrates for it to function properly. It's all about choosing which ones, and in which quantities.

"Slow carbs" are, in a sense, "good carbs." They are *unprocessed* carbohydrates, in the form of *vegetables*, *fruits*, and *whole grains*.

These "slow burn" carbs provide the body with a much more even, digestible form of carbohydrate, that can be easily assimilated into the body. They takes less insulin to process, and are much less taxing on our pancreas.

The "glycemic index" is the simplest method of determining if something is a "slow carb" or a "fast carb." A quick internet search will offer up a number of websites detailing the glycemic index for a wide range of foods. The higher the item is on the glycemic index, the more glucose it has, the faster your body converts it to sugar, and the more insulin is needed to process it. As discussed earlier, all white flour starches (donuts, cereals, white bread, pastries, etc.) typically fall into the "fast carb" category.

The "Good Fats": Essential Fatty Acids

Because our modern diet is inundated with refined sugars and fast burning carbs, obesity and diabetes have increasingly become a health issue. The endless array of "lose weight quick" diet fads over the past few decades have been an attempt to address this. The unfortunate casualty in all of this has been the "good fats." As already mentioned, our obesity problems are primarily due to a high intake of refined sugars and white starchy foods, and not necessarily from the fat itself.

The fact is, your brain is at least two-thirds fat.

However, there is one particular type of fat that your brain *absolutely* needs:

omega-3 essential fatty acids

Scientists have known for quite some time that the human brain made a giant leap in its development around 200,000 years ago. But, it remained a mystery as to what may have caused this. As the fossil records were examined in more detail, it was determined that groups of people *living near bodies of water* had a more developed brain than their inland-dwelling counterparts. What differentiated these coastal dwelling people was their more diverse diet, which consisted of higher amounts of seafood. The studies concluded it was the *omega-3 fats* in their seafood diet that caused this spurt in brain growth, which ushered in modern humans.

Zooming ahead to the present day, recent studies on depression have shown that societies with higher amounts of seafood in their diet (such as Japan) have significantly lower rates of depression.

Omega-3 fats are the ultimate brain food, and come from primarily two sources: fish, and certain seed oils, such as flaxseed oil. Interestingly, omega-3 fats can also raise dopamine levels by up to 40%. That's big news for us hunter-types. They contain what's known as an MAO inhibitor, which "inhibits" the monoamine oxidase (MAO) enzyme that breaks down dopamine and serotonin. Omega-3s, in essence, become protectors of these essential "good mood" focus/motivation brain chemicals.

The Importance of Live Greens, Vegetables, and Fruits

Since we were children, we've heard the phrase, "eat your vegetables." However, these "vegetables" were often canned, swimming in a gelatinous goo, and highly processed. I don't think I had actually eaten a really "fresh" fruit or vegetable until I moved to Kauai in the late 1990s. Eating fresh fruits and vegetables, properly grown (and not sprayed), was a stunning and revelatory experience. The taste was vibrant and complex – nothing like the usual grocery store fruits and veggies I was used to on the mainland.

The fact is, our bodies rely on fresh fruits and vegetables for countless nutrients, including *enzymes, vitamins and minerals.*

Enzymes are what constitute something being "alive." When our body becomes depleted of its finite store of enzymes, it decays, and eventually dies. Enzymes are killed when a fresh fruit or vegetable is heated over 114° F. This is the underpinning of the "raw food" movement – people who only eat raw, uncooked fruits and vegetables.

In regards to vitamins and minerals – even if you take supplements to get your daily dose, some of these nutrients may not be in a form that our bodies can easily absorb in this more concentrated form. Our bodies are designed to extract minerals from whole-plant sources.

Here again, this is where the "organic" label can be helpful. Although not always the case, if your fruits and vegetables are grown organically, there's a greater chance they'll contain more vitamins and minerals, because organic farmers tend to focus on "remineralizing" their land. Most standard factory farms have been monocropping the same area for many years, which leads to a depletion of minerals in the soil. Low minerals in the soil means low minerals in the produce grown on that soil.

Going back to my Kauai experience, I wanted to understand why these freshly-grown island fruits and veggies tasted so much better than what I had been eating on the mainland. The answer, as it turns out, was *minerals*. Kauai is one of the oldest islands in the Hawaiian island chain, and has mineral-rich soil. This soil is made up of volcanic rock that has been worn down, over millennia, into a powder. These higher concentrations of minerals lead to better tasting fruits and veggies.

Berries

When discussing hunter-type friendly fruits, berries (blueberries, raspberries, strawberries, etc.) should be especially noted. Berries definitely fall under the "brain food" category. They are packed with "good for the brain" nutrients, and have a lower glycemic index, compared to other fruits.

In a recent article on ABC news, the cognitive effects of eating berries was highlighted, citing the work of Dr. Elizabeth Devore (Brigham and Women's Hospital, Boston, MA):

> "Starting in 1995, cognitive, or intellectual, function was measured in the participants on two separate occasions. When Devore and her colleagues examined the data, they found that participants who had recorded increased servings of blueberries and strawberries preserved their brain function to a greater degree than those who had not."

Fresh organic berries, whether in smoothies, or on their own, are a great snack food to add to your daily routine.

Hunter-Types as Vegetarians

"Hunter-type" doesn't *necessarily* mean "omnivore."

I've been a vegetarian for going on 20 years now, and I easily get all my daily protein needs from vegetable sources.

People come to vegetarianism for numerous reasons. For some, it's ethical concerns about the treatment of animals, for others, because of its health benefits. Some vegetarians will occasionally eat fish and poultry, while others are strict vegans – eliminating all animal-based products from their diet, including dairy.

Any of these vegetarian "types" can adopt a hunter-type friendly diet, with one important caveat: *be sure you are getting enough amino acids in the form of complete proteins.*

If you're a hunter-type *and* a vegetarian, the "20 grams of a complete protein per meal" rule still applies. I can attest to this first hand. Those days when I forget to eat enough protein, there's a clear difference in my energy and focus levels. As stated earlier, the human brain evolved to its current state through humans eating animal protein. If we're going to keep our brain chemistry (dopamine, serotonin, etc.) in top form, we need a full dose of amino acids in the form of protein.

Also, being vegetarian requires some extra supplementation because we're not eating meat. Specifically, we can often be deficient in vitamin B12, and possibly vitamin D. Most vitamin supplements contain B12, and it can also be sourced from something like nutritional yeast, which also makes an excellent cheese substitute that's also high in protein. Not all vegetarians are low in vitamin D, but it's important to get a blood test every year or so to ensure that your vitamin D levels are good. Low vitamin D can cause numerous problems, including depression, and a greater likelihood of getting certain types of cancer.

A Diverse Diet Is a Healthy Diet

I realize that's a lot of information to take in. A simple rule-of-thumb that can be helpful when redesigning your diet plan, with an eye on getting the most amount of nutrients into your body:

Aim for a wide variety of colors when purchasing your fresh produce.

Coloring and nutrients go hand-in-hand. If you focus on getting a broad selection of colors in your fresh produce, you'll, most likely, be getting a good diversity of vitamins and minerals.

༄

DEFICIENCIES & FOOD ALLERGIES

Vitamin and Mineral Deficiencies

If your diet consists primarily of processed and "fast" foods, there's a good chance you have vitamin and mineral deficiencies. If these deficiencies are extreme enough, you may already be witnessing the effects. Here again, if your brain isn't getting the nutrition it needs, ADD/ADHD symptoms can become heightened. Vitamin and mineral deficiencies can lead to a whole host of problems: emotional, neurological, organs not functioning properly, et cetera. Depression, for example, can often be the result of low vitamin B12, B6, or vitamin D.

The good news is, deficiencies are usually easy to address.

Checking for Deficiencies - Blood Tests

If you have medical insurance, checking for deficiencies is as simple as scheduling an appointment with your doctor. Ask them to do a *thorough* blood test to check for vitamin and mineral deficiencies. They may require you to get a complete "physical" along with it.

Be sure to get a copy of the results, not just a phone call from your doctor telling you what you're low (or possibly high) in. Get a print out so you can look it over. Recently, it's become common practice for blood test results to be made available online. These reports provide extremely valuable information when developing a supplement program (discussed later in this chapter).

If you don't have medical insurance, there are local testing facilities in most every city (i.e. LabCorps, Quest Diagnostics). You'll be given a print-out that shows your primary nutrient levels, with deficiencies highlighted. Often, these tests are even more detailed than what you would receive from an HMO.

Identifying Food Allergies and Sensitivities

To add to the list of "items that make us more ADD/ADHD", food allergies clearly fall into this category. As discussed, chemical additives aren't helpful to anyone, but there's a number of common foods that may also be working against you.

Most of us associate "food allergies" with people eating shellfish, then having a violent physical reaction. Most food allergies are more subtle, and harder to track. "Food sensitivities" may be a better label for these types of reactions.

Some common food allergies/sensitivities:

- Dairy (lactose intolerance)

- Gluten (from wheat)

- Eggs

- Certain types of fish

- Soy

- Certain types of nuts

You may be eating a whole host of foods on a daily basis that are really sapping your energy and focus, and you're not even aware of it.

There are a few ways you can go about identifying food allergies. If you can afford it, a good naturopathic physician (ND) is trained to identify food allergies. An ND can also be helpful in dialing-in a very targeted eating plan for your specific body-type. Some medical insurance plans may cover naturopathic visits.

Another, more basic, option is to track your daily eating plan for a couple of weeks. Through varying your diet for a week or two, tracking how you feel after you eat certain foods, you can hone in on which foods may be causing you problems. I'll go into more detail on "tracking" later in the chapter.

Underactive Thyroid

The thyroid is often referred to as "the master gland" because it handles so many vital functions, including regulating hormones and metabolism. Studies have shown that ADHD-type symptoms can also be attributed to an underactive thyroid gland.

Here again, the diagnosis of an underactive thyroid (hypothyroidism) is pretty straight forward. A simple blood test (TSH) can check thyroid functioning. And there are numerous methods of treating this condition. Nutrition, once again, plays a big part in all of this. If you aren't properly nourished, your body won't be functioning optimally. The thyroid is no exception to this rule.

The Feingold Diet

The Feingold diet was developed by Dr. Ben F. Feingold, a pioneer in the fields of allergy and immunology. It's has been used for over 20 years to treat hyperactivity in children.

However, the same basic principles apply to adults. Much of what has already been discussed in this chapter fits well within the parameters of the Feingold diet. And there's a wealth of information about it online. It's definitely recommended reading if you want to gain an even deeper understanding of the link between ADD/ADHD symptoms and dietary choices.

Fibromyalgia

Fibromyalgia can sometimes be a catch-all term that refers to chronic fatigue, muscle pain, and sleep problems. ADD/ADHD is often lumped in with this diagnosis. In many cases, it's likely the result of chronic inflammation brought on by eating a less than optimum diet. Much of what's on the "what not to eat list" earlier in this chapter, falls into the category of "inflammatory foods."

If you have symptoms of fibromyalgia, an anti-inflammatory diet, with lots of fresh vegetables, and supplementing with omega-3 fatty acids (fish oil/flaxseed oil), has been known to be an effective treatment. Our body is remarkably capable of healing itself when given the nutrients it needs to do the work.

CREATING YOUR FOOD PLAN

In this section I'll offer some basic guidelines for constructing your own eating plan, taking into consideration all that's been mentioned thus far. At the end of the day, all of this should be filtered through the lens of "find what works for you." Once again, here is where "tracking" comes into play. Spend a few weeks trying various food combinations, note which ones make you feel the best, then refine.

Revisiting "The Basics"

The simplest method of mapping out your hunter-type food plan involves sticking with "the basics" mentioned earlier:

1. Higher protein / Lower carbs

- 20 grams of protein per meal (breakfast, lunch dinner)

- Omnivores: eggs, chicken, turkey, fish (aim for free-range/grass-fed/organic), vegetable protein sources.

- *Vegetarians*: "complete" proteins. Blend of seeds and legumes (hummus). Blend of grains and legumes (rice and beans). High protein grains (quinoa).

- Omnivores and vegetarians: select organic dairy (yogurt, cottage cheese), protein drinks.

2. Replace all foods containing refined sugars ("sugar", high-fructose corn syrup) and artificial additives (coloring, flavoring, preservatives) with healthier and satisfying equivalents.

3. Get your omega-3s.

- Omnivores and pescetarians: low mercury fish or fish oil (3 times a week for fish, or fish oil daily)

- Vegetarians: flaxseed oil, sea vegetable derived omega-3 (supplements)

Remember, when reviewing the previous list, keep in mind why you should be eating this way:

- *Higher protein* nourishes your brain with the amino acid building blocks needed to generate key neurotransmitters, like dopamine and serotonin.

- *Lower carb* provides a more even burn of energy, so you don't find yourself on the hyperactive end of the spectrum.

- *Replacing refined sugar and "artificials"* ensures that your body isn't being overly taxed, greatly optimizing all aspects of your health, especially focus and energy levels.

- *Omega-3 fatty acids* are pure brain fuel, optimizing your overall neural functioning.

Breakfast

For us hunter-types, breakfast may be the most important meal of the day. What you eat when you first get out of bed can make the difference between a day spent feeling clear, energized, and productive, or a day feeling scattered, mentally foggy, and lethargic.

The term *breakfast*, implies "in the morning," but this may not be the case for you, depending on your work schedule. So, I'll refer to breakfast as "what you eat after you first get out of bed from your primary sleep."

Here are a few higher protein/lower carb ideas for a quick morning meal:

- 2 Eggs

- Organic breakfast burrito (find one with at least 20 grams of protein. Just heat.)

- A bottled smoothie, blended with a some protein powder, or a pre-made "protein smoothie" (Odwalla, Naked Juice, etc.)

- Protein bar ("Builderbar" by Cliffbar has 20 grams of protein, is widely available, and is a personal favorite)

For the more adventurous, you may consider creating your own special morning smoothie blend that takes into account all of "the basics":

- Fresh fruits (especially berries)

- Organic yogurt

- Protein powder

- Flax oil (omega-3s)

- "Superfoods" like spirulina (also high in protein)

Big Breakfast vs Small Breakfast

For most hunter-types, a smaller *very nutritious* breakfast is often best. Avoid foods that will weigh you down. If you're accustomed to eating a big breakfast, and typically have challenges with focus and energy levels throughout the morning, experiment with eating a smaller breakfast.

Avoid eating heavy processed foods, like bacon, processed meats, fast food snack sandwiches, and sodas.

Lunch

Lunch provides you "afternoon energy." A medium-sized lunch typically works best for most hunter-types. Eating a large lunch, with lots of carbs, will almost guarantee you'll be sleepy in the afternoon. That's not a hard-and-fast rule, but most people would agree with this assessment.

There are countless possibilities for lunchtime. Again, review "the basics" to help make your decision. Also, convenience is usually a factor. Find restaurants in your area that offer healthier options. Avoid fast food chains if at all possible. This cuts down on the "temptation factor."

I'll often find the local health food store in an area and order from their deli. That's a very simple strategy for ensuring I can get a quick *and* healthy meal.

Here are a few lunch ideas to explore:

- A "wrap" (chicken, fish, tofu, tempeh) that contains fresh vegetables.

- Cooked protein (chicken, fish, turkey, veggie) with a small salad.

- Soup and salad.

- A large salad that includes protein (chicken, fish, etc.).

- Rice and stir-fry meat and/or veggies.

- Tortilla chips and hummus.

- A turkey/chicken/veggie burger on a whole wheat bun (avoid red meat and white flour buns)

Dinner

If you're wanting a heavier meal, dinner is usually the best time for it. However, this implies you don't need to do "focus" work afterward. Otherwise, a medium-sized meal is probably best. If you're really craving carbs, dinner may be the best time for them, provided you're getting some protein. However, if you're looking to lose some fat, a heavy meal at night, with no exercise afterwards, may not be your best option.

Snacks

What you snack on (in between meals) is of equal importance as your main meals. "The basics" apply to snacks as well.

There's a simple way of still having all your favorite types of snacks without paying the price in wild fluctuations of energy and focus – *find healthy versions of the same snacks you love.* Sure, you could just snack on nuts and fruits in between meals, but most of us won't be able to maintain this. It's easy to backslide into old habits if your snack foods aren't emotionally satisfying.

Look for snacks that use whole sugars, instead of refined ones. If it's chips (tortilla, potato, etc.), avoid eating ones with "partially-hydrogenated oils." Here is where a local health food store can come in handy. There's a good chance they'll have a very satisfying replacement for just about every snack food you can imagine. Gone are the days of "health foods" tasting like cardboard (although there are a few still out there). Whether it's ice cream, sodas, chips, or candy, look for foods that use organic sugar, evaporated cane juice, or stevia. These are types of sugar that your body can more easily process. It's still sugar, and too much of these foods can also lead to spikes and drops in energy level, but overall they'll provide you with a more even burn of energy.

Keep in mind, just because a snack has the right ingredients, doesn't *necessarily* mean you'll feel good after eating it. Again, track your energy and focus level the following few hours after eating *any* kind of food. Make special note of those foods that really bring your down and eliminate them (or, if they're relatively healthy, only eat them at times when you don't require focus the following few hours). Much of this is common sense. It's just a matter of putting it into practice on a regular basis.

TIPS FOR TRANSITIONING YOUR DIET

How to Transition Effectively

Now that we've mapped out the optimal hunter-type diet, the next step is how to implement it. There's a big difference between understanding something intellectually, and getting it into a form that is emotionally satisfying and *repeatable*.

Especially for us hunter-types, the complexities involved with transitioning our diet can get overwhelming. If shifting eating habits were simple, everyone would do it. It's the *emotional* attachment to food that is often the biggest obstacle. Most of us, understandably, use sweets and "comfort foods" to deaden emotional pain and make life more bearable.

When attempting to eat a healthier diet consistently, it's this emotional component that can often derail us. However, there are some steps you can take to ensure you're able to make changes to your diet and have them *stick*.

1. Be Clear about the Goal

Remember the goal:

> *Feel better, think clearer, be more productive,*
> *and have more energy to focus on creating*
> *the life you really want.*

Think in terms of *enjoying* what you eat. Be open to the possibility that this new way of eating can actually be more satisfying than how you've been eating. It's easy to get into the mode of "have to." Also, avoid seeking perfection. Aim for *consistency*. Work with a food plan that you know you'll keep to.

2. Know "The Essentials"

Review "The Basics" at the beginning of this section. Make a copy of it or create your own chart, then post it up somewhere in your kitchen. The refrigerator door is a great location. Daily reminders can go a long way in stabilizing this new way of eating.

3. Find Healthy Replacement Foods

This is essential, especially for finding healthy snack food alternatives.

The health food industry has evolved tremendously over the past two decades. There is a healthy and *yummy* replacement for just about any snack food you can think of: ice cream, chocolate bars, cookies, etc. The key is, *experiment*. If you buy a "healthy" candy bar that tastes like cardboard – keep looking. I assure you, there are a plethora of snack foods available at your local health food store that can match your current favorites.

4. Shop at Your Local Health Food Store

I can't stress how much this one step can make your entire eating plan flow much more smoothly. Health food stores have already done the groundwork of identifying healthy snacks, organic produce and meats, and deli items that fit within the "optimum" eating plan stated. Most of them *only* carry foods that are free of artificial colors, preservatives, and refined sugar.

If you don't have a health food store locally, look for something like a "Trader Joe's," which carries a mix of standard food items along side healthier alternatives, including organic meats and produce.

If neither are available in your area, you still have a few options:

Big chain stores

Check your local big chain grocery stores to see if they have a health food section. More and more, bigger food chains have started carrying healthier foods (like organics) because they've been losing business to health food stores in the area. Walmart now carries quite an extensive collection of organics.

Buy online

There are countless websites that allow you to buy organic foods, like soups, healthy snacks, and other packaged foods – often at significantly discounted prices, if you hunt around a bit. When buying online, consider buying in bulk. Many times this can really cut down on your monthly food costs.

5. Commit to "Two Weeks"

If you're having a hard time motivating yourself, try committing to at least two weeks with this new eating plan. The key in forming a new habit is setting doable goals, then sticking to them for a set period of time.

Telling yourself, "I only have to try this for 2 weeks," can be enough of an incentive to get yourself moving. But, if you say to yourself, "I'm on this new diet from here on out," there's a good likelihood you'll experience an emotional push-back at some point. Give yourself two weeks to – as consistently as possible – stick to the parameters of this new diet plan.

Then, after two weeks, assess. What's working? What's not? What foods are you enjoying, and which ones not so much. Do you have more energy? Is it costing too much? Are you concerned about being able to financially keep to this new diet? Look for ways of cutting down on your costs. Spend some time researching where you can buy food a bit more inexpensively.

The key is, *find a way to make it work*. Your physical health is the foundation of everything else in your life. It's worth the extra effort.

6. Slip-ups Happen

Be aware that "falling off the plan" will most likely happen at some point (especially in the beginning). If, after a few weeks of eating healthier, you find yourself once again binging on fast food, don't panic. Take it as a sign that you need to spend a bit more time identifying foods that are really satisfying to you.

As mentioned in #4, look for healthy replacements for your favorite snack foods. The less time you spend berating yourself for slipping up, the more time can be spent dialing-in a manageable eating plan. Work out what was the catalyst for the backslide. Were you particularly stressed that day? Have you yet to find foods that are a good emotional replacement for the less-than-healthy foods you usually eat?

Forgive yourself, assess, and refine.

7. Don't Bring It Home

If you find yourself snacking in ways you're not happy with, *don't bring these foods home*. Go through your cupboards and remove all those food items that you no longer intend to eat. If you have unopened non-perishable items, donate them to a local food drive, or a homeless shelter. Out-of-sight, out-of-mind. This is especially important when it comes to those midnight snack runs. Fortify your kitchen with healthy alternatives so your "inner kid" can feel he/she is not being punished on this new eating plan.

8. "Good" Is Often Better than "Perfect"

Perfect is rarely a doable option when it comes to eating habits. If you're constantly striving for perfection, more than likely, you'll rebel at some point. Finding the middle ground usually translates into long-term stability.

PART 3: SUPPLEMENTS

In a perfect world, proper diet and exercise would be enough to keep us clear, balanced, and on track. Unfortunately, we live in a complicated society that requires us hunter-types to function in ways not always suited for our temperament. Bills need to get paid, reports need to be filed, and our ability to sustain focus is absolutely essential for just about everything we do.

Therefore, extra supplementation is usually necessary. Used properly, supplements derived from naturally occurring compounds (extracts from herbs, vegetables, and other food products) can be just as (if not *more)* effective than pharmaceuticals – without a lot of unwanted side-effects.

Types of Supplements

There are four types of non-pharmaceutical supplements that we hunter-types should strongly consider integrating into our daily routine:

1. General Nutrients and "Superfoods"

2. "Brain Food"

3. Natural Stimulants

4. Natural Sedatives

There are two other categories of supplements that may be relevant to some hunter-types (covered later in the "Specific Health Challenges" section):

5. Natural Anti-depressants

6. Natural Sleep Aids

I'll go through each of these categories, one-by-one, to give you a general lay of the land, so that you'll have a deeper understanding of how each functions, what's available, and how to test them for their specific effectiveness on you. Here again, research, experimentation, then tracking what works, is a winning strategy.

Important note:

When shopping for supplements, always read the label for the recommended daily dosage. It is possible to overdose on certain supplements. Also, be sure to keep them out of the reach of children. If you are currently taking medications, be sure to consult your doctor before starting on a new supplement program.

Supplements by Category

If you do an internet search for "supplements ADHD" – you'll discover volumes of supplements that claim to treat ADD/ADHD symptoms. If you've ever gone into a vitamin store (or the supplement section at your local health food store), you were probably overwhelmed by the staggering array of types, sizes, brands, and combinations.

In order to simplify the process, it's necessary to identify "the essentials," so you'll know what to look for.

1. General Nutrients and "Superfoods"

Supplements, in the form of vitamins, minerals, and "superfoods" can help replenish your body of the nutrients it may be deficient in. Many of us have been running around on an "empty tank" for a long time. It's no wonder we require loads of caffeine and sugar to get us "hopped up," so we can feel relatively normal.

Recent studies specifically point to vitamin D and magnesium deficiencies in children as potential aggravators of ADHD symptoms. It's also been reported that zinc deficiencies can be a contributing factor to ADHD. If you've been eating the standard American diet (SAD), large amounts of refined sugars and starches can quickly deplete your body's store of essential vitamins and minerals.

The good news is, getting yourself back to sufficient levels of vitamins and minerals is a relatively simple task:

Take a high quality multivitamin/mineral supplement every day.

Not all vitamin/mineral blends are created equal. There's a big difference between the brands typically sold at your local supermarket, and the higher quality brands found at vitamin and health food stores. Mainstream brand vitamins often have added artificial coloring and other chemical additives that, as discussed, should be completely eliminated from the hunter-type diet.

If you have a problem digesting tablets or capsules, liquid supplements are also available. At the very minimum, be sure you're at least getting your daily allowance of things like vitamin C, B6, B12, Zinc, Vitamin D, Magnesium, Potassium, Folic Acid, Chromium, and Iodine, to name just a few.

"Superfoods"

If you read the news, there seems to be a new "miracle food" discovered just about every week. Although the health and wellness world tends to be filled with lots of hype and hyperbole, there are a few items that safely fall into the category of "superfoods" – foods that contain high concentrations of vitamins, minerals, protein, antioxidants, and micronutrients.

These are often included in higher quality multivitamin supplements, and don't necessarily need to be purchased on their own.

Volumes can be written about each one of these, but I thought I'd at least list a few well-respected superfoods to look for when shopping for your daily multivitamin supplements:

The "Super Greens":

Spirulina, Blue-Green Algae, Chlorella,
Wheat Grass, Barley Grass, Kelp

The "Super Berries":

Goji Berry, Acai Berry

Iron – Too Much of a Good Thing

If you're an omnivore, there's a good chance you're getting enough iron. Vegetarians (and some women), on the other hand, may need to supplement. A standard blood test can check your current levels. Iron overload can be dangerous, so unless you're deficient, be sure to look for supplements with *lower levels of iron or "no iron added."*

2. Brain Food

The second category of supplements I'll call "brain food." These are substances that have been shown to be specifically effective at nourishing the brain.

Omega-3 Fatty Acids

As previously discussed, omega-3 fatty acids are the quintessential brain food. Our brain is is about 60% fat. It needs omega-3 fats to functioning optimally.

There are three primary sources of omega-3 supplements:

- Fish oil
- Algae derived omega-3
- Flaxseed oil

Any vitamin or health food store will have a whole section of omega-3 supplements.

Important: With any of these omega-3 supplements, it's important to *ease in* your dosage. Start with 1/2 of what is recommended on the label, then slowly work up to the recommended dosage, over the span of a week or two. Too much of any of these supplements (especially in the beginning) can cause loose stool and diarrhea. I know people who've tried a high dose right away, had some "problems," and wouldn't touch it again. This is extremely unfortunate, given regular supplementation of omega-3 has so many health benefits, especially for us hunter-types.

Also, omega-3 supplementation can thin your blood, and is sometimes prescribed for people with high blood pressure. If you're already taking a blood thinner, ask your doctor before starting on an omega-3 supplement. Also, if you're getting nose bleeds, bleeding gums, or other signs of blood thinning, reduce your dosage, or stop taking it altogether to determine whether or not the omega-3 is the cause of the issue. These symptoms are rare, but should be noted.

Protein Powders

Protein supplements can be of noticeable benefit to hunter-types, for all of the reasons discussed earlier. Again, through an ample diet of high quality protein, you're providing your brain what it needs to function optimally.

The simplest method of supplementing your protein intake is *protein powder*. Make yourself a protein shake/smoothie in the morning, before starting your day. There are countless protein powders available on the market. Here are a few tips in finding one that best suits you.

For non-vegans, whey and egg white proteins may be a good place to start. Both are robust protein sources, densely packed with all the essential amino acids your body needs. Whey protein is derived from dairy. If you can easily digest dairy, then you may want to consider it.

However, many people (like myself) are lactose intolerant. When I have any dairy product (with the exception of yogurt), I quickly develop phlegm, and usually feel blah for at least an hour after. The good news is, there are numerous other options available:

- Rice protein

- Pea protein

- Hemp protein

- Blended vegetable-sourced proteins

These are typically a bit less dense in amino acids, and require slightly more for the same effect. However, they are often easier to digest, and can provide you with all the amino acids you'll need to start your day.

Whatever the protein source, read the label. Specifically, check for the amounts of *tyrosine* and *tryptophan* per serving. These amino acids are the precursors to dopamine and serotonin, respectively. Look for sources with higher amounts of these two for optimum effect.

Here again, the most important aspect of any protein powder is how you feel after having it. Even if you're meticulous in your research, at the end of the day it's all about its effect. Be willing to test out a few before settling on one. Some companies provide free samples, or a "single serving" packet at a lower cost. Try out a few, track how you feel after, then make your decision.

Other Brain Supplements:

There's a second tier of brain supplements that may be useful to some hunter-types. *Ginkgo Biloba* and *Gotu Kola* both deserve special mention here. These are herbal/leaf extracts shown to increase overall brain functioning. Both are available in capsules and tinctures.

Here's a list of other herbs and supplements that are believed to improve cognitive functioning:

- Choline

- Pine bark extract

- Grape seed extract

- Inositol

- Lecithin

- Phosphatidyl Serine (PS)

Important: Ginkgo Biloba, like fish oil, can be a blood thinner. Consult your doctor if you're already taking blood thinning agents, or stop taking if you experience issues like a bloody nose, or bruising.

Keep in mind, many supplements can have side-effects, especially if you take too much of them. Do your research. Educate yourself. Seek advice from a professional if you're uncertain.

3. Natural Stimulants

The medical definition of a "stimulant" is:

> *any agent that causes an increase in functional activity,*
> *usually of the central nervous system.*

Stimulants give us energy, motivate us, and oftentimes allow us to focus for longer periods of time than without them. Because genetically lower dopamine levels are the probable cause of ADD/ADHD symptoms, it's no wonder that we hunter-types have been turning to stimulants for a very long time. And, as mentioned in the "Addiction" chapter, just about any stimulant *can* be addictive.

So, the question is, which stimulants are the least addictive, the healthiest for us, and still effective in providing a boost in energy and focus?

Yerba Mate

Yerba mate (pronounced "yer-bah mah-tay"), is a relative newcomer to the supplement landscape, and it's my number one choice as a natural stimulant for hunter-types. Derived from the Holly Tree (*Ilex paraguariensis*) of the South American rainforests, its stimulant properties have been well-known to the local indigenous tribes for centuries.

It contains a naturally occurring form of caffeine, but it's also loaded with vitamins, minerals, and amino acids. In fact, in a 1964 analysis by the Pasteur Institute, it was concluded,

> "...it is difficult to find a plant in any area of the world equal to mate in nutritional value... [it contains] practically all of the vitamins necessary to sustain life."

What makes yerba mate unique, in my experience, is that it provides an even burn of energy, without the jitteriness and anxiety often experienced with other caffeine sources, like coffee (and sometimes green tea in higher doses).

Yerba mate has become increasingly popular and is now available in a number of different forms. The company, Guayaki, for example, creates a wide variety of products containing organic yerba mate, including soft-drinks, teas, and energy shots. Their "Pure Mind / Pomegranate Tereré" bottled blend also contains ginkgo and tulsi, which are both known to reduce stress and support concentration. One teabag, with some hot water, squeezed lemon, and a teaspoon of organic sugar, is a nice morning pick-me-up. It's quick to prepare, and can be poured into a any coffee thermos to bring with you on your drive to work.

Green Tea

Green tea's health benefits are legendary, and for good reason. Here are just a few of them:

- Increased focus and energy.

- Contains known cancer-fighting antioxidants, currently being used in the treatment of certain cancers, like CLL.

- Known to lower risk of heart disease.

- Boosts metabolism, providing potential weight-loss benefits.

- Contains the amino acid l-theanine, known for both its calming and focusing effects.

Green tea is the drink of choice in both China and Japan and can be a healthy caffeine replacement for coffee. Green tea comes in many forms, from supplements, tea blends, and ice teas, to chewable candies.

Always look for products free of refined sugar and artificial additives. Typically, products labeled "organic" tend to use a higher quality green tea than their non-organic counterparts.

Tyrosine

Tyrosine, the amino acid precursor to dopamine, falls somewhere between a "brain food" and a stimulant. You ingest tyrosine every day – it's one of the essential amino acids contained in just about any protein source.

I've placed tyrosine under "stimulants" because, for some, it can act as a stimulant. I'll sometimes take one capsule of tyrosine in the evening if I have some "focus" work to do, and I'm feeling a bit scattered or lethargic. It usually gives me an extra mental boost.

I place tyrosine lower on the list because, for some people, it can cause headaches. However, it's definitely worth testing out to see if it can be added to your arsenal of possible natural stimulants. I would consider it a secondary stimulant, with yerba mate and green tea as good day-to-day options.

It's recommended to take tyrosine (often labeled "l-tyrosine") on an empty stomach, along with vitamin B6 for optimum absorption. Looking for tyrosine capsules that also contain B6 is the simplest method for doing this. As with any supplement, test out a small amount (250 mg or so) to see if you have any adverse reactions, before moving to the recommended dosage.

Important notes on _all_ stimulants:

Some stimulants may cause heart palpitations, anxiety, nervous twitches, increased heart rate, tinnitus (ringing in the ears), fever, constipation, diarrhea, and other issues. Keep this in mind. If you experience any of these symptoms, reduce your intake, or stop using for a few days. It's important to find your specific tolerance level and the right stimulant for you, if you choose to use one.

Avoid taking any stimulant in the evening, for obvious reasons. They'll keep you awake. You may be able to gain some focus and energy in the short-term, but if you're not sleeping well, it's going to be working against you in the long run.

With any stimulant, it's best to regulate your intake. Taking too much can, over time, lead to them losing their efficacy. Use them mindfully, and in the lowest dosage possible for the intended effects.

Why Avoid Coffee?

Although coffee is definitely a stimulant, there's growing evidence that it can tax your adrenal glands, and deplete your body of vital nutrients (promoting the excretion of calcium, magnesium, potassium, iron, and trace minerals into the urine).

Stimulants like yerba mate and green tea, because they contain numerous beneficial nutrients and antioxidants, may not be as taxing to the body. They're definitely worth testing out. Instead of going "cold turkey," you may consider just cutting back on your coffee intake and picking up the slack with one of these other stimulants.

Why You Should Avoid Most "Energy Drinks"

Energy drinks/shots are ubiquitous and are sold in just about every liquor store and gas station. However, they're usually loaded with refined sugar and chemical additives. Also, if you're already taking a good multivitamin, there's a chance you'll be getting too much of certain vitamins, like B12 (commonly added to energy drinks). Too much B12 can induce anxiety (I know this from first-hand experience). It's best to stick with good nutrition and healthier forms of stimulants, as mentioned previously.

There are a number of natural energy drinks/shots available. Again, look at the ingredients, track how you feel, and avoid taking more than you need.

4. Natural Sedatives

A sedative is any substance that "mellows you out."

Hunter-types prone to hyperactivity are quite familiar with that feeling of being "totally wired," unable to sit still for even a minute. This is especially frustrating when you're trying to unwind at the end of the day, and it feels like 100,000 volts are coursing through your veins. This can really affect your sleep patterns, productivity, and ability to focus the following day.

It's no wonder why hunter-types often self-medicate. Challenges with hyperactivity can easily lead to vicious cycles of abusing sleeping pills, anti-depressants, and illegal substances, just to "find normal." It can be maddening if we don't get a break from that constant surge of energy and jitteriness.

Here again, the question becomes, "are there natural substances we can take to take the edge off, without a lot of unwanted side-effects?" Here's a list of a few natural sedatives that are broadly considered safe and effective.

Chamomile

Chamomile (especially taken as a tea) is always a good first choice as a natural sedative. Its use goes back centuries and is found in many cultures throughout the world. Derived from a daisy-like flower, it has countless other benefits as well, including anti-inflammatory and anticancer properties. Drinking a cup (or two) of chamomile tea mid-evening can provide remarkable sedative effects, and may just get you to sleep at a decent hour.

Calcium and Magnesium

Often sold as a combined supplement, the sedative effects of calcium and magnesium are well-documented. In fact the old adage of a "glass of milk before bedtime to get you to sleep" relates to the high levels of calcium found in dairy.

Theanine

The amino acid theanine, commonly found in green tea, is noted to have both calming and focusing effects.

Other Natural Sedatives:

There are numerous other natural sedatives available. Here are a few you may want to consider:

Lavender

Passionflower

Skullcap

GABA

Valerian Root

Shopping for Supplements

Shopping for supplements can be overwhelming, with so many brands and blends to choose from. There's also the cost factor. Higher quality supplements can get pricey. Here are a few tips to simplify your shopping process and make your supplement plan more affordable.

1. *Start with the essentials.* It may be helpful to start with just one or two of the products mentioned, then test them out thoroughly before adding any more to the mix. Too many products at once can get confusing. It also can make it harder to track which ones are working, and which ones aren't. Avoid the temptation to do a "complete overhaul" right away.

2. *Local means convenient; online is usually less expensive.* If you're concerned about cost, try doing your "research and testing" at your local health food or vitamin store. Often, their prices are competitive with what can be found online. Certain specialty stores like "The Vitamin Shoppe" are located throughout the US and carry high quality products at a relatively low cost.

When buying online, check Amazon, Google Shopping, and other tools that allow you to compare prices side by side.

3. *Some generic brands can still be of good quality*. Many health food stores will have their own generic brand of common supplements, and they're often significantly less expensive than name brands. Speak to the sales person. Try to get more information on where their products are sourced. They may be the same exact products you'd pay twice as much for, just with a different label.

4. *Buy in bulk*. Buying in bulk often means getting a substantial discount, especially online.

5. *Try "subscribing" to the products you know you'll need every month*. Some websites offer a "subscription" service, sending you a particular supplement the same time every month, at discounted prices. This can be a great way of ensuring you don't forget to reorder supplements, and you'll also be paying a bit less.

6. *Use a pill holder*. If most of your supplements are in pill form, try picking up a 7 day, 4 times a day pill holder. Fill it up once a week. This can really simplify your morning routine.

7. *Use reminders*. Developing good methods of reminding yourself about your health routine is half the battle. See the "Time Management" chapter for more details on reminder options you may want to explore.

An Effective Supplement Plan: The Basics

Now that we've gone in-depth into which supplements would be most supportive to hunter-types, let's simplify the list so you'll know where to start.

Morning

Multivitamin supplement
Take a high quality multivitamin supplement with breakfast every day. This should be a constant.

Omega-3
Take an omega-3 supplement (fish oil, flaxseed oil) with your other morning supplements. Start at 1/2 the recommended dose, and gradually increase. Dial back if you are having any intestinal issues.

Natural stimulant (i.e. yerba mate or green tea)
Take a natural stimulant in the morning to provide the focus you'll need throughout the morning. Use the minimal amount for the desired effect (i.e. start with 1 bottle of an yerba mate drink, or 1 cup of green tea).

Protein shake/smoothie
Mix a high quality protein powder with a bottled smoothie, (or one you blend yourself), to ensure you're getting enough protein. If you're already getting 20 grams of protein from your breakfast, this may not be necessary.

Early Afternoon

Natural stimulant (only if needed, and not after 3pm)

Evening

Natural sedative (if needed)

Those are the basics. For many hunter-types, this exact routine can be very effective, without much alteration, especially when combined with a healthy diet and exercise program. Later in this chapter we'll discuss specific methods of tracking the effectiveness of your supplement program.

Isn't This Going to Be Expensive?

At first you may be concerned about the outflow of money needed to purchase supplements. Relatively speaking, if you shop around and look for good deals, the cost will be nominal in comparison with the *many* potential benefits. The way I've learned to look at "health expenses" (like supplements) — the clearer I am, the better I feel, the more productive and creative I'll be.

Health is an investment, not just an expense. It pays countless dividends and is the bedrock of all real prosperity.

PART 4: SPECIFIC HEALTH CHALLENGES

Depression (The Biochemical Connection)

Although emotional challenges can feed into depression (as discussed in the "Navigating Emotions" chapter), there is often a strong biochemical link. Poor diet, vitamin and mineral deficiencies, lack of sunlight, and minimal exercise, all can lead to long periods of feeling quite miserable and depressed. Hunter-types, based on all of the available information, are extra vulnerable to depression.

Longer-term chronic depression is often associated with lower levels of serotonin (see the "Hunter-type Brain" Chapter for a more in-depth look at this essential neurotransmitter). Also, according to professor Robert Sapolsky of Stanford University, up to 20% of depression can be the result of hypothyroidism. When it comes to depression, there's never a one-size-fits-all approach. However, there *are* a few key steps you can take to minimize the biochemical aspects of depression.

The general plan put forth in this chapter (exercise, diet, and supplements), can be considered a natural "anti-depressant" strategy. Once again, by properly nourishing your body, you're greatly increasing your odds of having a more stable mood. In fact, I was first introduced to "amino acid therapy" (the groundwork for all the dietary suggestions in this book) through assisting a friend who was suffering from depression. After much research, I came upon the work of people like Dr. Daniel Amen and Julia Ross (whose book, "The Mood Cure" provides the most in-depth natural treatment plan for depression I've found to date.)

Taking a high quality multivitamin, omega-3 supplements, and a high protein / low carb diet are all key steps for anyone wishing to work with their depression in a non-pharmaceutical manner.

Natural Anti-Depressants

You may be familiar with the term SRI (serotonin re-uptake inhibitor). An SRI is any substance that prevents the body's normal metabolism from breaking down serotonin – the neurotransmitter most associated with generating feelings of well-being. Through preserving serotonin, more is available in the brain.

There are natural forms of SRIs available you may want to explore before trying pharmaceuticals. There are three well-know, well-documented, natural antidepressants that deserve mentioning:

- St. John's-wort

- SAM-e

- 5-HTP and l-Tryptophan

There are supplement blends/combinations of these also available. A product called "Eskaloft" has been helpful for a number of my life coaching clients, and can be found by doing an internet search for that term.

Important Note:

DO NOT take any natural anti-depressant while using pharmaceutical anti-depressants, sedatives, or OCD medication. There may also be adverse reactions to over-the-counter medicines. Always consult your doctor to discuss potential side-effects if you are currently taking _any_ medications. Always follow the recommended dosage, and avoid combining multiple types of natural anti-depressants.

Sleep Problems

Lack of sleep can make common ADD/ADHD challenges almost crippling. I've watched numerous hunter-types really struggle with sleep issues, and I know it's a very common issue for many of us. If we're feeling a bit more stressed or anxious than usual, it's easy for this to disturb our sleep patterns.

The effectiveness of over-the-counter sleeping pills often comes at a high price. I've watched friends really suffer as a the result of taking them regularly. They *did* get sleep, but they were often in a fog the next day, and over time, the effectiveness waned. The potential for addiction to sleeping pills also looms large.

Once again, it comes back to properly nourishing your brain. There are some key strategies to consider when tackling sleep issues:

1. *Get enough sun (15 minutes of direct sunlight per day)*

The average person needs 15 minutes of direct sun every day in order to generate adequate levels of melatonin to get a good night's sleep.

If you live in a climate where getting enough sunlight is an issue, purchase a full-spectrum lamp.

2. *Watch what you eat and drink before bed*

> "The best bedtime snack is one that has both complex carbohydrates and protein, and perhaps some calcium. Calcium helps the brain use the tryptophan to manufacture melatonin. This explains why dairy products, which contain both tryptophan and calcium, are one of the top sleep-inducing foods." – William Sears, M.D.

With the exception of dairy, avoid eating protein three hours before bed. Too much protein can keep you awake.

3. *Have a "wind down" plan in place*

As mentioned earlier, try drinking a cup of chamomile tea mid-evening. This can help mellow you out, and increase the likelihood you'll get to sleep at a decent hour.

4. *If necessary, try a natural sleep aid.*

There are numerous natural sleep aids available that can be as effective as pharmaceutical sleeping medication. There are three to especially consider:

- Valerian root

- Melatonin

- Chamomile

Once again, do a little research to ensure there won't be any adverse reactions with medicine you're already taking. Read the label for warnings. You may want to start with an amount half of what is recommended, and ease in.

Transitioning Off Medications

If you're currently taking medications for ADD/ADHD and/or depression, and are considering other options, it's ***extremely important*** to do so under the supervision of your doctor.

Sadly, it's far too common for suicides to occur during the tapering-off period of a psychopharmaceutical drug. During the writing of this book, an acquaintance of mine took his own life during a time when his doctor changed his medication. It was devastating, both to his family, and his community of friends. Don't assume you are mentally strong enough to do it on your own. You should be monitored closely by a trained physician. Discuss with them any supplements you plan to take to ensure there won't be any adverse reactions. I can't stress how important this is. Always err on the side of caution.

PART 5: PLANNING AND TRACKING

Experimenting, Tracking, Assessing, and Refining

Be it exercise, a food program, or supplements, identifying *what works* and *what doesn't work,* then putting it into practice, is the protocol. This involves:

1. *Experiment* with numerous options first.

2. *Track* – make regular notes on your mood, energy, focus, productivity, etc.

3. *Assess*, through reviewing your tracking notes.

4. *Build habits* based on what works best.

5. *Continually refine* your habits over time.

Tracking

While tracking can be done simply through journaling once a day, I suggest the following process for monitoring the effectiveness of your exercise, diet, and supplement program. I've included a sample tracking sheet so you'll have an idea of how to structure your own.

"Effectiveness is the Measure of Truth."
– Hawaiian Proverb

Every evening (possibly right before going to sleep), make note of the following items based on your experience from the day. On a scale from 1 to 5 (1 being the lowest score, 5 being the highest), track the following:

- Mood
- Focus

- Energy Level
- Productivity

Along with these, note:

- Did you experience a *crash/meltdown*? (whatever that means for you.) Just write a simple yes or no.

- *Exercise* (what you did and for how long)

- *Diet* (what you ate for breakfast, lunch, dinner, snacks, etc.). This doesn't have to be overly detailed. In fact, you may want to devise a simple code for those items you eat every day (i.e. chicken stir-fry = CSF)

- *General notes.* These are points that will be helpful when reviewing your tracking at a later date. Consider this a simple journal entry that goes into more detail on how your day went.

Commit to doing your tracking, as best you can, every evening for two weeks. If you miss a day or two, it's not a problem. Just do your best. After two weeks, you'll at least have some basic information to work with. Many people find this process surprisingly satisfying, once they get into the habit of it.

After two weeks, look over your tracking notes. Specifically review:

Were there any noticeable effects on your mood, focus, and productivity, the day or two *after* you exercised?

Which exercise routines did you most enjoy?

If you experimented with eating different types of foods, how did these affect your mood, energy, focus, and productivity levels that day?

Regarding supplements – did you notice any positive or negative effects? Which ones worked as you intended, and which ones generated no noticeable effect. Keep in mind, supplements like vitamins often have a much slower incremental effect, whereas the effects of a natural stimulant will be noticeable almost immediately.

On the days you had a crash/meltdown, what happened that led up to it? What were you eating? Did you get enough exercise? Were you under a lot of pressure, or not gotten enough sleep the night before? Spend some time to work this out. This is extremely valuable information.

TRACKING SHEET

Overall Mood *from 1 to 5* (1 = Depressed/Anxious, 5 = Happy & Fulfilled)	
Energy Level *from 1 to 5* (1 = Low, 5 = High)	
Mental Focus *from 1 to 5* (1 = Fuzzy, 5 = Very Focused)	
Productivity *from 1 to 5* (1 = Not Productive, 5 = Very Productive)	
Any Major Crashes or Melt-downs? (yes/no)	

Physical Exercise:

Meals:	**Supplements:**

Notes:

There are countless more questions you can ask yourself, however, these are good ones to start with. You can now start constructing your daily/weekly habits (exercise, food, supplements) based on your results.

Planning, Scheduling, and Reminders

With a few weeks of tracking under your belt, you should have a basic understanding of known steps that minimize your ADD/ADHD challenges and maximize your productivity and well being. In the "Time Management" chapter, I'll go into much more detail on ways of using a planner (or scheduling software) to create a sustainable daily/weekly/monthly schedule. I'll also share specific methods for creating reminders for yourself, to ensure you're sticking with the health plan you've mapped out.

To pull together all of the main suggestions contained in this chapter, here's an overview of what may be helpful to integrate into your daily/weekly routine:

Daily Routine

- Take a high quality multivitamin, and an omega-3 supplement every morning.

- Be sure you are eating at least 20 grams of a high quality protein at every meal.

- If helpful, take some form of natural stimulant (yerba mate, green tea, etc.) 1 to 2 times a day.

- Replace *all* refined sugar products with whole sugar alternatives. Find ones you *actually* enjoy eating.

- Eliminate *all* food products that contain "the artificials" (coloring, additives, preservatives, sweeteners, etc.). Replace them with satisfying alternatives.

- Reduce carbs and starches from your diet.

- Identify food allergies, and eliminate these foods from your diet.

- Schedule in "wind down" time at the end of the day. Take a natural sedative (tea, supplement, etc.), if necessary, two hours before you'd like to go to sleep.

Weekly Routine

- Exercise (3) times a week, 30 - 45 minutes per session:

  - Make it a good cardio workout.

  - Find exercise routines you really enjoy.

  - Ideally, exercise outdoors, somewhere in nature.

  - Schedule exercise on your calendar and set reminders for yourself.

  - If possible, stick to the same days each week to exercise (to form a habit).

  - If you have a challenge with more rigorous cardio exercise, go for walks instead.

- Schedule one day a week for extended chill-out time. This is "do nothing" time to recoup from the week.

Finding Your Way

Once again, I encourage you to ease in to all of this. Try starting with just two weeks of tracking your exercise routines. Then, take another two weeks to focus on your diet. Then, two more weeks experimenting with and tracking supplements. It may work best for you to leave a few weeks in between each of these "sessions" to integrate the habits and schedule you've created for yourself.

There's no right or wrong way to do this, just keep to the overarching goal of "feeling better and being more productive." The process of getting to this place will look different for everyone, and hopefully this basic system of tracking, assessing, and refining will be enough of a structure to get you going.

10

TIME MANAGEMENT

For us hunter-types, good time management tools are essential. How we manage our time directly relates to our productivity and overall well-being. Without them, anxiety and chaos ensue. Before diving into the nuts and bolts, it's important to first zoom out a bit and discuss "the big picture" of time management and scheduling.

Ideally, you've spent a little time working on goal setting and visioning, as discussed in the "Life Visioning" chapter. It can be helpful to do this first because, if you don't know the direction you want to move, it's easy to get lost in handling the day-to-day tasks of life, while not necessarily moving any closer to your intended goals.

How you achieve your goals is directly related to the choices you make day-to-day – items you put on your schedule, people you meet with, time set aside for specific work, etc... These are all the small interlocking pieces that make up the greater vision of your life.

Therefore, at the outset, I would encourage you to think of all the many action items in your life as fitting into two basic categories:

1) Items related to your life goals
2) Everything else

Obviously, just about everything you do, from paying bills to feeding the dog, indirectly relates to your life goals in some way. If you don't pay your rent, you'll get evicted, which could put more than just a slight crimp in your lifestyle. However, by thinking in terms of these two basic categories, you can simplify and prioritize your life in a way that ensures forward motion.

The tips and techniques we'll explore in this chapter are models that have both worked for me and my life coaching clients. Once you understand them fully, I *highly* encourage you to adapt them to best serve you and your lifestyle. However you design your time management system, one of the main goals should be – it becomes *transparent*. That is, it should be consistently effective in ensuring you are making appointments and keeping commitments to yourself, without having to think too much about the process itself.

Projects, Action Items, and Scheduling

Over the years I've explored various time management techniques. After many trials and tribulations, a system began to take shape that was simple and consistently effective.

To provide some context – I've spent most of my adult life engaged in media production, in one form or another. This usually involves *numerous* small projects, all happening simultaneously, each with its unique action items to be accomplished within a particular time frame. As time went on, I realized the same systems I used for my business also worked extremely well in many other areas of my life.

The system boils down to three basic categories:

1. Projects

2. Action Items

3. Scheduling

Projects

Every aspect of your life, if you think about it, can be organized into various "projects":

Personal Finances is a project

Home is a project

Work is probably a series of smaller projects

Family is a project

etc...

To cope with the many different demands of life, our brain needs to *label* activities – placing them in some kind of mental box, in order to process what to do and when to do them. Many people can do this naturally, but with us hunter-types, it tends to get all jumbled up together. *We have to train ourselves to place things into categories so that they become manageable.*

Understandably, it can feel a little creepy to refer to something like "Family Life" as a project – however, your brain has been doing this already whenever you organize your time, so you might as well make it a conscious process. And you don't have to use the term "projects" – you may want to call them something like "life categories." Find a label that works best for you.

Action Items

All *projects* consist of *action items*.

Simply put, an "action item" is anything you'll be doing in relation to a particular project. For example:

Project: Finances
Actions:

> Invoice Charlie for $250.00
> Cash check at bank

Project: House
Actions:

> Clean and organize living room
> Do the dishes

Scheduling

Scheduling is the process of placing action items and upcoming events onto your calendar. All actions, whether or not you add them to your calendar, happen "in time." However, many of these actions *will* need to be placed on your calendar in order to complete them – to ensure they don't reside forever on your action items list.

჻

Putting the Pieces Together

Now that we've laid out the basic system, the next step is putting together the tools needed to make it all function properly. After exploring countless time management tools over the years, I've found there are two simple rules of thumb that make for a useful system:

1. Simple is effective
2. Aim to be *functional*, not "perfect"

Making your system too complex can easily lead to the system breaking down. Hunter-types especially have a tendency to be "overly creative" with time management systems.

The essential tools for any time management system are:

1. A calendar
2. An action items list
3. Reminders

No matter how technology shifts and evolves, these basic tools will remain constant. Only the forms may change.

Calendar

This is a single place where you list and track all of your appointments.

Action Items List

This is a list where all your intended actions reside.

Reminders

A "reminder" is any method of reminding you of your actions, appointments, and intentions. This can be as simple as post-it notes you place around your house, or as sophisticated as your phone beeping to let you know you have an appointment 45 minutes from now.

ॐ

HIGH-TECH AND LOW-TECH TIME MANAGEMENT SYSTEMS

There are high-tech and low-tech methods of time management. Whether you are tech-friendly, or more of a traditionalist, it can be helpful to familiarize yourself with both systems.

A Paper-Based Planner – The Low-Tech Approach

Using a paper-based planner can be a very effective time management tool, and countless people use them. For many years, this was my primary time management system, and I carried it with me wherever I went. I personally prefer Franklin-Covey planners because they have a wide selection of sizes and add-in sheets. I also enjoyed having two pages for each day, which some planners don't offer.

If you are going to use a physical planner, here are some helpful tips:

1. Bring it *everywhere*. From my experience, this is the only way it's really going to be effective.

2. Write *all* your appointments and events in it.

3. Keep a section for *notes*. You can either have separate pages for specific projects (i.e. health, work projects, goals, etc...) Or keep a linear set of notes, writing the date and project name at the beginning of the note.

4. Have a section just for your main *action items list*. Again, try to keep all your action items in one spot. This makes the whole process simple and more likely to get used.

5. Review your schedule and action items list *every morning,* so you'll be clear of any appointments you've scheduled for the day.

6. Every Sunday afternoon or Monday morning, look over your schedule for the upcoming week and, ideally, for the next month. This is another good habit to get into. It allows you to be more proactive by looking ahead. When you imagine your life in terms of weeks and months, instead of just day-to-day, you'll naturally become more proactive, and most likely circumvent upcoming challenges because you "saw them coming" ahead of time.

7. If you're new to using a planner, commit to using it everyday for one month. If a month sounds a bit too daunting, then aim for one week. The key is to turn it into a *habit* – make it a daily ritual. It may be a little awkward at first, but chances are, it will become second nature after a few weeks. Regularly, look over your system and see if you need to refine or adjust any element of it to make it more effective and easier to use.

8. Buy at least *one year* of pages. There's nothing more frustrating (and *disorienting*) than having your primary time management system become nonfunctional because you ran out of pages. Place a reminder in your planner at the end of November to "buy pages" for the next year. Make this a priority so you can start the new year off on stable ground.

9. Avoid using a computer calendar in conjunction with your paper-based planner. If you use a desktop computer, there's often a tendency to want to use it in tandem with the physical planner. Avoid this. From personal experience, this can easily lead to confusion and missed appointments because your calendar is spread between two different systems, and neither are synced up with the other. Pick a system and stick with it.

Paper-Based Action Item List

Most planners will come with a section for tasks/action items — usually with a check-box next to each line to denote whether or not it's been completed. I prefer using a simple lined page instead, so I'm not trying to cram items into the space they've provided.

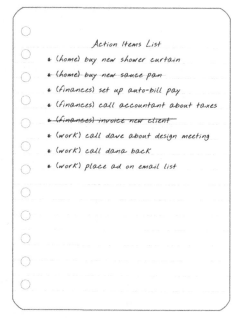

Depending on what's going on, I also lean towards having just *one* main action item list, versus one for each project. This is a personal preference. If you find it more effective to create an action item sheet for each project, go for it. Just be sure you're staying consistent with using this system. Having just one list *tends* to make things simpler. *One* list, *one* place to write an action item. Simple.

❧

Time Management Systems for the "Tech-Friendly"

Although many people have a love-hate relationship with technology, the one thing tech is really good for is time management.

Here's why:

Computers allow for non-linear editing — it's much easier to move things around. With a physical planner, you have to erase, re-write, cross-out, etc... It gets messy. And there's no way for a paper planner to remind you of tasks, if you forget to crack it open (something I've had happen on numerous occasions).

Many of us have either a laptop, a tablet, or a smart phone – sometimes all three. So, in relation to the "high tech" time management system I'll discuss, having some mobile device is a prerequisite, as opposed to a stationary desktop computer. You'll need something that will be with you wherever you go.

You may be able to simply use a smart phone and a desktop computer, if they're always synced up via an online calendar. I'll go more into detail on this later in the chapter.

What If I Don't Have a Mobile Device?

If you don't have a laptop or a tablet, and are concerned about the expense – check for sales. Look for online deals, or see if a friend or family member has upgraded recently and would be willing to give you theirs. You can always check for a used one on websites like Craigslist or eBay.

To handle things like basic scheduling, email, and web browsing, it doesn't have to be a super powerful system. Anything made in the last four or five years will be fine for handling the basics, provided it's in good working condition. If you get a used one, you may want to clear off the disk drive and re-install the operating system. This can drastically improve it's speed and performance.

If you are unsure how to do this – ask a friend, check online, or go to your local computer store – they're usually quite forthcoming with free advice.

Calendar Software

Most operating systems (Mac, PC, Linux, iOS, Android, etc.) come with some kind of calendar program pre-installed. Macs comes with iCal, and PCs often come with Microsoft Outlook.

There are also a number of free calendar programs available. In the "Bibliography & Resources" section at the end of the book,

I've listed a number of them for various platforms. Each of them handles "the basics":

    1. Events can be added to the calendar quickly

    2. Events can be easily moved around.

    3. The program will remind you before an event happens, via some pop-up window or sound alert.

The Action Items List (High-Tech Approach)

As mentioned previously, I prefer having just one action items list, instead of one for each project.

Here's how I do it:

I have a file on my desktop called "ActionItems.txt". This is a simple text file. Every operating system (i.e. Mac, PC) has a basic text/notes program – no bells and whistles (ability to change fonts, justification, etc.), just text. I find this to be a very hunter-type friendly environment – no distractions.

I've devised a simple system for writing out my action items, which I'll go into more detail on in the "note-taking" section a bit later in the chapter. It looks like this:

    * action item
    + accomplished item
    (project) project name for the action item

So, an action on my list would look like:

    * (Finances) Invoice Charlie

If it's completed, I just change the * to a + :

    + (Finances) Invoice Charlie

In the morning, after I check my schedule, I also look over my main action items list. I will see what needs to get done, and then add it to my schedule for the day. I will also mark off those items that have been accomplished with a "+" instead of a "*", possibly moving them up out of the to-do items using cut and paste. My completed items are at the top of the list, and my "live" actions are at the bottom. Sometimes I'll just delete an item when it's completed.

My main action items list ends up looking something like this:

> + (Finances) Finish Taxes
>
> + (Health) Call Laura about appointment
>
> * (Music) Book slot at festival
>
> * (Finances) Invoice Charlie
>
> * (Family) Call mom

Using a Separate Action Items List for Specific Projects

From time to time, you may need to have a separate action items list for specific projects. Keeping a unique list for certain projects can also prevent your main action item list from getting too long, making it unwieldy and unmanageable.

However, keeping all your action items for the upcoming week on your *main* action items list is still a good idea. If I know something needs to get done soon, I'll move it *from* the project list *to* my main actions list. After that, it will probably end up being scheduled as an event on my calendar, to ensure it gets done.

Reminders

For us hunter-types, it's far too easy to have an action item *not* get done because you forgot to look at your action items list or calendar (if it made it that far). Life gets busy, and it ends up getting swept under the rug.

This is where smart phones, laptop software, and online calendars can really come in handy. Reminders are essential. They are, in a sense, a way of your calendar tapping you on the shoulder about a specific item or appointment. And having *multiple* reminder systems is even better. If one fails to get your attention, there's always a back up.

Reminder System 1: Calendar Software

My first round of reminders comes from my calendar software. It beeps, flashes, or plays a sound whenever an event is coming up. This works well, but *only* if I have my laptop open at the time of the reminder. By default, most calendar software can be set to *always* remind you about an event a set number of minutes before it occurs, with a sound notification of some kind. If this isn't the default, and you have to tell it to do so for every event, go into the "Settings/Preferences" of the program and change the default setting.

Reminder System 2: Email and Smart Phone Reminders

If you're like me, I check my email numerous times throughout the day – both on my smart phone and on my laptop. I find email reminders to be immensely valuable, and they've saved me numerous times from missing important appointments, or essential bills that needed to be paid.

Yahoo! Mail and Gmail both have free online calendars that will send you an email reminder regarding an event you've created. For important events, it really brings me peace of mind to have that extra level of backup, in case I miss the pop-up from my primary calendar software. This is especially helpful for bill reminders.

Typically, once you've signed up for the account, you'll just select the equivalent of "Add New Event", and one of the options will be, "Email me a reminder to this email address:" It will also ask you how many minutes/hours before the appointment you would like to be reminded.

You may prefer not to use an online calendar for your *main* scheduling because there may be times when an internet connection may not be available. I always want to be able to look at my schedule, no matter what's going on. That being said, the ideal situation is to have your local calendar (saved on your laptop or tablet) synced with an online calendar. This system can be very helpful if you have a smart phone, because then *all* of your devices can be linked up. That way, when you add an event to your calendar on your smart phone, it will automatically sync to your laptop or tablet calendar.

This can be a little tricky to set up, but there are lots of tutorials online to do this. Once they're all synced together, you'll receive reminders from your smart phone (popup and/or sounds), letting you know about upcoming appointments on your main calendar.

Wrapping Up

This system is not an exact science – and over time I've allowed for a certain degree of flexibility. But, for the most part, I use it exactly as stated. It's become quite transparent.

Regardless of your system, be sure to handle the basics: calendar, action items, reminders. The specifics of how you do this are less important. However, if you do take the high-tech approach, be sure to back up your data on a regular basis!

To reiterate – this is what works *for me*. You'll need to adapt and refine a system in a way that works best for your life and your tendencies. Again, a good time management system should be something that you don't think too much about once it's in place. It works, and you keep using it because it's easy and gets the job done. If you find yourself really struggling or stressing out – forcing yourself to conform to your system – you probably need to re-think it.

NOTE-TAKING

Hand-in-hand with a good time management system is having an effective way of taking notes. Whether it's attending a meeting, a class, or mapping out a project, knowing how to take good notes has countless benefits. And the content of your notes *often* yields action items that end up on your schedule.

This note-taking system is one I've refined over time. It brings together all of the previously mentioned time management categories: projects, action items, and scheduling – with the addition of one extra category: ideas.

Like most of us, I was taught the "outlining method" in school.

    I. Main Item Heading

     A. Sub-point Heading

      1. Sub-point 1

      2. Sub-point 2

Outlining always frustrated me. It felt very limiting – much too linear for how my brain worked. I didn't feel *intuitive*. If I needed to add something to an outline – it usually involved scratching things out, erasing, and eventually the whole thing would have to be remade. *Very* frustrating.

So, throughout school I never really had a system of note-taking that worked well for me. I'd just scribble down a series a rough points and ideas that, when it came time to take a test, I would be fumbling through, trying to make some sense of it.

It wasn't until I started my own business in my mid-twenties that I was finally let in on "the secret" that unlocked a much more efficient and intuitive method of note-taking.

Effective Note-taking: The Basics

Time is linear. When taking notes during a meeting, for example, points of information flow one after another.

My old practice was – attempt to organize my notes *as* I wrote them down. Here's where the outline system fails miserably. The act of trying to organize *while* note-taking is stressful and ineffective.

Also, during a meeting, something being said may spark an idea I may want to come back to later and review. Additionally, an *action item* may occur to me, or I may agree to do something in relation to what is being discussed.

Here's a different method of taking notes:

> Take *one note after another*. Don't try to organize. Use a simple code that identifies what each note item refers to.

When I was let in on this note-taking technique, it was a a major "ah hah" moment. I was quickly able to devise a system that I've now been using for the past 20 years.

Here's the "code" I use:

> * = action item
>
> ! = idea
>
> KP = key point
>
> (project) = project name

Here's how it would look in practice:

> * (Kids Website) Call Charlie about getting distribution
>
> KP - Based on the survey, 9 out of 10 people said they enjoyed the last production

> KP - The client wants a light blue and beige color scheme that matches their new promotional material.
>
> ! (Museum Project) Suggest they invite children from local schools to the grand opening.

Let's take a look at this. In this example, these are notes from a client meeting on a "Kids Website." As I go through the meeting, the first note is a clear *action item* that relates to *this* meeting.

> * (Kid's Website) Call Charlie about getting distribution

After the meeting, I can quickly scan my notes, and add *all* the action items listed to my main action items list, and possibly to my calendar.

The second and third notes are key points (KP). These are general notes I may need to reference later.

> KP - 9 out of 10 people said they enjoyed the last production
>
> KP - The client wants a blue color scheme

Neither relates to an idea (!), or a specific action item (*). Later on, when I hold the design meeting for the project, I may want to go back and double check the color scheme the client requested. I *know* that it will be a key point (KP) – so I can easily scan my notes to find it.

> ! (Museum Project) Suggest they invite children from local schools to the grand opening.

This last note is about a project completely unrelated to the current meeting. Something discussed from the meeting sparked an idea for some other project, in this example, the "Museum Project." After the meeting, this item should be added to the notes for this project.

This system has become the backbone for how I function in the world and has served me well. It has been used successfully on countless projects. In fact, this entire book was created using this note-taking system.

And it can be used for just about anything you can think of:

- Meetings

- Tracking good ideas

- Brainstorming with friends or co-workers

- Mapping out your day

- School lectures

- Taking notes from video presentations

I encourage you to adjust and adapt it in a way that most suits your needs.

Ideas

Capturing "good ideas" so they can be easily referenced later can be helpful in countless areas of your life. Most people, when they have a good idea, will just scrawl it down on a sheet of paper. This scrap then seems to float off into the cosmos – lost in pants pockets, or stacks of paper – never to be seen again.

I suggest keeping a file on the desktop of your computer, or a section in your planner, called "ideas." In it, make a habit of recording any ideas you have throughout your day that you'd like to revisit. Perhaps it's a a vacation you'd like to go on, a new creative project, or a possible business venture. Get into the habit of taking down every "good idea" you think of. Then, at the end of the day, transfer them into this file. If you have a good idea while driving, and can safely call your voice mail, leave it on there – then transfer it to this file later that day.

From my experience, it's as much about the "awareness" involved in doing this, as the action itself. You're far more likely to do something with your creative ideas *if* you have a system for "capturing" them. You'll probably generate countless ideas you'll never explore, but it only takes one good idea that you *do* pursue that can completely transform your life.

FROM GOALS, TO MILESTONES, TO DOABLE ACTIONS

Going back to the "Life Visioning" chapter, once you've created a vision and identified your goals, the next step is turning these goals into specific actions to get you there.

This was the part I struggled with for a long time. It turns out the key, once again, is *simplicity*.

1. Break up a goal into smaller action items.

2. Set milestones for yourself.

3. Do your best to meet your milestones, but stay flexible.

4. Get items *off* your action item list and *onto* your calendar.

5. Always be willing to ask for support.

Break Up Complex Tasks into Smaller Ones

This is age old wisdom. If you were to study a complicated task (like building a communication satellite), it will always be made up of a host of smaller, more manageable items. And you've been doing this your whole life, whether or not you've been aware of it.

If you're faced with a complicated task – something that feels completely overwhelming – see if you can break it up into simpler steps. Then, just focus on the *first one* – don't worry about the rest until that one is complete. This sounds obvious, but many of us hunter-types forget to do this.

Milestones

Setting milestones – points in time when a certain *part* of a goal is reached – creates a bit of urgency, which can be very helpful for us hunter-types, who tend to thrive on stimulation.

Take a goal you're working on, and see if you can come up with some key milestones that will indicate you're on your way to completing your goal.

For example:

> Within one year, my goal is to make $1000 a month selling my paintings online.
>
>> Milestone #1: Within (3) months have my website online.
>>
>> Milestone #2: Within (6) months I've sold 3 paintings online.

Creating these smaller goals along the way can really help in getting clear on what needs to happen within the next couple of *days* and *weeks*. Your first milestone of "getting the website online within three months" suggests a number of specific actions.

> * Call Charlie and ask him who's hosting his website and how much it costs.
>
> * Research web hosting and pricing.
>
> * Find a local web designer – or see if there is a way I can build my own from an existing template.
>
> * Do an internet search for "tips on creating an art website."

If you have well thought-out milestones, the action items to meet each milestone should come to you quite easily.

CREATING A "BALANCED" SCHEDULE

Over-scheduling

A common issue that arises, especially after becoming inspired to make significant shifts in your life, is to put a large amount of new items on your schedule in order to make a "fresh start."

Sometimes this can be helpful, but many times there can be a backlash. There's a big rush of inspiration, then a "come down" because there was no *realistic* way of maintaining the breadth and scope of the new schedule. Oftentimes, this can lead to discouragement, possibly feeling even *worse* than when you started.

Knowing Your Edge

Everyone has their own personal thresholds. Some people have seemingly boundless energy and thrive on a packed schedule. Other people, like myself, do best with quite a bit of down time, to balance out the times of high energy and hyperfocus. If I have too many things on my schedule, I can easily go into overwhelm. Over time, I've recognized this, and have adjusted my schedule to take this into account.

Finding your personal edge is part of the journey of self-discovery. My advice is – continue to refine your schedule until you find that "sweet spot" where you're working at your optimum pace, at the top of your game, *consistently.*

Scheduling with a Mindfulness of Your Natural Tendencies

To continue on the previous point, the antidote to "burnout" is:

*be honest with yourself about
your natural tendencies.*

For example, if you know that after a long day at work, all you want to do is crash out, rest, and recover – *don't* schedule the art project you really want to accomplish after work. Chances are, you'll be wiped out from the day, and you'll just add another layer of self-criticism, because you didn't accomplish your art goal. *Many* people have this tendency – they *conceptualize* their schedule without taking into account their *actual* energy and focus levels on a daily basis.

MY NATURAL TENDENCIES

On a blank sheet of paper, draw (7) equally spaced vertical columns labeled Monday through Sunday.

Then ask yourself:

When do I feel most clear to do mundane tasks (i.e. paying bills, going through the mail, etc.)?

When am I most naturally creative?

When do I most enjoy spending time with others?

When do I really want "alone time?"

When do I really like being out in nature?

When do I most enjoy exercising?

When do I most want to "chill out?"

Shade in and label these areas on the sheet of paper.

Once you've mapped them all out, you can now use this as a template for creating your *optimum* weekly schedule.

As an example of what can happen from doing an exercise like this, I no longer schedule *any* phone calls or appointments before 11am. I've been self-employed for over 15 years and, in the past, I would let other people's schedules completely dictate *my* schedule. This often led me to being "off my center," and sometimes less-than-prepared for meetings. Occasionally, I'd have to reschedule because I just couldn't get myself into the head-space to meet with someone. I was in "reaction mode" most of the time. This is a common experience for many of us hunter-types.

After looking very honestly at my natural tendencies, I made the bold decision not to schedule *any* business meetings or phone calls before 11 a.m.

What was the result? I no longer had to wake up to an alarm clock. I wake up when I'm fully rested – which most times is somewhere between 8 a.m. and 9 a.m. This schedule allows me to make the most of my "creative" time – which usually is between 9 p.m. and 1 a.m. Then, I have plenty of time in the morning to do my yoga and meditation practice. Most importantly, I have ample time to prepare for phone calls and meetings. Overall, I find myself being *far more* productive, and the quality of my work has increased noticeably.

Scheduling for optimum performance is less about *forcing,* and more about getting clear about how you *already* function. Keep in mind, your energy and focus levels can be greatly improved through a healthy diet, regular exercise, and proper supplementation. Recognize that your energy/focus rhythms may shift over time. But, it's essential to start *where you are now.*

Without this piece firmly in place – a full and honest understanding of your overall life rhythms – no time management system will be very effective for an extended period of time. However, even a little awareness in this area can go a long way.

Creating Your Weekly Schedule

Once you have a pretty good idea of your optimum times for completing certain tasks, the next step is to create your *actual* weekly schedule to work from. As mentioned, the best place to start is where you are *right now*. In the future, you may change jobs, start your own business, or take on new hobbies. But, to get any real traction, it's essential to start with your life as it is today.

MY IDEAL WEEKLY SCHEDULE

As with the previous exercise, take a piece of paper and create a (7) column graph, Monday through Sunday.

On this schedule, enter all the events in your life that happen at *regular times* during the week. This could be anything from your work schedule, to picking up your kids from school. These items are consistent and rarely change.

Now, highlight all those times in the week that can be considered *free time*. A highlighter pen may work best, but you can just as easily make boxes around these areas on the schedule. You may have events that float in and out of this time area, but for the most part, this is "flex time" – time you can now start filling with items in relation to your life goals, physical exercise, play time, connecting with friends, et cetera.

Next, examine those times on your schedule that you think are *inflexible*. Take a moment to reflect on whether or not these items can be adjusted in a way that would most harmonize with the insights from the previous exercise. Is there a way to adjust these items to better fit with your natural rhythms and tendencies?

For example, look at your work schedule. Can you make any adjustments to it? Is there an opportunity to work from home for even for part of the week? Can you make a request of your employer to adjust your schedule so as to be more in alignment with your natural rhythms?

You may want to go through this exercise a few times, continually refining your "ideal schedule" so you have a clear model to work from. Any new items added to your schedule will filter through it.

Case Study – Scheduling for Balance

Dave, a life coaching client of mine, had a job that required him to work 10 hour shifts on a regular basis. He often slept over 8 hours a day. Some days he would find himself sleeping in for 10 to 14 hours. He had immense self-judgment about this. He was desperate to be productive and accomplish his goals in his free time.

The conflicting needs were: *rest* and *sleep* vs *meaning, purpose,* and *accomplishment.*

Adding to this, he found he was making commitments with others without a full awareness of his need for getting enough rest. If he ever missed or had to reschedule an appointment, it only added to his inner conflict.

The Experiment

We decided his best move was to set aside one day a week that he could sleep in *as long as he wanted to*. Then he'd continue with the rest of the week as usual.

He also agreed to "tune in" before making any appointment, ensuring he would always be able to sleep in long enough.

The Result

There was a *noticeable* shift. He got more done in his off time. He always had a day to recoup after a long week, and he was much more consistent with making and *keeping* appointments. This simple awareness of his natural rhythms paid off abundantly.

Maintaining a Balanced Life Under Pursuing Your Goals

To revisit a major point from the "Navigating Emotions" chapter – everything that we do is motivated by "needs." This means any goal we set for ourselves is connected, in some way, to meeting a set of needs. This awareness can be extremely beneficial when creating your schedule.

A very easy trap that many people fall into – they put needs associated with big goals out somewhere in the future. "I will get this need met when *this* event happens."

For example:

> "I will get proper sleep once I've completed graduate school."

> Needs: *Rest and Balance*

"I will spend time with friends as soon a my business is successful."

Needs: *Connection and Community*

The needs-actions list process, mentioned in the "Navigating Emotions" chapter, provides an excellent means of getting yourself out of this trap.

Scheduling with the Needs-Actions List

Through identifying and addressing your essential needs, regularly, you'll keep yourself in balance *while* moving towards your stated goals.

If you went through the needs-actions list exercise, it most likely yielded up some valuable insights that can be quite useful when scheduling your week.

As you develop your schedule, if you place an emphasis on "balance," not just on "accomplishment, you're more likely to be productive *and* enjoy your life a whole lot more. If it's the other way around – when all of your energy is focused on accomplishment and meeting goals – the most predictable outcomes are burnout, stress, and overwhelm.

Using your needs-actions list for scheduling is relatively straight forward. Look at your list and see which actions you'd like to schedule into your "flex time."

Start with those items you most enjoy, ones you *know* meet multiple needs on the list. Also, be especially aware of needs that usually go unmet. Ensure that these are given priority.

For example, perhaps the action "play racquetball with Dave" meets needs for: play, exercise, friendship, and relaxation.

That's one activity that probably should be on your schedule regularly. This may seem totally obvious, but most of us have a tendency to get caught up in life and forget to do those things that most nourish us. Through making sure they're on your calendar, you're more likely to do them.

The key to working with the needs-actions list is *experimentation*. Test out one action at a particular time. Did it really meet the need? If not, can it be placed somewhere else on the schedule? Can it be associated with another item to make it more effective?

Ex: go to the gym *after* dropping off the kids

It's this process of fine-tuning your schedule that, over time, can make the biggest difference in both your productivity and overall well being.

Making Peace with <u>Not</u> Achieving Your Goals "On Time"

It's so easy to become disheartened when a very treasured goal is not achieved in the time frame you've set for yourself.

As mentioned earlier, this is connected with another common hunter-type tendency of "flexible" time horizons. It's easy to see a task getting completed *in our imagination*. But tasks often take longer in the real world than we expect.

> "I love deadlines.
> I like the whooshing sound
> they make as they fly by."
> **– Douglas Adams**

Making some peace with this tendency can greatly assist you in achieving your goals. It's connected to the ability to *keep going*, even though you may experience some discouragement. A good attitude is, "this is taking longer than I expected, but that's to be expected. This is just part of the process."

Don't Let Your Action Items List Rule Your Life

Working with an action items list can get tricky, psychologically speaking. It's easy for it to become oppressive. Many people who are self-employed are actually tyrannically employed by their task list. This is backwards.

Keep in mind:

> Your action items list will be incomplete the day you die. *Don't let it rule your life.*

This thought can help put things into perspective. Use your action items list as a tool to only support your well-being.

Remember: Life Gets Messy

No matter how "dialed in" your time management system is, it will undoubtedly get shoved, pushed, and contorted by the day-to-day ebbs and flows of life. Keeping doggedly to your schedule *no matter what the cost*, can be a recipe for stress and exhaustion.

Create your ideal schedule, keep to it as best you can, but remain flexible. This process of "allowing" is crucial in maintaining a reliable time management system.

Recurring Events and Reminders

Whether you use a physical planner or a mobile device for your time management system, having *recurring* events can be extremely helpful in reminding you about goals, thoughts, ideas, affirmations, etc.

If you use a mobile device, it's as simple as creating a "recurring event." All scheduling programs have this option – including the ability to play a sound at the time of the event.

If you use a paper-based planner, you can spend a little time writing key reminders on your schedule that will occur over the next few weeks or months. In this case, it may be be helpful to write them in the "notes" section of each day, if your planning includes this area. Most planners come with a place-holder (usually something that looks like a ruler) that snaps into the margin to help you mark the day of the week. You could also write up a list of reminders and tape it to this, knowing you'll be looking at it every time you open your planner.

To give you an example of what this may look like, one reminder I always keep on my schedule is:

> *Be mindful before making any commitments.*

This just sits on my schedule – and gets emailed to me once a day. It's usually in the background most of the time, but occasionally – every few weeks – I'll read it. There have been numerous times when just seeing that reminder prevented me from over-scheduling.

That's how reminders work. They're in the background most of the time, but, because they're always sitting *where you're looking* on a regular basis, they sink in. And you should revisit them occasionally to keep them fresh.

"Burn" Then "Burnout"

A very common tendency for us hunter-types is to "burn" on something, then "burnout." This is most likley a bi-product of our lower dopamine levels. As mentioned in the "Hunter-type Brain" chapter, when we're in a low dopamine "brain fuzz" state, we'll feel unmotivated, and it will be difficult to focus.

However, in those times when we're "on," the tendency is to think:

> *"I feel clear now!! I'm actually being productive!*
> *I need to milk this energy for all it's worth because it may not*
> *come back any time soon!"*

That's when burnout happens. And it usually throws off your whole schedule.

As you refine your diet, exercise, and supplement program, and adjust your schedule to be more in harmony with your natural tendencies, "burnout" rarely happens. And if it does, it's a clear indicator some part of your life is out of balance. Revisit some of the exercises in this book – see if you can identify the problem area and make some shifts.

∽

The Art of Time Management

Time management is as much an art form as it is a skill. It's a creative process. And just like any creative process, there's no right or wrong way of doing it. But it helps to have some basic guidelines to work from.

All of this takes time to master, but the rewards of a good time management system are well worth the energy invested.

11

TIPS & PRACTICES

Restructuring Your Life to Be "Hunter-Friendly"

Taking time to restructure your life, taking into account your hunter-type tendencies, can be immensely rewarding. This chapter is a bit like a cookbook. It contains a number of "recipes" – tips for making your life more hunter-type friendly. It expands on many of the topics already covered in previous chapters.

As you read through these various tips and suggestions, consider how they may apply to:

- Your work life

- Your home life

- Your living space

- Your creative ventures

As with all the other suggestions in this book, think of this as "a good place to start." Feel free to adapt them to meet your own specific needs.

IMPROVING YOUR MENTAL FOCUS

As discussed in earlier chapters, hunter-types are *not* deficient in attention or focus (as the term *Attention Deficit Disorder* suggests). In truth, we are capable of immense focus and concentration.

Our challenges with mental focus usually manifest in three very specific areas:

- Being able to focus on mundane tasks and/or subjects we don't find stimulating.

- Problems with focus and overwhelm when we're feeling mentally "fuzzy."

- Sustaining focus for longer periods of time.

Here are a few tips to improve your overall ability to focus.

1. Exercise

Regular exercise is absolutely *essential* for us hunter-types. For the last few years, I've tracked my energy and focus levels on a daily basis. Across the board, the day or two after exercising for at least a half an hour, my focus and productivity levels *noticeably* increased. This result was both consistent and predictable.

If you find yourself feeling overwhelmed or mentally fuzzy, ask yourself, "when was the last time I exercised?" Reference the "Exercise, Diet, and Supplements" chapter for numerous tips on creating an enjoyable and *sustainable* exercise routine.

2. Healthy diet and targeted supplements

The second question to ask yourself when in the grips of mental fuzziness is, "what have I been eating lately?"

If you're not putting good fuel into your body, you'll be feeling the effects. Remember, hunter-types are usually more sensitive to dietary choices than the rest of the population. Here again, revisit the "Exercise, Diet, and Supplements" chapter for specific dietary tips.

3. Take regular breaks

Whenever you're doing "focus" work, once every hour or so, stop. Take a break, get outside, breathe in some fresh air, and stretch. This sounds deceptively simple, but it can have a profound influence on your ability to *sustain* focus. This is because:

- You are getting more oxygen to your brain

- You are in *motion* (always helpful for us hunter-types)

- You are giving your mind a chance to "stretch out" – which many times allows for insights on problems you may be working on

4. Movement

Continuing on from the previous point, anytime you're in movement – walking, jogging, driving a car, riding on a train – it can help improve concentration. We hunter-types seem to be wired for this. Identify those activities that bring you the most clarity, and utilize them *consciously*.

Perhaps, after getting a work assignment, the best possible action you could take is – *go for a drive*. If that really works for you, don't force yourself to stay at your desk because that's what you think you *should* be doing. Note what activities best clear your head, give you perspective, and help you problem-solve – then utilize them.

5. Eliminate distractions in your environment when you are needing to focus

Hunter-types have an inborn tendency to "scan the environment," which would have served us well when we were hunter-gatherers. In our modern world, this can be quite frustrating. If the TV is on, or you're surrounded by lots of movement and noise, there's a good chance it will be difficult to focus on the task at hand. Before you start working, see what you can do to eliminate as much stimuli as possible. Noise canceling headphones can be especially helpful in shutting out a particularly loud environment.

Eliminating *visual* distractions is equally as important.

6. Shift up your work environment

If your job allows you to be more mobile with your work activities, consider bringing your laptop or paperwork to a quiet coffee shop or library. Experiment a bit to see which work environments are most conducive to focusing on specific tasks.

7. Listen to loud percussive music

This may sound completely counter to the last point, but studies have shown that listening to loud percussive music stimulates the prefrontal lobe and cues dopamine production in the brain.

I've tested this out while writing this book, and I can testify to its effectiveness. Whenever I would start to feel "fuzzy," I'd take a break, put on my headphones, and pop on some tunes. I found, within just a couple of minutes, I was thinking clearer and could start writing again.

8. Practice breathing deeply

Oxygen assists concentration. Most of us are used to taking shallow breathes. As a result, our brains can become oxygen-deprived – resulting in less-than-optimal mental functioning. When you remember to take deeper breathes, not only are you bringing more oxygen to your brain, you are also releasing tension in your body.

9. Drink lots of water

Just like plants, we humans need sunlight, air, and water, in order to function properly. If a plant is deprived of any of these three, it will die.

A good practice is, *keep clean water with you at all times.* Ideally, pick up a stainless steel water bottle and keep it filled with filtered water throughout the day.

Avoid tap water. Tap water usually tastes pretty bad, and is often loaded with chlorine and other chemicals. If you're not used to drinking water throughout the day, you may get a little annoyed with having to go to the bathroom more often. Think of it this way, we hunter-types need movement, and your bladder is just reminding you to take breaks and move.

10. Meditate once a day

There are countless benefits to a regular meditation practice. If practiced regularly, it can substantially increase your ability to focus for longer periods of time. I highly recommend making meditation a part of your daily routine. In the "Spirituality" chapter, I've laid out a few meditation practices to experiment with.

11. Get out into nature at least once a week

Being in nature, away from the man-made modern world, can assist you in temporarily shutting off the judgmental part of your brain that tends to place labels on everything it sees – often directing its critiques towards yourself. This mental process can create tension in your body, making it harder to focus, and it definitely affects your physical health.

Find a location you really enjoy going to. If you live in the city, is there a lake nearby? Can you drive out to the beach? Is there a hike that you've always wanted to go on? If you can't get out of the city, find a nearby park. Ideally, find a place that doesn't have a lot of man-made sights and sounds, so that the *dominant* energy is that of nature.

Also, consider integrating your meditation and exercise practices with your excursions into nature.

12. Create a structure for your life that minimizes the times when you're mentally "fuzzy."

Much of this book is about moving towards this goal. It's about looking at your life *as a whole* and optimizing all your activities to be "hunter-type friendly."

IDEAL TIMES FOR MENTAL FOCUS

Either on your computer, or on a sheet of paper, think back to those times when you found yourself really being able to focus well. What were you doing? Write all these out.

Then ask yourself, "When do I feel most clear during the day? Is it in the morning? Afternoon? After going to the gym? While taking a shower?" Write these out.

Now, list all those times (or activities) that most challenge you mentally – items that can be overwhelming to deal with. Perhaps it's paying bills, sorting through your mail, or some mentally challenging task at work.

Now, look through what you've written.

See how you can arrange your schedule so that you're using your "optimum" focus times to tackle those tasks you find most challenging.

You may want to revisit this exercise every few weeks, especially as you're testing out other exercises from this book.

ORGANIZATION

"Keeping yourself organized" is a big topic. There are already countless good books on the subject available, including a number geared specifically to people with ADD/ADHD challenges. I don't want to reinvent the wheel, so in this section I want to cover just "the basics," along with a few points I haven't seen mentioned elsewhere.

Tips for Being More Organized

One of the most common labels placed on hunter-types (people with ADD/ADHD challenges) – is that we're tragically disorganized. The "Hunter-type Brain" chapter goes into the many biochemical reasons why this is so. However, I can attest to the fact that it *is* possible to be a hunter-type *and* be well organized. The key, once again, is "smarter not harder."

To exist in our modern world, it's nearly essential to have *multiple* systems of organization:

- Filing systems for finances and important papers

- Cleaning your house

- Paying bills

- etc...

Having good organizational systems can make your life so much easier while reducing stress levels significantly.

Designing Your Systems of Organization

As with your time management systems, the first step in "being organized" is to zoom out a bit and look at the big picture of your life.

Here are a few things to consider when designing your systems of organizing, whatever their application:

1. Simplicity equals effectiveness

Keep your systems as simple as possible. If they're overly complicated, your odds of continuing to use them are low. Bear in mind, you'll probably be using them at times when you're feeling mentally fuzzy.

2. Design them around your natural tendencies

Design your organizational systems around how you *already* do things. There are countless tips in books and on the internet covering how best to organize your life. However, if they aren't built around your natural tendencies, they're probably not going to last.

3. Be consistent

Once you've found a system you like, stick with it. If you start straying from it, bring yourself back. Commit to using a system for *at least* one week, without altering it in any way. You can't really tell if a system will work until you've spent some time with it.

Physical Filing Systems

There are countless methods for organizing important documents, both for home, and at work. Here are a few things to consider when developing your *physical* filing system:

- *Keep all your files in one spot* (in a filing cabinet, or just a filing box, if you don't have much paperwork).

- *Order your documents in meta categories*: finances, legal documents, health documents, etc.

- *Try using the "projects" system outlined in the "Time Management" chapter. This can be helpful in getting clear on where to place written notes, ideas, etc.*

- *Organize your physical and computer file systems as similarly as possible.* For example, if you have a section of your filing cabinet labeled "Health Documents", create this same folder on your computer, and organize it in a similar manner.

- *Keep a box of empty folders on hand at all times.* Go to your local office supply store and stock up. It's easy to run out of folders, without them your system ends up being just a messy stack of papers.

The most important thing to remember when dealing with paperwork: *get it out of the pile* and into your filing area, in a way you'll be able to find it again later, if you need to. That should always be your primary goal.

Effectively Dealing with Mail

Both for myself, and with many of my life coaching clients, dealing with mail (sifting through bills, junk mail, and important documents, etc.) can be quite a daunting task. And, mail can easily build up over time, creating anxiety and stress.

This is primarily due to the fact that "sifting through mail" is not a very hunter-type friendly task. It's just not very stimulating, and can easily become overwhelming:

"Is this important? Should I file this? If so, where?"

"Do I need to respond to this now?"

"Oh shoot! I forgot to pay this bill!"

"Hey, here's a coupon. Should I use this? I don't think I want to buy anything from there – but I may want to later..."

On and on it goes. No wonder people will endlessly procrastinate going through their mail.

Here are a few tips that may help:

1. If it's not absolutely important, *recycle it!*

2. *Drop it in the appropriate file, envelope and all.* Often, what takes time is tearing things open, removing all the extra marketing info, and just filing the bill or statement itself. If it's a bill or a statement, and you don't need to open it, just drop it straight into the file.

3. *Start using online bill paying for as many bills as you can.* This can drastically cut down on the stresses of sifting through mail, because the majority of important transactions can now happen online – and many of these can be automated.

If you've got a stack of mail that's really built up, get creative. Call a friend. Ask them to come over and hang out while you go through your mail. It doesn't have to be a grueling process. The more you can be creative, and think "outside the box" for boring tasks, the more likely they'll get done in a timely fashion, and not end up turning into "giants."

Reduce Junk Mail

Junk mail is terrible for the environment. We're cutting down groves of old-growth forests just for mindless catalogs and irrelevant ads that just get thrown away without ever being read – not to mention the endless amount of pollution involved in transporting this "trash" to you.

Additionally, many of us have already transitioned into using *email* as our primary method of corresponding with companies and organizations. Email can be *far* easier to manage than physical mail, if done properly. And, it doesn't take up any physical space.

Take a few hours and contact (call or email) the main companies that are sending you junk mail, and request that you be taken off their mailing list. You may also want to encourage your friends and family to do the same.

Try visiting the website www.donotmail.org, or do an internet search for "stop junk mail," to find a whole host of tips on ridding yourself of the endless barrage of junk mail we're all afflicted with.

House Cleaning

Our external environment *greatly* influences our inner life. If you're in a room that's cluttered, you'll probably *feel* cluttered.

One of my clients struggled with keeping his house clean for a long time. He'd clean it, things would be in order for a while – then life would take its toll. It would then quickly regress back into a giant unorganized heap. And this just added to his preexisting feeling of overwhelm.

He decided to hire a friend to come in to clean and organize once a week. He enjoyed spending time with them, and he now knows – no matter *what* is going on in his life, or how disorganized his place gets – it will never last more than a few days. He found the minimal financial investment was *well* worth it.

Some people just have the gift for organizing. Calling upon them to assist you, especially when getting new systems together, can make things a lot easier. If you can't afford to pay someone, consider offering a trade for services.

Avoid Creating Clutter

This may sound overly simplistic, but I've found this to be a very helpful rule. My mother used to drill this point into me as a kid, and she was right. If I just spend a bit more focused energy on *not creating clutter in the first place*, far less energy will be required for cleaning later.

I know many of you may be saying, "that's all well and good, but you don't know how chaotic my life is!"

This maybe true, however – the simple intention of *not creating clutter* can go a long way. Intentions, when spoken clearly, regularly, and with focus, drop into the subconscious. Over time, you'll mostly likely stop creating so much clutter. It will become a habit.

Consider installing this thought into your consciousness:

*All of my actions now create
greater order and peace in my life.*

Write this 10 times every morning for a few days, or set it as a reminder on your smart phone. The more you bring this thought into your conscious mind, the more it will affect your subconscious.

Because your *external* environment affects your *internal* one, there's a good chance you'll be more productive if your work and home environments are relatively ordered. And I'm not inferring you obsessively clean every single day. I'm talking about a *manageable* level of order, and only you know where that line is.

Keep in mind, you probably will go through cycles. Things will get a bit cluttered, you'll clean and organize, then they'll get cluttered again. Accept some clutter, but know where your threshold of overwhelm is, and don't allow things to ever get that far.

෴

Computer File Systems

Over the years, I've headed up projects that involved *multiple* people having to share and work on the same computer files. Without a good system, it's easy for things to devolve into chaos.

In the late 1990s, I worked with a man named Leland Russell, head of a company called "Geo Group," which organizes large-scale corporate innovation events and projects. He shared with me his computer file organization system. It's simple, clean, and I've been using it for over 15 years, with little modification.

This system is an extension of the "projects" system mentioned in the "Time Management" chapter.

On your computer, in the root directory of your hard drive (if you're on a PC, it's usually C:\), or on your desktop, make a folder called *Projects*. Then, inside this folder, make two folders: *Active* and *Archive*.

> *Active*: All of the projects you are currently working on, including ongoing ones like finances, health, etc...

> *Archive*: These are all projects that have been completed, or no longer being worked on.

Inside these folders, make a folder for each project, and place all your files for this project there: text files, images, word processor documents, etc.

So, the tree would look like this:

```
📁 Projects
    📁 Active
        📁 HomeImprovement
                photo.jpg
                5-15-10 Research.txt
        📁 Health
                MyEyeglassPrescription.txt
                9-22-10 LetterToDoctor.doc
    📁 Archive
        📁 CharliesBirthdayParty
        📁 Wedding
        📁 NewHouse
```

Additionally, you may want to include a *Media* folder along side your *Projects* folder, to store videos, music, and photos.

    📁Projects
       📁 Active
       📁 Archive
   📁Media
       📁 Video
       📁 Music
       📁 Photos

Why I like this system:

- It's simple

- I always know where to put things

- I can quickly track down what I'm looking for when I need it

- It's easy to back things up. If I need to backup my computer, I know *all* of my important information will be stored in the "Projects" folder

Date All Documents

Whenever I create *any* document – either on the computer, or on a sheet of paper, I always date it. This makes it easy for me to track it down later. I may not be able to remember the exact file, but I *usually* remember the general date when I created it.

Even though your computer *does* date a file when it's created – I've found this is not always reliable – especially if you experience a computer crash, or something gets corrupted when moving the file to an external hard drive.

If it's a computer file, I always place the date *first* in the file name:

   1-15-11 BookNotes.txt

Mind Mapping

This book would not exist if it weren't for mind mapping. Mind mapping is a nonlinear method of outlining made popular by Tony Busan in the 1980s, and seems to have been tailor-made for us hunter-types.

I was first introduced to mind mapping in the mid-1990s by the head of the "Best Practices" department at Texas Instruments. He assured me that it was a "life changing" tool. And sure enough, he was right. It was a complete revelation.

Mind mapping is designed around how your brain *actually* functions – unlike traditional *linear* methods of outlining (I,II,III - A,B,C, etc.). Thought is *nonlinear,* and is made up of an endless host of associations. By having a tool that is *also* nonlinear – that mirrors these cognitive patterns – it makes it much easier to get ideas out of your head and onto paper (or onto your computer).

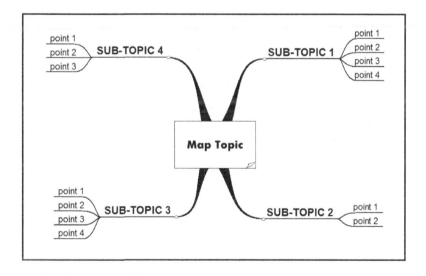

Mind mapping is basically a tree graph that starts in the center, with a "central topic," then extends outward into branches and subbranches.

I've found so many valuable uses for mind mapping, including:

- Planning my day

- Mapping out projects (like this book)

- Decision making (weighing pro's and cons)

- Brainstorming

- Outlining talks and workshops

The practical applications of mind mapping are virtually limitless, and there's a number of mind mapping software packages (and smart phone apps) available. My suggestion is – start by learning the basics of mind mapping *on paper,* then move to using software, once you've got the basics down.

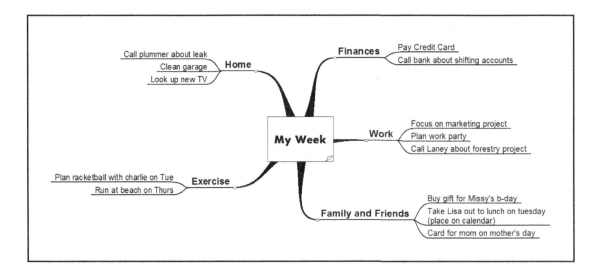

A word of warning, mind mapping can get addictive. You may find yourself mapping out just about everything in your life. However, from my experience, mind mapping is really good for certain things, but not for others.

For example:

You *can* take meeting/class notes with it, but I haven't found this very effective, because you'll need to organize things into categories *while* you're mapping. It tends to slow things down.

However, it works really well as a *group* brainstorming tool – as long as someone then converts it into useful action items.

When writing this book, I used mind mapping software to organize and refine my chapter outlines. It made it easy for me to drag-and-drop outline points, continually refining the sections of each chapter. This cut down on my prep time considerably. It also yielded a comprehensive and concise outline to write from.

FINANCES

Hunter-types often have challenges with finances (paying bills, tracking expenses, doing taxes, debt, etc.). Dealing with numbers can be boring and tedious – definitely not very stimulating. This can make budgeting, and keeping our accounts in order, quite difficult for many of us.

Here again, some of the previously mentioned tips apply:

1. Create simple and effective systems for handling your financial tasks.

2. Once you have a working system, stay with it.

3. Get support. Hire a bookkeeper or at least someone to help you get your money systems setup.

4. Use life coaching sessions to assist in maintaining and refining your systems.

5. Be creative. Make the act of doing your finances as stimulating as humanly possible.

Schedule One Day Each Month for Finances

We hunter-types are often plagued with the experience of having countless little details all flooding together in our brain (paying bills, tracking expenses, budgeting, etc.). All those small items can quickly add up to one big pile of overwhelm.

Once again, the key is – *have a good system*. Create a container for these details so they're handled *by the system*, and not constantly bouncing around in your head.

A good beginning strategy is:

Pick one day a month to do your finances.

Choose a day, possibly during the last week of the month, to handle as many financial tasks as possible:

- Paying bills
- Budgeting for the next month
- Tracking income
- Transferring money into savings
- Making financial decisions
- Taxes

A very helpful tip to remember – *schedule your finances at a time when you do your best detail work*. Ensuring you've had a good cardio workout the day before can make a big difference. Having some natural stimulant before hand (yerba mate, green tea, etc.), can also improve your focus and mental clarity. The better your brain is functioning, the easier the process will be.

If you're really struggling with keeping to your scheduled day, try integrating finances in with your life coaching sessions (see the "Creating a Support System" chapter). If possible, take a few minutes during the session to *start* working on your finances.

Most often, once you get over "the hump" of resistance, finishing the task is usually much easier.

Automatic Bill Pay and Financial Software

Automating the many tasks around finances can greatly eliminate stress and anxiety. Most banks offer free "automatic bill pay" with their accounts. Nearly all of your bills can be paid in this fashion. If you have a predictable income, and know the money will always be in the account to cover your payments, I *highly recommend* taking the time to setup automatic bill pay. If you're confused about how to do this, just give your bank a call, or visit their website. They often provide instructional videos online.

If your income is a bit less predictable, you can still pay your bills online *manually*. This still takes less time than the paper-based approach once it's set up (provided you are comfortable working with a computer).

Money Management Software and Reminder Systems

There are countless money management software packages available – and you may already have one installed on your computer. Some are simple and straightforward, while others can be confusing, offering way too many features than you'll ever need.

If you go online, most of them will offer a free 30 day test run. Download a few, play with them, and find one that really clicks for you.

A good money management application will:

- Track bill payments

- Interface with your bank's online bill pay

- Track your account balances

- Track your income and purchases for use at tax time

- Remind you when bills are coming due

- Work with your smart phone

- Provide charts showing spending habits

If you already work with an accountant on your taxes, you may want to ask them what software they recommend.

And you can do all of this *without* a software package. I simply use a spreadsheet that I fill out once a month. It tracks my account balances, income from various sources, and calculates a certain percentage of my income that I transfer into savings. I then use email and smart phone reminders to let me know when bills are coming due.

Dealing With Debt

Another common predicament many of us hunter-types get into is *debt* – spending beyond our means. Coming back to our ongoing discussion on dopamine and stimulation – spending money can be a rush. The obvious downside is the potential to rack up a huge mountain of debt. With debt comes anxiety, self-judgment, low self-esteem, relationship issues, and a whole host of other problems.

Here are a few suggestions in getting this psychological weight off your shoulders:

1. *Forgive yourself.* Most of us weren't taught how to manage our finances and had to learn as we went along. It may not have been until you read this book that you fully understood your "wiring." Your actions were unconscious, and – had you been aware of these unconscious tendencies – you probably wouldn't have gotten into debt in the first place.

2. *Start fresh now*. With this new awareness of your tendencies, make a conscious decision to improve your relationship with money.

3. *Educate yourself*. If you're being hounded by bill collectors, realize you have the law on your side. Bill collector calls *can* be stopped (or at least managed), and there's a plethora of information online on how to do this. Stopping the harassing phone calls may only involve one or two short conversations. Try googling, "stop bill collector calls."

4. *Get rid of your credit cards* and replace them with debit cards that allow for Visa/MasterCard purchases. You can still use the card to buy things, but they will be deducted from your *existing* funds. You'll no longer be postponing payment out into the future.

5. Place a strong emphasis on *creating new money,* versus constantly dwelling on what you owe. The time you waste worrying about money doesn't help the situation. Focus this energy on being creative, brainstorming on ways to get more money. This is always a helpful financial discipline, whether or not you're in debt.

6. *Get support*. There are numerous free nonprofit debt relief services that can assist you in consolidating your debts, negotiating them down, and getting you back on track. If you have feelings of shame around taking this step, consider this: if you get sick, you go to the doctor. Do you feel shame for getting sick? Then, you shouldn't feel any shame if you need a little help with your finances. We all slip up from time to time. The people that succeed, after some personal failure, usually make the decision to ask for help when they need it. It may feel *momentarily* awkward, or embarrassing, but in the long run, you'll be much better off.

7. Listen to an audio series on "creating prosperity." Piping in *positive* thoughts surrounding money can provide some much-needed inspiration to turn things around. See the "Bibliography & Resources" section at the end of the book for recommendations.

Start a Financial Support Group

Many people have challenges with handling their finances – hunter-type or not. Consider pulling together a group of friends once a month to:

- Brainstorm on income ideas

- Research and implement effective money management systems

- Utilize the "group mind" to help each individual overcome specific money-related challenges

Talking about money with friends is often taboo in our society. It's often the subject people feel least comfortable discussing. By pulling together a group that meets regularly to discuss money *openly* – much of these fears can be diffused, and real progress can be made.

Finances for the Self-Employed

We hunter-types are often entrepreneurial. Being self-employed offers countless benefits, but one of the downsides can be: getting your personal and business finances all muddled together. Especially if you're working from home, keeping these two separated can be a bit challenging.

Here are a few tips that may be helpful:

1. If you have an accountant that already does your taxes, schedule a meeting with them to discuss the best ways of organizing and separating your personal finances from your business.

2. Create separate bank accounts for your business. Then, get a debit card for your business account that can be used as a Visa/MasterCard. The charge goes through as a credit card, but the funds get transferred right away. Make all your business purchases with this account. That way, you'll have a clear record at tax time of all your business expenses.

3. Educate yourself: read books, watch videos, read articles, subscribe to lists. There are *volumes* of good information available on how to manage finances for a small business.

⁓

WORKING FOR YOURSELF

Hunter-types often gravitate to starting their own business. There are a number of reasons why self-employment can be well-suited for us:

- It can provide us more freedom to create an income based on what we're passionate about.

- We can often make our own hours.

- We have to rely on "our wits" and creativity to provide for ourselves.

- Depending on the business, we may be able to design our schedule around our natural rhythms. For example, if you're an artist, and work best late at night, working for yourself affords you this opportunity.

However, there are some very specific skills involved in successfully earning enough from your own business to support yourself. One of the biggest challenges – especially if you work from home – is the *lack of external structure*. Because of this, a good deal of self-discipline is involved in managing your business in this distraction-filled environment.

In this section, I'll offer a few basic tips that may be helpful if you have, or are considering, starting your own business.

Creating an Optimal Work Environment - Internally and Externally

Whatever your line of work, mindfulness of your work environment can go a long way in the success of your business. It's always best to start with the *internal* one – your physical health, your thoughts, and your emotions.

From my experience, self-employment places a much greater importance on nourishing yourself properly, both physically and emotionally. If you're off center, your business grinds to a halt – and with it, your ability to provide for yourself. It's very much connected to survival. If you're just off in the clouds plotting all the wonderful things your want to do with your business, and you're not focused enough on your internal environment, odds are, things will get tumultuous.

Much of the information shared in this book was derived from my own necessity to find balance in order to pursue the work I love. Viewing the material in the "Navigating Emotions" and "Exercise, Diet, and Supplements" chapters through this lens, may offer up some key insights in being able to keep your business ventures thriving.

On the *external* front – every business is unique in its set and setting. Here are a few general tips that may be useful in making your work environment more hunter-type friendly. I'll revisit a few points already mentioned.

1. Regularly clean and organize your workspace.

For some of you, this may sound like a Himalayan task, however I've found sometimes the most effective thing I can do is spend some time cleaning and organizing. This act, in and of itself, often brings internal clarity.

Your external will affect your internal. Through organizing and cleaning your external environment, you greatly assist your thought process in being more clear and focused.

2. Good oxygen flow is essential.

I can't stress this point enough. I'm continually surprised how many people work in a virtually hermetically sealed environment. If you have a window where you're working, *open it!* It can make a huge difference in your ability to focus if you're getting fresh air.

If you don't have a window, *take regular breaks*. Get outside. Breathe deeply. If you are in a city environment, find a tree and spend a few minutes under it. Trees give off oxygen and purify the air around them. If you have more oxygen in your body, you'll be more alert and able to focus for longer periods of time.

3. Healthy lighting can make a big difference.

Numerous studies have been conducted on the effects of lighting on productivity and overall health. One such study, conducted in Canada on elementary school students, came to the following conclusion:

> "The results indicated that over the two year period, students under full spectrum fluorescent lamps with ultraviolet supplements developed fewer dental cavities and had better attendance, achievement, and growth and development than students under other lights. Students under the high pressure sodium vapor lamps had the slowest rates of growth and development as well as the poorest attendance and achievement."
>
> – "A Case of Daylight Robbery. A Study Into the Effects of Types of Light on Children."
> *Warren E. Hathaway, Ph.D.*

If you work in rooms that have florescent lighting, consider replacing them with standard iridescent lighting, or install full-spectrum florescent bulbs instead. Full-spectrum bulbs are widely available, and can easily be worth the extra few dollars if they bring you greater focus and well being while you're working.

Have Good Systems in Place

Once again, we hunter-types *thrive* when we have good systems in place. A good system can minimize mental confusion, and allow us to focus the bulk of our energy towards the task at hand. You shouldn't have to "re-invent the wheel" for each new project and client.

Here's a list of a few systems that could be helpful to map out when starting a new business, no matter what your work or service is:

- Invoicing

- Budgeting

- Expenses tracking and assessment

- Tax planning and accounting

- Meetings (format and general structure)

- Note-taking and referencing for each client/project

- Marketing

- Client relations and correspondence

- Scheduling

Work Scheduling

All of the tips mentioned in the "Time Management" chapter apply to work scheduling.

A common trap many people fall into, especially when they first start out, is not having a clear idea *when* their work day starts and ends. This easily turns into working at all hours of the day and night, and on weekends, which can easily lead to burn out.

It can be very helpful to write out a basic schedule for your work week. Map out when you'd like to work, and when you'd like to schedule other things into your life that will bring balance (like exercise, time with family and friends, rest and chill-time, etc.).

Then, to the best of your ability, keep to this schedule. If you don't want to work after 6 p.m., don't schedule a client call at 7 p.m. If that's the time that works best for them, either say "no," or tell them this isn't your typical work time, but you'll make this *one* exception.

I've followed this principle for many years. If I stick to my schedule, and create strong boundaries around my personal life – willingly saying "no" to clients when things don't work within my schedule – people tend to have much greater respect for my time. As I continued with this, I began attracting those clients and projects that work best within my schedule. All of this led to me being more skilled at what I do, doing a much better job, and the being able to charge more for my services.

When you're just starting out, there's usually a lot of feelings of insecurity, because running your own business is new to you. This can lead to being a "people pleaser." Keep this tendency conscious – make note of those times when you sacrifice your schedule for a client, when you really didn't want to. Over time, just through the act of being conscious of your actions, you'll do it for less, and you'll find ways to keep stronger boundaries around the rest of your life.

You probably want to work for yourself because you enjoy the freedom it brings. Don't let your business rule you. Remember, you're the one in charge.

Working Out How Much to Charge for Your Services

Coming up with a clear hourly rate for your services is an essential exercise for just about any business you're in. Even if you're selling a product, it can be immensely helpful to get clear on what your time is worth, so you can assess whether or not your sales goals are honoring the time you're putting in. There's a few ways to arrive at this.

The simple approach is to find out what is common in your industry, based on your general skill set. This is critical information to have. You need to know what people are use to paying for your service.

Another method is to work backwards, based on what you'd like to be making on a monthly and yearly basis. Here's an exercise I've found quite useful. It is adapted from Fredric Lehman's *Prosperity Consciousness* audio series. This is one way to arrive at how much you'll need to charge for your services in order to make your expenses *with* money left over (profit).

 CALCULATING YOUR HOURLY RATE

Pick a yearly income that reflects what you'll need to earn to cover all of your basic needs (food, shelter, etc.).

Now, pad this by at least 20%.

For example, let's say this number is $42,000.

Divide this by 12 (months).

42,000 divided by 12 = 3500

This gives you your projected income for one month: $3500.

Next, divide by 4 (weeks).

$3500 divided by 4 = $875

This gives you a rough estimate of your target *weekly* income.

Divide this by the number of hours you have available to work per week, while leaving enough time for other important activities in your life. For this example, we'll say that's 35.

875 divided by 35 (number of hours you'd like to work) = $25/hr

You now know if you charge $25 an hour for your services, and work 35 hours a week, you will make your goal of $42,000 a year. If you work (5) days a week, this means your daily income goal is: $175 a day.

This exercise takes an abstract number like $42,000, and puts it into terms you can wrap your head around. If I ask you, "how do you make $42,000 a year from your business?" – you may feel a bit overwhelmed. However, if you tell yourself, "all I need to do is charge $25 an hour, and work 35 hours a week", that feels far more doable.

This is a good example why it's important to break things down into their basic components. This process tends to reduce overwhelm, making your income goals feel much more attainable.

Knowing How Long It Will Take

Another key to success in *any* business involves good time assessment – *accurately predicting how long things will take.* Whether you're a writer, an artist, or in construction, knowing how long things take leads to clarity on how much to charge for a project. Or even on a more fundamental level – whether or not a project is worth pursuing in the first place.

An ability to do this *accurately* usually only comes from experience. However, the best way to refine this skill starts with taking good notes, and reviewing them regularly.

If you charged $2000 to do a project, figuring your time is worth $75/hour. How long did it *actually* take to get done? Not all businesses bill in this fashion, but if yours does, this is an essential skill to develop.

If you're creating a product, a good rule of thumb is to charge at least three times the cost of materials.

Don't Overbook Yourself

As a hunter-type, when considering your work schedule, there's one key point to remember – *know your limitations.* Avoid overbooking yourself, taking on more projects and clients than you can handle at a given time. It's easy to get into the mindset "more work is always better" or "more work *always* means more money."

The reality is, when you overbook, your work will suffer, and you'll most likely get burned out. This often leads to getting physically ill. If you're the only employee of your business, when *you* go down, the *business* goes down. Period.

Mindful scheduling practices, taking into account your limitations, is essential in maintaining a successful business.

Seek Out Support

Running your own business, especially if you're the only employee of your company, can be a lot of work. It's easy to lose perspective, feel discouraged, or get lost in the minutia of work-related tasks.

"Business support" can come in many different forms:

- Business coaches

- Life coaches

- Networking groups

- Business support groups

- Mentors (business owners/entrepreneurs)

Having someone you meet with on a regular basis to discuss your business can be the difference between a thriving business and one that is just "getting by." If you pay for this service, you can write it off on your taxes.

〜

OTHER LIFE TIPS

If Possible, Avoid Homework

Hunter-types typically don't do well with "homework." And I'm not just referring to school work.

Take the following scenario.

While talking with a friend, they ask if you'd be able to write up a "letter of recommendation" for them.

Without thinking, you say "yes." Then, five minutes later, you find your inner dialog sounding something like this:

> *"WHY DID YOU DO THAT!!! I already have so much on our plate! I'm going to obsess about this for weeks, not do it, then just feel guilty about it!"*

Either you'll spin on this for a few days until you finally get up the energy to do it. Or endlessly procrastinate until it creates resentment between you and your friend.

And this is just one possible scenario. Hunter-types will have multiple examples of this kind of situation.

Let's look at this example in more detail. The "homework" involved – writing a letter of recommendation – is typically *not* a hunter-type friendly task to begin with. It evolves a good deal of focus and sustained mental clarity.

Here's one possible solution:

> *schedule these kinds of tasks with someone else.*

In this case, with the person making the request.

> Friend: "Would you be willing to write me a letter of recommendation?"
>
> You: "I would, but I'd like to schedule a phone call with you to do this, perhaps sometime in the next few days. We can go through it together."

This completely changes the situation. Once you've scheduled this task with another person, *it no longer resides all on your shoulders.* Therefore, it's no longer homework. You can brainstorm with them about it *in real time*, write it together, and the task is complete by the time you get off the phone.

Look at your own life. Identify areas where you can enact a "no homework" policy. I assure you, this strategy can be immensely effective in reducing stress and making tasks more enjoyable.

As you become more mindful of making commitments in ways that really work for you, it helps everyone around you. You become more effective, *and* more reliable. As a result, your sense of self-esteem goes up, and you'll probably have more energy as a result.

Take Time to Unplug

Many of us hunter-types are addicted to stimulation. In modern life, this usually comes in the form of technology. Television, the internet, our mobile phones – all of these provide high levels of constant stimulation. There's nothing intrinsically wrong with any of these, but if you need them *all the time*, you no longer own them, *they own you.*

The effects can be quite far reaching. You may spend less time connecting with friends and family, or you'll be incapable of being present with them, even when you are *physically* with them.

On another level, technology and modern life tend to be *fast-paced*. Whereas, the subtler pleasures of life require a certain degree of stillness to fully appreciate them.

Here's an exercise that you may find helpful.

"UNPLUGGING" EXERCISE

Take at least one day a month to completely unplug – no cell phone, no computer, no TV. Pick a day and mark it on your calendar.

Then, try heading out into nature on this day, or spend time with your friends and family. Cherish the experience of just "being in the moment."

This may be the most rewarding time in your entire month. Or, you may find you're crawling the walls because you really *need* to check your email, get on the internet, or watch something on TV. Good. This shows you *exactly* where your attachments to technology are.

Perhaps you may be inspired to face this dragon head on by taking *one day a week* to unplug – or unplug for two or three days in a row. You may want to plan a camping trip where you unplug for a whole week or longer. Again, the goal here is strengthening your will so you can *consciously create your life*, instead of your habits and addictions always running the show.

"Simplify My Life" Session

Most of us have highly complicated lives. Merely by living in the modern world, our life amasses complexity.

When I was 25, after building a relatively successful business, I decided to sell everything I owned, get down to a guitar and backpack, and travel. This was one of the scariest *and* most liberating experiences of my life.

I ended up settling in Hawaii, drastically simplifying my life. I didn't have a car, I walked everywhere, spent a lot more time in nature, and had *far more meaningful* interactions with others, because so many distractions had been eliminated.

When I've given talks, I find that people really connect with this story. I think it's because most of us are so weighed down by life and obligations that we often feel trapped. We don't see a way out.

The good news is, you don't have to give up everything in order to touch this sense of freedom. It simply involves strengthening your ability to "let go." Think of it this way, the muscles in your hand that are responsible for grasping are usually much stronger than the ones that allow you to let go of something.

By going through a regular practice of "letting things go that no longer serve you," you strengthen that unseen muscle that gives you the ability to remove yourself from things that are holding you back. And the ability to do this opens up new space for new and useful things to come into your life.

"SIMPLIFYING MY LIFE" EXERCISE

Either by yourself, or with someone else, brainstorm on ways you can simplify your life. What is "taking up too much room" – either physically or mentally? It may be items you no longer need, ways of behaving, or people whose presence is somewhat toxic to you.

As you go through this exercise, you may end up listing lots of small things. Or, you may realize you want to make bigger changes, like changing your job, taking time off, or even moving to a new location.

This is about looking at your life through the lens of "how can I feel *more* free, and have *less* complexity and distractions?" With this as your focus, you'll most likely come up with a whole host of ideas. Some of them will be practical, while others may not be so doable – but it will feel good to at least consider them. They'll probably offer you a bit of perspective on your current situation.

Most of us have far more control over the course of our lives than we realize. By taking a little time to step outside it, examining our patterns and habits, we may find there's a whole host of things we can do to improve our *overall* sense of well being and freedom. Often, this starts with letting some things go.

Hunter-types and Travel

Hunter-types *thrive* on movement and stimulation. We can often feel stagnant if we're in one location for long periods of time. If this is you, regularly scheduling trips outside your immediate area can be a very helpful strategy.

Here are a few benefits to regular travel:

Perspective

By getting outside of your local area, you can get perspective on problems you may be having, as well as insights into your next life moves.

Movement

Hunter-types need movement. We tend to feel more alive, and mentally clearer when we're in motion.

New stimuli

Connecting with new people and being exposed to a different environment can be reinvigorating, allowing us to return home with a renewed sense of energy and purpose.

A time to journal and reflect

Traveling is often the optimal time to reflect, journal, and write down insights.

If you're feeling a bit lost or stagnant, try getting out of town for a few days. It may just be the "magic bullet" you're looking for to get you back on track.

༄

Survival Strategies for Hunter-types in the Modern World

Life in our modern world gets complex. Good strategies and tools are essential, especially when you're in a pinch. Much of this chapter was derived from insights gleaned from dealing with challenging situations, both in my own life, and in assisting my life coaching clients.

Once again, take what works, adjust or let go of what doesn't.

12

CREATING A SUPPORT SYSTEM

Creating an effective support system is one of the most vital (and often overlooked) aspects of working with ADD/ADHD challenges. How do we create a context for receiving useful support from others on a regular basis?

A "support system" can take many forms (one-on-one life coaching, business coaching, groups, etc.), but it should always address one very important need – *consistency*. To achieve our goals, and maintain balance, consistency is essential. And for us hunter-types, it's typically the vitamin we're deficient in. Although we tend to have tremendous gifts of creativity and out-of-the-box thinking, these gifts often come at a cost. Consistency, especially as it relates to mid-to-long term planning, can be extremely difficult for us, even if we're doing all the right things to support our health.

So, what does an effective support system look like, and how do we create it? This is the place where many of us get stuck.

In this chapter, I hope to offer you clear, road-tested methods for receiving ongoing support from others, specifically designed to address our unique set of challenges. These techniques can provide the context for establishing meaningful support from others, regardless of your current financial situation.

How I Discovered Life Coaching

For many years, even after homing in on a supportive exercise and diet plan, I watched myself continually struggle with achieving my goals – bringing *my own* projects to fruition. I could partner with other people, and watch my *collaborative* work succeed. But my own projects kept getting derailed.

The reason was simple – *I couldn't maintain consistency*. I'd lose touch with the initial inspiration, get disheartened, or just feel overwhelmed by all the details necessary for its completion. And this persistent inability to achieve my goals really ate at my self-esteem.

It became imperative for me to seek out some *external* means of support to keep me going when times got tough – to help me stay on track when I got waylaid.

What Is Life Coaching?

Life coaching is a fairly recent phenomena. The term itself didn't enter into our modern lexicon until the mid-1990s.

Still in its infancy as a profession, it's most commonly associated with business coaching, and has become increasingly popular for people who are self-employed. And for good reason. Life coaching, when done skillfully, can have dramatic results. It creates a context to receive support in a way that really didn't exist previously in our society.

Although it can take many forms, life coaching is primarily about support. It's a process by which a person receives focused support in all aspects of their life, on a *regular* basis. It involves looking at "the whole picture" of your life, so you don't get caught up in all the tiny little details that tend to weigh us down on a daily basis.

Life coaching has already proven itself to be an extremely effective tool for us hunter-types. In fact, there are now *many* life coaches that specialize exclusively in working with people facing ADD/ADHD challenges.

The Birth of the "4 Step Life Coaching Process"

I've had the privilege of working with a number of very talented life coaches. These were people who allowed me the space to co-create a coaching system uniquely suited for my life.

A few years into receiving life coaching, I was asked by a friend, after assisting him through a particular rough time in his life, to be *his* life coach – a profession I had no real interest in pursuing. It turned out to be a major turning point in my life. I found the work to be deeply meaningful, and I gained new-found respect for what consistent support can do.

In working with another "hunter-type" on a regular basis, someone with classic ADD challenges, I was able to fine-tune the coaching system I had been using for myself the previous few years.

To my surprise, the process quickly stabilized, and I witnessed how – it was the *process itself* that was doing most of the work. This was then verified by other life coaching clients, as my practice expanded.

In many ways, the process I'll be sharing with you is the culmination of my many years voraciously devouring personal growth books, workshops, and spiritual practices – filtering everything through the same questions: "Does this work? Is this effective at making my life better? And, as in attempting to prove a scientific theorem, can it be consistently replicated?" All of this percolated up into a form that, I believe, can be used by just about anyone, whether or not they have past experience with life coaching.

For hunter-types especially, life coaching can provide us an anchor. If you're like me, you often wake up feeling like a *completely different person* than you were the day before – the goals and intentions from that previous day like faint lights off in the distance. A regular life coaching session can offer a kind of mooring to tie off at – keeping us from continually getting swept out to sea.

There's one more aspect of life coaching that directly applies to you, *in this moment*, as you read these words. A common pattern I've seen, over and over again – both in myself and with friends and clients: you read a book, attend a seminar, and get *really* fired-up to change your life. Then, after a few weeks and a couple of setbacks – the energy fizzles and you're right back where you started – probably a bit more jaded than when you began.

As I've watched this pattern in myself, it became absolutely clear that *ongoing* support was the key to integrating new habits and sustaining positive changes in my life.

Addressing the Affordability Factor

Although having a professional life coach to speak with on a weekly basis can be immensely supportive, not everyone can afford this. This coaching model provides a means of getting effective support *right now* – regardless of your current financial situation.

To be clear, this model is *not* ADD/ADHD specific – it can be used by just about anyone (or any group) interested in making positive changes in their life.

THE "4 STEP" LIFE COACHING PROCESS

The "4 Step" life coaching process involves setting some time aside in your regular schedule to focus on key areas of your life with another person.

In reviewing the process, I'll refer to two specific roles:

> The "client" – the person *receiving* coaching.

> The "coach" – the person *facilitating*.

It's important to understand both roles, especially if you are interested in exchanging life coaching with someone.

Preparation

Whether it's a phone call, a one-on-one session, or a group, there are a few steps necessary to optimize your environment in order to get the most out of this process.

> 1. *Establish specific beginning and end times <u>prior</u> to the session.* Be sure there is a clear understanding between you and your coach as to this time-frame, before getting started.

> 2. *Ensure your environment is free from distractions* (turn off your cell phone, the TV, etc.). Inform others not to interrupt you during the time frame of the session. If you are using a computer to read notes from, close your email program, web browser, or anything else that may distract you.

> 2. *Be prepared to take good notes.* Both the person acting as coach, and the client, should be prepared to take notes (pen and paper, laptop computer, etc.).

> 3. *Map out the session.* Before each session, the client should review their notes, goals list, and write out their intentions. What are you most wanting support on? Make

note of what specific items require focused attention – especially anything that feels overwhelming or confusing.

You may also want to create a simple list of your wins and challenges since the last session (to be discussed in detail a bit later).

Session Length

If you plan to do a coaching session once a week, *one hour* is typically enough time to go through the entire process. If it's once every two weeks, or once a month, then allot at least *an hour and half*. From my experience, these time durations work well for most people. If it's your very first session, set aside an hour and a half.

The "4 Steps"

The four main sections to the life coaching process are as follows:

1. Review

2. Check-In

3. Brainstorming

4. Scheduling

1. Review

This first section consists of reviewing:

- Goals (short-term and long-term)

- The needs-actions list (to be discussed later)

- Any ongoing reminders compiled from previous sessions.

The "Review" section sets the stage for the entire session. By reviewing your goals first, *before* addressing any challenges that may be occurring in your life, it addresses one major need – *perspective*. It's far too easy to "get lost in the trees" and not see the forest.

Reviewing your goals *in the beginning of the session* offers you a broader perspective on your life. From this vantage point, effective plans can be made that *not only* address current challenges, but allow you to be proactive in taking steps to meet your goals. This particularly addresses a common hunter-type challenge with mid-to-long-term planning.

Once you've created a goals list, it's essential you actually look at it occasionally. This may seem obvious, but many people (as I've done in the past) just store it somewhere, never to be seen again. It felt good to write it out, but nothing ever happened with it. And, even if you *do* have your goals posted up somewhere in your house – many times it just becomes part of the scenery.

Through *actively* reviewing your goals on a regular basis with someone else, you remind yourself about your dreams and intentions – those items you really want to accomplish.

Here's what this section of the coaching process looks like:

> Either you or your coach (decide which works best for you) reads through your short-term and long-term goals list.

> As you listen to each item, make note of which ones "jump out."

> For example, if one of your long-term goals is:

> > *"Move to New York and study acting."*

> And, as the goals list is read, that one really connects with you, let your coach know. Have them write all these items down so that they can be covered in the "Brainstorming" section later in the session.

How to Work with Your Goals List

A tendency many people have, when going through a list of their life goals, is to feel frustrated or overwhelmed because they tell themselves, "I *should* have gotten that done! I didn't work on that *at all* last week. I'm so lazy!"

If viewed in this context, your goals list becomes just a big weight, a reminder of all the things you think are wrong with you.

A much more productive method of working with them involves seeing them as *suggestions* – as *potential* items to pursue. There will always be goals on your list that you won't be currently addressing – especially if your goals list is quite large.

Use your goals list to spark you – to get you *inspired* to take action. Going back to the previous example:

"Move to New York and study acting."

Instead of hearing, "this is just another thing I have to work on." Connect with the feeling, "I'd *love* to do that! I really want to focus some time on this today during the session."

And, as you read through goals that *don't* spark you, just let them go. If they're connected to something that will benefit you, they'll come alive again at some point. Leave them on the list, knowing you'll revisit them in the next session.

Another common experience is, you hear a goal being read, and it brings up some sadness. Occasionally, it may even cut pretty deep. You may feel disappointed about your previous attempts to meet this goal that didn't quite work out.

It's *equally important* to note these items as well. Place them on the "brainstorm" list, so you can discuss them later in the session. Perhaps it's simply a matter of coming up with slightly different actions, or perhaps the goal itself needs to be reframed in some way.

Working with goals in this way keeps you connected to your life force. Over time, I've watched this practice really shift how people perceive their goals, creating an overall feeling of lightness around them. You're more likely to pursue your goals when they don't feel like obligations.

The Needs-Actions List

The "needs-actions list" is an essential component of the life coaching process. As discussed in the "Navigating Emotions" chapter, needs are like vitamins. When a need goes unmet for any length of time, the results can be depression, anxiety, and even health issues. This list is designed to help you maintain balance, no matter what's happening. It provides a clear method of scheduling activities that address core needs, thereby reducing times of overwhelm and emotional instability.

However, the primary reason for using this list on a regular basis is – *life can become much more fulfilling*. You now have a tool that helps you home in on those activities that most nourish you, and ensure they actually end up on your schedule. Through reviewing this list during every life coaching session, you exponentially increase the power of it.

Start by re-reading the "needs-actions list" section of the "Navigating Emotions" chapter. Create at least a short list to work from. It will continually expand and grow over time, so don't be too concerned about making it "just right."

However, you could also start the coaching process *without* a list in place. There is time set aside in each session to address the needs-actions list. With the support of your coach, you can start from scratch, talk it through, and build it over the course of a few sessions.

Here's how the needs-actions gets used in this segment of the coaching session:

1. Start by looking over the needs list on page 123. Scan through it, or have your coach read it to you aloud.

2. Make note of which needs "jump out" as being either *not* being met, or *definitely* being met. Then, tell your coach so they can write them down. This is not a conceptual process. Trust your gut-level response.

For example, if you read through the list and the need "respect" really jumps out at you, make note of this. Don't try to figure out *why* this need isn't met, just identify it.

3. Once you have your list of met and unmet needs, look over your needs-actions list (if you have one). See which actions you've already identified that can address the unmet needs. Identify which actions can go on your schedule, then have your coach write them down. Their job is to add them to the "Scheduling" section of their notes, to be reviewed at the end of the session.

If you *haven't yet* identified potential actions to meet a particular need, have your coach add this need to their "Brainstorming" section notes. Later in the session, you can spend some time addressing ways to get this need met.

For the needs that *have* been well met recently, let your coach know what *specific* activities met these needs. These then can be added to your needs-actions list.

For example, if your needs for "friendship" and "connection" were really met since last session, perhaps the activities that met them were:

*Spent two days with an old friend
while they were in town.*

On your needs-actions list, you may then want to write:

Needs:

Friendship and Connection.

Actions:

Schedule lunch with a friend.

Schedule a phone call with a friend.

Avoid associating a <u>particular person</u> with getting a need met. It can create a situation where you associate *this one person* as being absolutely necessary to meet this need. Although it's common for many of us to do this, it's a good habit to break.

4. Once you're complete with this process, see if there are any *other* actions you would like to add to this list. You may want to experiment with a few new activities. Again, this is an ever-evolving document. It's important to continually refine it over time, as you shift and grow.

2. Check-In

The second main section of the coaching process involves the client sharing both their *wins,* and their *challenges,* since the last session. As you'll discover, just about everything in your life can fit within these two categories. This section is specifically designed to meet needs like: perspective, clarity, listening, understanding, celebration, and empathy – to name just a few.

For most of us, there are very few times in life when we receive active listening – to share what's going on in our life without being continually interrupted. For us hunter-types in particular, this part of the coaching process can be immensely supportive because it allows us to gain clarity on all the details that have been banking around in our brain – going through them, one by one, so they can be addressed.

For this section to really be effective, the process should be free-flowing and engaged. Even if the "client" has prepared a list before hand, they should be encouraged to connect with what they've written. Through keeping this process "alive," it often spontaneously yields solutions to address specific challenges. This "processing out loud" can be extremely helpful for us hunter-types.

Wins

A "win" is any perceived accomplishment since last session. Wins can be anything from real-world accomplishments, emotional wins, to personal revelations. They don't *necessarily* have to relate to items on your goals list, but they're often connected in some way. Perhaps you'll only see the connection as you go through this process.

This first reason for listing your "wins" is to identify what *is* going well in your life. So many of us get completely fixated on reaching our goals, or dealing with challenges, that we forget to celebrate all the smaller wins along the way. Regularly celebrating "wins" often provide us the fuel we need to meet bigger challenges.

Another reason for noting your wins involves *tracking*. You'll want to track the effectiveness of your life coaching sessions – noting which actions, planned in previous sessions, are *actually* working for you. In this way, this section feeds your needs-actions list, because you're spending time identifying *what works*.

This is where the life coaching process can have a *cumulative* effect. As you get into the habit of being mindful of your "wins," there's a good possibility you'll start doing this on a daily basis. You'll start becoming more aware of what actions are working, and you'll train yourself to celebrate every win *in the moment*. This definitely has a positive psychological effect, and can improve your overall mood.

If you're the coach:

Your job is to make note of *all* wins shared by the client – either on your computer, or on paper. Using a computer is often preferable because you'll have the ability to email the notes to the client after the session. Keeping an ongoing record of your coaching sessions is essential for tracking purposes. Even if the person has a prepared list of wins, undoubtedly more will occur to them in the midst of the process.

In order to stay fully engaged, avoid the temptation to interrupt, unless you're needing clarity on a particular item. Your role is to listen and take notes. Specifically, make note of anything that should be discussed in the "Brainstorming" or "Scheduling" sections.

Perhaps, as the client goes through their list of wins, they'll say something like, "I *really* enjoyed working on that project. I'd like to revisit it again at some point in the near future." Make a note and add it to either the "Brainstorming" or "Scheduling" section, so they can follow up on it later in the session.

Sometimes a client will have a particular challenge that's really clouding their ability to list any wins. If this is the case, you may suggest *starting* with "challenges" then go back to wins afterward.

Another option is to make the request, "how about we make note of this point, then address it in *challenges*, once you're complete with listing your wins?" Be sure to phrase this in the form of a question, so the client has the space to decide what would work best for them.

If they're unable to list more than two or three wins, ask them what they're grateful for in their life right now. Do your best to draw it out of them.

Questions you may want to ask:

> Do you have any wins regarding items on your goals list?
>
> What did you do since last session that felt rewarding?
>
> Do you have any wins in relation to diet or exercise?
>
> Did you receive clarity on something that's been on your mind?
>
> Any wins from work?

At the end of the "wins" segment, you may also want to ask, "is there anything from your list of wins you want to add to the *Brainstorming* or *Scheduling* sections?" Share what you've written – see if there was anything you missed.

Challenges

This next segment of the "Check-in" involves identifying all those items that are causing the client discomfort. A "challenge" is anything going on in their life that is unpleasant, taxing, or confusing. If it's a problem, it's a "challenge."

Oftentimes, this is the "unburdening" part of the session. Here again, simply through the act of being listened to while sharing their problems, *without* being interrupted by someone trying to diagnose or fix the problem, can be immensely therapeutic in and of itself. Often, just this quality of listening is all that is required to diffuse or resolve a particular issue. People spend lots of money going to a therapist merely to receive this kind of listening.

Typically, once you share a problem with someone else, the weight of it no longer feels like it's all on your shoulders. The psychological benefits to this can not be emphasized enough. Many people experience extreme emotional suffering due to feeling they have no one to turn to for help. Scheduling this kind of support into your regular routine can drastically reduce feelings of alienation and separateness.

For the client:

It can be helpful to establish what you feel comfortable sharing *prior* to your session. If you haven't reached a certain level of trust with the person you're working with yet, you may want to avoid sharing more personal challenges until this kind of trust is established.

For the coach:

As with the "wins" section, the coach's job is to quietly listen, *without* interrupting, unless there's a strong need for clarity on a particular point. Specifically, make note of those items that should be added to the "Brainstorming" section. If it's an unresolved issue, put it on the list. Don't worry about whether or not it's "important," just add it. You'll be going through the list with the client a bit later, to prioritize.

This is *not* the time to resolve the challenges being mentioned. However, there may be a *strong* tendency to do this. It can often be difficult to listen to another's pain without offering a "solution" to their problem right away. This definitely requires some self-discipline, and it takes practice. Simply listen and make notes.

This also helps create a strong container for sharing in future sessions. If the person feels *fully* listened to, it can build their sense of trust in you, and for the process. As mentioned, oftentimes the solution to a particular issue may come to a person *after* they've been fully listened to.

After the client has shared their challenges, depending on the severity of the issues mentioned, you may want to offer some empathy, saying something like, "it sounds like you've had quite a difficult week." Or, you can simply ask them, "how do you feel now that you've shared all of that?" But, don't force it. If it's not authentic, just allow for silence and move on to the next section.

Carry-over Items – Reviewing Notes from Last Session

At the end of the previous coaching session, a list of actions and scheduled items was arrived at. This is the time to review all the items that may not have appeared in the "wins" or "challenges" check-in. It's important to do this later in the session because the client is usually a bit more present. They'll be better able to hear any items that *didn't* get done without as much self-judgment.

For example, in the previous session, the client may have set the following action item:

> *Contact three people to get testimonials for my consulting business.

The coach can review the notes from last session and ask how that went. Perhaps, in relation to the above example, the client *did* contact a number of people to get testimonials from, but only heard back from one of them. This should probably be added as a "Brainstorming" item.

Some people want to dive deep into to all the reasons *why* something didn't happen, and work out ways to improve their ability to be effective in the future. Others may feel so much self-judgment about not getting something done that it becomes counter-productive to go into this process of self-examination. It's very easy to have an incomplete action item turn into negative self-talk – which is the *exact opposite* of what is intended for this life coaching process.

Also, there is a *big* tendency for many people, especially early on in the coaching process, to create *way more* action items than are *easily* doable. By not pushing too hard during this segment, the unnecessary items will shake out – while the essentials will naturally float to the top.

That being said, I have one *big* rule of thumb to address items that stay on the list for more than three sessions:

Schedule it with another person!

This works extremely well for mundane and overwhelming tasks. Again, smarter not harder.

Avoid spending too much time on this segment. It should take, at most, five minutes – ideally, just a minute or two.

The "Check-in" Process – For the Client

Is it essential for the client to prepare a wins/challenges list *before* the coaching session?

It's preferable to get into the habit of doing this, but it's not essential. Especially if you've been facing some difficulties, the ability to do this may not be with you in the moment. Most of the time, you know full well what your wins and challenges are. Most people, once they get going, usually find it quite easy to rattle off a number of them without being prompted.

Even if you *have* made a list, it's typical to remember a few more once you get going. Once they've unburdened themselves a bit listing challenges, it's quite common for the client to remember a few other wins.

3. Brainstorming and Problem Solving

By this point during the session you should have a full list of "Brainstorming" items, derived from the earler sections. These will consist of potential action items, goals for the upcoming week, intentions, and usually quite a few challenges that need to be worked out.

Before diving into the list, it's important for the coach and the client to read through the list together and prioritize. Combining items that are in some way connected is also important.

For example, the coach may have assembled a list that looks something like this:

Schedule more physical exercise this week.

Schedule time in nature.

Work out what to do about the Margaret situation.

Get clear on what actions to take in marketing my services.

Pay parking ticket.

Finish taxes.

Unmet needs: connection, rest, play.

From this list, the client may conclude that the "Margaret situation" is really bothering them, making this the first item in the list. They may also feel *strongly* about getting more clients for their business, so item #4 should be moved to the #2 slot. And so on...

Even though there may be a *number* of urgent items that require addressing, it's a good practice to ensure there are *always* a couple of items related to the client's goals list on the brainstorming agenda.

There's no right or wrong way to brainstorm. It's just a matter of going back and forth, one item anat a time, discussing potential strategies. Once clear actions have been identified – the coach's task is to write these out, placing them in the "Scheduling" section notes, to be reviewed at the end of the session.

Problem Solving

Much of the "Brainstorming" section involves problem solving – developing strategies to effectively address issues that are weighing the client down.

For the coach:

Your job, first and foremost, is to *ask good questions.* Assume the person, somewhere deep down, already knows the best actions to take regarding this particular item. However, feel free to offer suggestions. This is definitely an *interactive* process. Assist the client in gaining a wider perspective on the problem. And, most importantly, help them to get clear on their *intended outcome.* What's the "best case scenario?" If you can arrive at this, it becomes much easier to work backwards from this place of clarity to a potential solution.

4. Scheduling

The "Scheduling" section distills all the insights from the session into *clear action items*, placing many of them on the client's schedule. Throughout the session, the coach will have compiled a list of action items, starting with the "Review" section. These may be:

- Actions involving goals

- Actions addressing the "needs-actions" list

- Items mentioned in the "Check-in" section (wins, challenges, carry-over items)

- Items arrived at during the "Brainstorming" section (the majority of action items usually come from here)

For the coach:

Review the notes taken from the entire session. Ensure you have a complete list. Then read the list to the client. Ask them:

Which items are the greatest priority?

Which items should be placed on their schedule?

Which items should be scheduled with someone else to ensure they'll get done.

The most effective way of ensuring an action item will be accomplished is to put it on your schedule. Having an action items list is essential. However, placing an action item on your schedule greatly increases the likelihood of it getting done.

Unless the client has already shown they are quite good with working from an action items list, encourage them to place numerous items onto their calendar (planner, laptop, or possibly their smart phone). If they are using calendar software, suggest they create a reminder for themselves for each item (email, mobile alert, etc.). This is especially important if this is one of the client's first sessions. See the "Time Management" chapter for more information on creating "reminders."

Closing the Session

Once scheduling is complete, the session is just about complete. Two items should be discussed prior to ending the session:

- Establishing a time and place for the next session.

- Reviewing how the session went. What worked, and what could be improved upon next time?

1. *Establishing a time and place for the next session*

Setting a time for the next session *greatly* increases the likelihood there will be a next session. People get busy, forget, and fail to carve out enough time, and sessions endlessly get postponed. Again, this life coaching process has a cumulative effect, and works best when done on a regular basis (weekly, bi-monthly, etc.).

2. *Reviewing how the session went.*

As with any process, you always want to know what works and what doesn't. Taking a little time at the end of the session to identify what still needs to be refined can be immensely helpful in making the *next* session flow even more smoothly.

For the coach:

Here are a few questions to ask the client:

> What was most helpful?

> What was most challenging?

> What can be done differently next time to make the session more useful and satisfying?

Write all these down in your "coaching notes," so they'll be seen at the beginning of the next session.

For the client:

Going through this process also gives the coach clear feedback on how they were able to benefit you. This is immensely important. If the person coaching you *doesn't* feel they've been of value to you, especially if they're not receiving coaching in return, they'll probably be less willing to do another session with you.

However, contributing meaningfully to another person is a deeply rewarding experience. If you're the client, keep this in mind – be sure to clearly express your gratitude. Even if the session didn't go well, there will have been at least *a few things* that were helpful.

A Few More Notes for the "Coach"

If you're taking the role of coach, do your best to be transparent. Meaning, if you are feeling confused about how to handle a particular issue – or are unclear about what a client may be needing in a particular moment – share this. It keeps the process alive, and the tensions low. If you can go into a situation knowing it's OK not to have it all together, the more likely you'll be able to offer meaningful support.

Also, be sure to share your notes with the client after the session. Both people should have a copy of the coaching notes. This is why taking notes on a laptop (or even a tablet) is ideal. They can easily be emailed to the client at the end of the session.

I recommend using *just one* text file for all your session notes, adding in the date before starting each new session.

Typing out the name of each section at the beginning of the session can be helpful. It gives you a clear structure to enter your notes into. It will look something like this:

10-1-14

Review

Goals

Needs-actions

Check-in

Wins

Challenges

Carry-over items

Brainstorming

Scheduling

THE "4 STEP" LIFE COACHING PROCESS

1. REVIEW

- Read through the client's goals list
  Short-term goals
  Long-term goals
- Read through the "needs-actions" list.
- *Client* chooses whether to read, or have the coach read.
- During the reading, if an item resonates with the client, they inform the coach, and it gets placed on the "Brainstorming" list.
- Starting with the "Review" section provides a big picture context for the rest of the session. It may remind the client of what they most value, and perhaps allow them to see their current challenges in a different light.

2. CHECK-IN

- *Wins*
  Client shares all perceived accomplishments since last session.
  Wins can be real-world accomplishments, personal achievements, overcoming of obstacles, etc.
- *Challenges*
  Client shares all challenges since last session.
- Coach does not interrupt, unless needing clarity – or for offering time reminders.
- Coach makes note of all items shared during the "Check-in" that could possibly go onto the brainstorming list.
- At the end of the check-in, the coach reviews their notes from the previous session for items not mentioned.

3. BRAINSTORMING

- By this part of the session, a list of brainstorming items has been assembled from the previous sections.
- Together, the coach and the client *prioritize* the list – based on both urgency and the accomplishing of items on goals list (both are given equal importance).
- If the client has challenges that are keeping them from feeling centered in the moment, start with these items first. Typically, the goal-related items will be easier to work with once the emotional challenges have been cleared.
- The role of the coach is to *ask questions, brainstorm*, and assist the client in getting to *doable actions* for the upcoming week(s).
- Actions get placed on an "action items" list to be used in the "Scheduling" section.

4. SCHEDULING

- Action items are reviewed and (as many as possible) are placed on the client's schedule – at specific times (ex: Tuesday 10am, go running).
- Action item *reminders* are also created (smartphone/computer, email reminders, post-it notes).
- Actions that consistently go incomplete week-after-week get *scheduled with someone else* for added support.
- The client's schedule for the next few weeks is reviewed and refined. Is it balanced? Is it realistic (filled with doable action items)?
- Non-addressed or carry-over items to be reviewed next session are noted.
- Feedback for the coach is offered by the client. What was helpful and what could make the next session better?
- Next session is scheduled.

Some Final Notes on the Process

By this point, you should have at least a general understanding of how this process works. Although there are numerous details to consider, it's actually quite simple in practice, and can be easily memorized.

When first starting out, it can be helpful for the coach to read directly from the book. This makes the process a bit like following a recipe. Don't expect to get everything right the first time around. Assume they'll be lots of little potholes, and possibly a bit of awkwardness in the beginning. However, after doing a few sessions with the same person, the process will naturally become more streamlined.

In the beginning, it's helpful to follow the process as closely as possible. Then, once you have a clear grasp of how everything works, feel free to adjust things to best fit your needs.

If you're the one *receiving* coaching – the more you're clear about how the process works, the easier it will be to explain it to someone else, if you ever have to seek out a different person to be your coach.

〜

Be Mindful When Choosing Your Life Coach

When selecting someone to be your life coach, whether it's a trained life coach, a friend, or a family member, there are a few points to consider. The right person for the job will leave you feeling inspired and clear at the end of a session. The wrong person may leave you feeling worse off than when you started.

My advice is – *try someone out first*. Don't make a long term commitment until you know they are able to support you effectively.

Also, ensure you're offering something in return for their time and energy. If you aren't trading coaching, and not paying them, try offering something else in return. Perhaps you can trade some other service to keep things in balance. Even if it's a family member, it's easy for things to get uncomfortable when there isn't an even exchange of energy. Doing this will greatly increase the likelihood your "coach" will enjoy the process, and be more interested in scheduling future sessions with you.

How to Find a Life Coach

Hiring a life coach is ideal for many people. It gives you someone to talk with on a weekly (or monthly) basis who is 100% dedicated to helping you get clear, track your goals, and support you in the process of integrating positive habits into your life.

And the agreement is very clear. You pay them, and they provide you with a service.

There are many different types of life coaches, with a wide variety of personalities, skills, and systems. My advice is, *interview a few people before settling on a coach.*

Many life coaches offer a free session. I personally haven't found this very useful. I've tried this in the past when I first was looking for a life coach, and found I was revealing too many things about myself to someone I had yet to establish trust with.

The approach I recommend is to simply interview them. Request a 15 to 20 minute phone call to speak to them about their process. Make it clear up front that you are not interested in a free session. This let's them know what to expect.

On the phone call, ask them a bit about their process, and their background. Notice how you feel talking to them. Do you feel guarded or relaxed? Get a sense of their personality type. Does it mesh well with yours? Do you have a sense of trust in their abilities, or do you find yourself questioning whether they can provide you with a stable ground to work from? Trust your gut. Recognize, the more you feel comfortable talking to this person, the more likely you'll get the kind of support you're looking for.

Some specific questions you may want to ask:

> "Do you have a set method of coaching, or do you tailor your process for each person's particular needs?"

> "Do you have experience with coaching people with ADD/ADHD?"

> "Do you have any experience with health coaching (diet, nutrition, exercise)? If so, what's your background and philosophy regarding health and wellness?"

> "Can I do a *test run* for one month?" Many coaches will be willing to do this. However, if they say they prefer longer commitments – you might consider looking elsewhere. Coaching can be a significant financial investment. If you've never experienced it before, a trial run is a good way to start."

Also, get clear about what they charge for their services – and what exactly they'll provide you in return. How many sessions per month? Is there a fee if you have to reschedule?

You may consider looking for a life coach that has some knowledge of health and wellness – or if you can afford it – you can always look for a *second* coach just for this, with an emphasis on someone with prior experience with ADD/ADHD. This can be especially helpful if you are wanting to shift to healthier eating habits. Again, interview them, listen to their background and philosophy, and see if it meshes well with yours.

One last point. *Avoid making a hasty decision.*

As much as you probably want to hit the ground running, take your time in interviewing potential coaches. In the meantime, you may want to start with the "4 step" life coaching process with a friend or family member, to ensure you are getting support right away. Then, you can easily move this work into the sessions with your new life coach.

Life Coaching with a Friend or Family Member

Let's face facts, not everyone can afford a few hundred dollars a month for a life coach. For many people, this is just not a financial reality. The "4 Step" life coaching process is designed to be useful, even with people that have no experience with life coaching.

And there's a possibility that a friend or family member may end up being a very talented life coach in their own right. Start by identifying someone in your life that you *trust* – ideally someone who's a good listener, and someone whose opinion you respect. Avoid choosing someone that might be prone to offering negative feedback and criticism. This can make the whole process challenging and counter-productive.

As mentioned, it's ideal to find someone who is *also* interested in getting life coaching support as well. Everyone (and I mean *everyone*) can benefit from support in achieving their goals. Most people are starved for it. It should be relatively easy to find a willing participant.

Arranging a Life Coaching Session

Here are a few points to consider when arranging your life coaching session with someone other than a professional life coach.

Start with a shorter commitment

Some people may feel a bit concerned about committing to something for an unspecified period of time. A good first step is – agree to one month (2 to 4 sessions), then check-in at the end of that time to see if it's still working for the both of you.

Stick with an agreed upon time limit.

If you're doing a trade with someone, keep track of the time, and be sure to make even for the both of you. Typically, an *hour* to an *hour and a half* per person, per session, is a good rule of thumb. If you're planning to do a few sessions, a few days in a row, this time can be less.

Avoid going over your set time limit. Also, be sure to give the other person extra time if you go over with yours. Creating good habits like this will increase the likelihood that both people will stay with the process, week-after-week.

Take a break between sessions.

If you're trading life coaching with someone else, either schedule their session on another day, or take at least a *15 minute* break between sessions. This ensures the second person gets the same amount of focus and awareness as the first. This also gives the first person some time to integrate their session, and possibly take down some notes after. You may want to switch up who goes first in each session.

Lock in a set time for coaching sessions.

It's ideal to choose *one specific time and day* every week (or couple of weeks) for your coaching sessions. This makes it easy to track, and creates a certain level of reassurance, knowing that you've set aside a specific time to receive support on a regular basis. As you start seeing the benefits of life coaching, you'll most likely want to guard this time from being encroached upon by other things.

Pay attention to set and setting.

As mentioned earlier, it's essential to have a quiet and focused environment to work in. If you're meeting *in person*, avoid loud public places where you may feel distracted, or uncomfortable about sharing certain things. Also, avoid doing coaching sessions on the cell phone while your driving. A little focus can go a long way.

If you're doing an *in person* session at someone's home, be sure you won't be interrupted by other members of the household. It may be helpful to tell roommates or family members not to disturb you during the time you've established for the coaching session. Turn off your cell phones (and house phones, if possible).

What to do if your support person decides they can't keep doing it – or has scheduling conflicts?

This is a common occurrence. Don't panic! Because you already have a system in place, it can be fairly simple to migrate to another life coaching partner. Put the word out to friends. After working with someone for a while, you may be a bit clearer about the type of person you'd like to work with in the future. Be clear about your intention, make some phone calls, or possibly post something to your social media accounts.

Pulling Together a Life Coaching Group

A life coaching "group" that utilizes the "4 Step" process is another possible method of receiving regular support. And the group *does not* have to be hunter-type (ADD/ADHD) specific. You may want to call it a "life visioning group" – or make up a unique name of your own.

The basic intention is:

> *Create a group that actively supports*
> *each other in achieving their goals and*
> *working through life challenges.*

There are a few possible forms to consider.

Form 1:

The first possible form involves going through the sections of the "4 step" process, one-by-one (goals, check-in, brainstorming, and scheduling), with *each person* sharing in the context of *that section*. Then the group moves on to the next section.

You may consider using some kind of "talking stick" – an object that gets passed around that denotes when it's each person's turn to speak. When the person has the stick, no one interrupts. It's a physical cue that reinforces the idea to listen attentively to the person sharing.

It's also *very* helpful to select a moderator, at the beginning of each meeting, to direct the flow.

This form may be useful if you find people get bored or distracted when going *one person at a time* through the entire process (form 2).

Form 2:

The second form involves going one person at a time *all the way through the process*. The group places it's entire attention on the person who's turn it is. With this form, it's important to take a short "stretch break" between participants.

Making the Most of "Group Life Coaching" Sessions

Regardless of which form you choose, here are a few suggestions to optimize your group sessions:

- *Three to five people is ideal.* Avoid having more than 5 people because there won't be enough time to get to everyone in a session.

- *Set clear time limits before starting.* Keeping to a set time limit *per person*, and establishing a definitive time to complete the group session, helps everyone. It allows people to plan ahead.

Depending on the size of the group, *2.5 to 3 hours* is a good length of time. If you are always going overtime, some people may find it challenging to make time for the group. A set time limit increases the likelihood of keeping the group together.

To work out the time limit for each person, take the overall length of the meeting, subtract time for breaks, opening, and closing. Then, divide by the number of people in attendance.

For example:

> *Length of meeting:* 3 hours (180 minutes)
> *Total in attendance:* 4 people
> *Time for opening:* 10 minutes
> *Time for closing:* 5 minutes
> *Break time between each person:* 5 minutes
> *Total time available for sessions:* 10+5+5+5+5+5 = 35 (adding all "extra" minutes)
> 180 - 35 = 145 minutes (total time minus extra minutes)
> *Time per person:* 145 divided by 4 = *36.25* minutes (available time divided by number of people)

- *Appoint a time keeper.* The time keeper alerts the group when someone's segment is nearing completion, and when you're approaching the established time to close the meeting. This person ensures that the group always finishes on time, and everyone gets a chance to receive a good session.

- *Map out the form of the session in the beginning.* If you've selected a moderator for the session, it's their job to remind the group of the basic structure of the session, including time limits and general "rules."

- *Request order.* "If you need to leave early or use the restroom, please do so quietly." Instruct people where the bathroom is, and encourage everyone to take notes as people are sharing.

- "If you have something you would like to share with the person talking, write it down. Please don't interrupt. There will be time later to offer your feedback."

- *Focus on being supportive.* Encourage the group to be supportive in their comments. If there's a person who is consistently critical or disruptive, pull them aside and try making some requests. If they're unable to shift their behavior, you may want suggest they find a different group, or start their own. Everyone is different. They may thrive in a different environment.

- *Have a set ritual for opening and closing your meetings.* Have some regular activity the group does at the opening and closing of each meeting. Perhaps you'll simply read an inspirational quote. I find it helpful to start with a short meditation. The moderator instructs the group to take one minute, sit in silence, and allow themselves to be "fully present." I find this simple act makes the group more focused and productive.

  For the closing – a short "around the room" check-in usually works well. What did people get out of session? What would make the next session better?

- *Pick and announce the time for the next meeting.* Ideally, have someone agree to email/call the group the day or two before for the next meeting. With social media, this could also be done as a "recurring event," using something like Facebook or Meetup.com.

What to Do When a Group Dissolves

Groups usually shift and grow over time. Having a group dissolve is a common occurrence. If possible, try pulling the group together one last time for closure.

Once the group is complete, ensure you move to a new method of receiving support as soon as possible. Perhaps you'll want to try working with a professional life coach – or identify someone to partner with from the group for *one-on-one* life coaching sessions.

Make this a priority. It's easy to get disappointed when a group dissolves, then stop getting support. Plan your next steps and take action.

∽

Maintaining Good Support Systems

An effective support system pulls together nearly all of the topics covered in the previous chapters, from *life visioning*, *time management*, and *emotional support*, to tracking the effects of *diet, exercise and supplementation*.

It all boils down to:

1. Identify what you're needing support with.
2. Ensure you are getting this support on a *regular basis*.

With a good support system in place, you'll make steady and consistent shifts in your life that will ultimately yield greater balance and well-being.

13

THE CREATIVE LIFE

Life, by its very nature, is creative. It expands, grows, and connects. Staying in touch with your creativity is staying in touch with life itself. So many of us hunter-types are artists. Along with our many challenges come countless gifts. For the vast majority of us, our cornerstone gift is *creativity*.

Making a Living as an "Artist"

A high percentage of hunter-types gravitate towards the creative arts. In fact, the running joke amongst people working in the entertainment industry is, "all of Hollywood is ADD."

However, having a particular creative gift usually isn't enough to pay the bills. There are a specific skills required to turn your creativity into something that financially supports you. Unfortunately, many *very talented* artists get relegated to jobs that crush their spirit because they (understandably) need to keep a roof over their head and food on the table.

Having some basic business skills can go along way in making a successful living as an artist. The better your skills, the more you'll be able to do the kind of work you're most passionate about.

In this chapter, I'll go through a number of insights I've gleaned over the past 20 years using my creativity to make a living. I'll discuss a number of challenges that tend to plague us hunter-types as we pursue our creative endeavors, and offer a few road-tested methods for addressing them.

Who Is "An Artist?"

Although I believe each and every person has creative abilities, hunter-types seem to be particularly gifted in this arena. The term "artist" covers a broad spectrum of creative pursuits. Artists aren't just painters or sculptors, they can be: musicians, actors, graphic artists and designers, filmmakers, stand-up comedians, writers, ad agents, architects – to name just a few.

Essentially, anyone who actively engages with their creativity on a regular basis is an artist. In this broader definition, many entrepreneurs could also fall into this category.

Helpful Skills for the Hunter-type Artist

Many of the topics discussed in previous chapters apply to hunter-type artists:

- visioning and goal-setting

- time management systems

- note-taking skills

- good exercise, diet, and supplement routines

- clear systems for organizing yourself

"...and I wrote the first bare line,
bare, without substance, pure
foolishness, pure wisdom
of one who knows nothing.
And suddenly I saw the heavens
unfastened and open."
– Pablo Neruda

All of these comprise the groundwork necessary in being successful making a living as an artist.

Creativity, Consistency, and Completion

Probably the most common challenge for hunter-type artists is *completing* the creative projects we start. Typically, there's a big burst of energy in the beginning, then as the initial inspiration wanes, we're off to the next one. Because we tend to be *inspirationally* driven, it's often challenging to summon the energy and focus necessary to make it to the finish line.

If this relates to you, here are a few tips I've found quite useful:

1. *Develop a "habit of completion."*

2. *Keep examples of completed projects by artists you respect close by throughout the project.* Continually refer back to them to get your "creative juices" flowing again.

3. *Don't bite off more than you can chew.* Before embarking on a project, take some time to reflect on what is *actually required* to complete the project. Is the scope of it too broad? Can you select one aspect of it and complete that first?

Always break down bigger projects into smaller ones so you can feel a sense of accomplishment all along the way.

4. *Set milestones.* Do your best to put specific dates on your calendar, then meet them. Over time, your ability to predict how long a project takes will improve, especially if you practice this kind of mindfulness early on in your creative career.

Developing a Habit of Completion

Forming a "habit of completion" is like building a muscle. Every time you complete a project, you increase the likelihood that you'll do it again on future projects. Whether or not you're 100% happy with the results is not as important. Most artists will tell you that getting to that 100% mark rarely happens. There *usually* will be aspects of a creative project that won't meet your expectations.

But at least you've *completed it.* You've added to your reservoir of "completion energy" that will serve you well in the future.

> **"...nothing once begun should be abandoned, unless proven to be morally wrong."**
> **– Mahatma Gandhi**

One Stroke on the Canvas

Another tip that can help you complete a project, especially if you're feeling stuck, is to think in terms of "one stroke on the canvas." This is an old painter's trick.

It can feel daunting to revisit a project once the inspiration isn't there. The inner talk is usually something like, "I'm really bored with this project," or, "I'm really confused about where to take this, so I just can't work on it right now."

One remedy to this creative block is:

Make a commitment, once a day – or even once a week – to do *one small thing to it.*

A painter, for example, would commit to making at least "one stroke" of paint on the canvas of a particular painting. When framed in this way, it can be much easier to summon the energy to work on the project.

Of course what usually happens once you start working on it – the inspiration returns and you're able to get a lot more done. It's merely about getting over the first hurdle of *starting up again*.

However, if you take one action and the inspiration just *isn't* there, no problem. You've at least met your quota for that day and kept the project alive.

WORKING WITH CLIENTS

For many creative professions, you'll be interacting with a "client," in one form or another. This is someone who is paying you to use your creative gifts to benefit them in some way. This dynamic is quite different than a nine-to-five job, where you receive a regular paycheck and have set hours.

Some of this material may not directly apply to your profession. However, I'm confident a number of these points can be repurposed to apply to just about any creative field.

Balancing Your Creative Projects with "Client Work"

Making a living with your creativity, doing *exactly* the work you want to do, is the "Holy Grail." It's what every artist wants. However, along the way, we have to pay our bills, and this often requires us to lend our creativity to someone else's project or business.

There *is* a way to keep your own projects alive during this. However, it requires *explicitly* setting aside time for your own endeavors. And I know, first hand, this is easier said than done. Creative work can be all-encompassing. A client project can absorb all of your "head space" and creative juices, not allowing much room for your own projects.

Strong boundaries are key. Do your best to establish at least one day a week to devote to your creative life *outside* of your client work. This is where good time management skills are essential. The better you are at setting aside this time – staying vigilant about keeping it clear on your schedule – the more you'll be able to keep your own creative projects alive.

It can also be helpful to schedule this time with another artist. If you find it difficult to keep to your own creative schedule, making plans to meet with another person on a regular basis can help "ground" that time. Find someone that may have the same need, even if their work isn't in any way connected to your own. In fact, this is often preferable. Just agree to meet, support each other, and possibly just sit in the same room and work on separate things. It may sound a bit strange, but I know it works. I often suggest this to my life coaching clients.

However, there can be great value in artists working for other people when first starting out. Client work, in whatever form it takes, can help build good creative disciplines that will serve your own projects later in your career. I've learned *volumes* working for other people. They helped me hone my craft. And even though I often felt frustrated because I didn't have total creative freedom and say over my time, in hindsight, I'm immensely grateful. My own work is better because of them.

Client Skills

There's a clear set of skills necessary to develop when working with clients, and these skills are rarely taught in schools. You typically learn them through trial-and-error, or from mentors in your field.

When I first ventured out as a 3D animation artist in the early 1990s, I had no clue how to work with clients, and made all kinds of mistakes. These mistakes led to many uncomfortable situations with clients, a whole lot of stress, and many spells of feast and famine.

It took me a number of years to develop *systems* that consistently yielded good results, ample pay, and happy clients.

1. Educate Yourself

The one smart thing I did quite early on in my career was to *educate myself*. I spoke to other artists who were doing what I wanted to do, and asked them how they ran their business. I also consumed vast numbers of books, audio books, and personal growth workshops. Although it took me a long time to integrate the material, that "study time" was invaluable.

2. Know Your Limitations and Set Clear Boundaries

I can't stress enough how important this is. Knowing what you're capable of and approximately *how long it takes* to complete specific tasks affects all aspects of your life, not just your "work."

When going into an agreement with a client, be clear about:

1. *What can <u>realistically</u> be delivered in a certain time frame.*

2. *How much you'll need to get paid in order to make your living expenses <u>on time</u>.* Ideally, aim for receiving a good deal more than you'll need (if the "going rate" for your skill will allow for it, and the client is willing to pay it.) Again, this sounds obvious, but – in the heat of the moment – especially when you're really needing money, it's easy to forget to do this.

3. *The time you have available to devote to this project.* If you're working on a number of projects simultaneously, ensure you're not over-extending yourself.

3. Manage Expectations

Memorize this phrase. It will serve your well:

"Under-promise, over-deliver."

Reminding yourself of this, especially as you are making agreements with clients, can make your life a whole lot easier.

When I first heard someone use the term "expectation management," it was a revelation. Managing your client's expectations is something you have more control over than you may think. And this goes hand-in-hand with *knowing your limitations*. Going into a project, your client will most likely know the quality of your work, because it's usually what gets them to contact you. What they don't yet know is – *how long will it take you to complete it.*

Managing expectations has a lot to do with creating a realistic schedule for yourself, then letting the client know what that schedule is. One thing to keep in mind – the more you can be firm about your boundaries *in the beginning*, the better the work you'll do because you won't be stressed out as you're working on it.

Throughout the project, develop good communication between you and your client. Keep them up-to-date. Avoid "going into your cave" and working without communicating for long periods of time. This can easily breed tension. Even if it's a short phone call or email saying, "just wanted to keep you posted – everything is going well. I'll have something for you shortly." This usually keeps clients happy because they feel reassured you're on the job.

4. Create Smart Billing Schedules

Getting paid *on time* is one of the key aspects of making a living as an artist. Although every industry has certain standards for billing, remember that ultimately *you* have the final say in how you want to get paid. Then, it's up to the client to decide whether or not they want to work with you based on your terms.

The tendency, when first starting out, is to take on every project offered to you because you need the money. You're probably feeling a bit insecure because you're still getting familiar with the business aspects of being an artist. Because of this, it's easy to make mistakes, especially in relation to billing. Unfortunately, these missteps can force you back to a nine-to-five job, because you weren't able to maintain your business.

Over time, after you've completed a number of client projects, you'll develop more self-confidence and it will become easier to set boundaries.

Here's some hard-won wisdom regarding billing:

1. *Get money up-front whenever possible.* This advice applies to many creative professions. If it's a short-term project (1 to 2 months), see if you can get 50% up front, and 50% upon completion. For longer projects, request *some* money up front, then set regular milestones throughout the project to get paid once they're completed. Again, be sure you will *easily* be able to make your monthly living expenses – especially if it's a long-term project.

2. *Have a written contract prepared for all new clients.* Spend some time on this. Speak to other people in your profession and see what's typical.

3. *If a client won't sign an agreement (especially regarding a larger project), just walk away.* Don't even waste your time. If they're serious, they'll sign. If they're not, you probably wouldn't have gotten paid anyway, and you just saved yourself a lot of time and suffering.

That being said, be flexible. Discuss the points in the contract and see what changes can be made so that both parties are happy. Listen to their concerns and see what can be worked out.

If you're a performer, *respect your time*. Although it's common at the beginning of a performer's career to give away your services while you're learning your craft, *respect your time*. If someone can't pay you, suggest a trade. Marketing and promotion trades are extremely useful and typically don't cost your client anything, just a little time.

Get comfortable making requests. The sooner you start getting paid for your work, no matter the amount, the sooner you'll have the confidence to attract higher paying gigs.

MARKETING YOURSELF

Marketing is as old as time itself. It's simply the act of letting other people know what you have to share with them. You can have all the talent in the world, but if no one knows about it, it won't make a bit of difference.

For artists, understanding the basics of marketing is essential. It's beyond the scope of this book to go into all the details of marketing, however there is one golden rule to remember:

focus on benefits and values

Whatever form your marketing takes (internet, print, word-of-mouth, etc.), place your attention on "how does your service or product *benefit* and *provide value for* someone else?"

Whether you're selling a product (music album, book, film, etc.), or a service, your marketing should always answer this one simple question:

*"How does this make someone's
life more satisfying?"*

That's it. If you keep that as your focus, your marketing will be successful, because that's what we're all looking for. We all look for items and services that will make our lives more enjoyable.

Build Your Mailing List

No matter what type of artist you are, having a mailing list is essential. Now, with email, this process costs next to nothing. Staying connected with people who you've done work for in the past, or people who enjoy your art, is *the number one most trusted method* of growing your business in the internet age.

Send out regular emails, share stories, free items, et cetera. Make a connection. These are *your* people. Treat them well and they'll go out of their way to help you expand your business.

Tracking What Works

Whatever form it takes, one of the most important aspects of successful marketing is noting *what works* and *what doesn't*. Even if you're using the internet, and most of your marketing doesn't cost you anything, it still involves your time. Avoid wasting your time with marketing that doesn't yield good results.

Continually test out new forms of marketing, let go of what doesn't work, and focus the bulk of your marketing on what has brought good results. This sounds obvious, but this is a mistake many people make *over-and-over again*. It's easy to slip into the mindset, "This *should* work! Everyone else does it."

Often, the best marketing comes from word-of-mouth – a client that's happy with your work recommends you to someone else. That doesn't cost you a dime. You may even consider emailing your clients every few months with a request for referrals, possibly offering them an incentive for every new client they bring to you.

As mentioned, the internet can be an amazing resource for marketing. *Educate yourself.* Keep up-to-date with the latest in Search Engine Optimization (SEO) and social media. There are numerous websites that send free emails with internet marketing tips on a weekly basis. Subscribe to them and study up.

If marketing isn't your bag, set aside a certain percentage of your income to go towards paying someone to do your marketing for you.

CULTIVATING A SUCCESSFUL "INNER LIFE"

Knowing What Inspires You: The Key to Long-term Creative Success

Inspiration can be a mercurial thing. Some days it's there, and other days it isn't. It's easy to arrive at the conclusion that inspiration is something completely beyond our control. We have no way of consciously summoning it when we need it.

> "To be nobody-but-yourself in a world which is doing its best, night and day, to make you everybody else – means to fight the hardest battle which any human being can fight; and never stop fighting... Does this sound dismal? It isn't. It's the most wonderful life on earth."
> **– e.e. cummings**

This was my thought for a long time. However, I now know this *isn't* the case. We all have far more control over inspiration than we realize. The key is knowing *what* inspires you. If you're a painter, perhaps looking through the artwork of some of your favorite artists may be just enough to "light you up." If you're a musician, listening to one of your favorite albums, or discovering a great new artist, can set you in motion.

The point is, do this *consciously*.

You may be concerned you'll end up copying the work of someone else, losing your own sense of individuality along the way. This almost never happens. On some level, *all art* is derivative. We don't exist in a vacuum.

For me, a good source of inspiration will meet my need for *excellence*. It calls me to continually refine whatever I'm creating – taking it *all the way* to the most realized end result. And this looks and feels different for every artist.

The "Home Stretch"

Depending on what you're working on, it's often the "home stretch" that involves the most amount of work. The "wrap up" on a project typically consists of refining lots of small details. Expect this, and plan accordingly. Many people will give up on a project at this point because they didn't expect the home stretch to be so difficult and time consuming.

Emotionally prepare yourself for this ahead of time. If your head is the right place, you'll be able to pull through, knowing you're traveling the same road, and sharing the same challenges, that countless other artists have faced before you.

Managing the Ups and Downs

Some days, no matter what you do, the creative energy just isn't there. It's important, when these days arrive, to not beat yourself up over it. Although, as mentioned earlier, we can establish the *general conditions* necessary for creativity to "happen," there's always a part of it that will remain a mystery.

There's a big difference between being able to *nudge* yourself into creative action, and punishing yourself when the energy just isn't there. On these days, it can be helpful to journal or have a conscious inner dialog (see the "Navigating Emotions" chapter for more details on this).

There *will* be days when you'll have zero access to your creativity. That's just how it goes. Accepting this can bring a great deal of peace. If it's in relation to a work/client project, ensure you've included enough time in your agreement to allow for these days, because *they will happen*. Spend these down days working on more ground plane, mundane tasks.

On another level, the more you can associate *enjoyment* with your creativity, the more creative you'll be. You do this by not pushing yourself too hard. We all know what our "edge" feels like. Our body tenses up, there's a tightening of our muscles, and an overall feeling of frustration. While some claim the act of "pushing themselves to the edge" yields more creativity, I'm not convinced this a stable *long-term* practice.

I'm firmly convinced that creativity and child-like wonder go hand-in-hand. The most creatively brilliant people I've ever worked with *all* had one thing in common – there was an innocence to how they worked that allowed them to stay connected to their creative spark.

We all know this intuitively. If we see someone who looks rigid and "controlled," we usually associate that with not being very creative.

Playfulness and creativity go hand-in-hand. The more you can create an environment of *play* around your creative life, the more consistent your creativity you will be. I find, if I'm pushing or badgering myself to create, it's best to stop, check-in, and see if I'm really enjoying the process. Is this a *get to* or *have to* situation?

Even if it's a work-related project, if I can frame it in terms of "a creative challenge" *for myself*, the more I'll be pleased with the outcome. And the client will ultimately benefit from this as well.

Dealing with the "Post Project Dip"

Many artists experience an emotional dip after they've completed a project. If this is common for you, it's helpful to *make plans for it.* Woody Allen, the famous film director, reportedly counteracts this dip by starting work on a new film as soon as he wraps with the previous one. If he finishes a film on a Friday, he'll start work on a new film the following Monday.

This "dip" is very common, and you've probably been through a few of them, if you think back. Be mindful of this if you find yourself in the doldrums after wrapping up a big project. Sometimes, just allowing yourself to wallow in it for a few days can be helpful. Often, just giving into the "funk" can give birth to the inspiration for your next creative venture.

The Life of an Artist

Artists make the world a better place to live in. Even though learning institutions often marginalize the importance of creative occupations, the fact is – we make life worth living. We inspire people. We make people laugh, cry, and feel things deeply. Our work can comfort people when they feel alone, and fire them up to take action. Societal and cultural revolutions are fueled by artists. We, through our ability to tap into the Great Mystery, can harness the collective imagination, and provide vision.

It's hard to imagine a more noble and worthwhile occupation.

OPTIMAL

DAILY ACTIVITIES
Utilizing the systems below, optimize your day-to-day actions to be "hunter-type friendly. Focus on "smarter not harder".

ACTIONS

CALENDAR
Have one place for tracking all calendar items and events (paper planner, computer calendar, etc...)

ACTION ITEMS
Utilize one method for tracking all action items. Discipline yourself to always use this method.

SCHEDULING & TIME MANAGEMENT

TRACKING
Track your energy, productivity, focus, and diet, at the end of the day to optimize daily routines.

COACHING
Incorporate regular life coaching sessions with a life coach, friend, or family member.

REMINDERS
Develop an effective system of reminders for action items, goals, and appointments.

SUPPORT SYSTEM

AWARENESS
Make mindfulness a priority. Practice meditation and "needs awareness". Make them a regular part of your life.

INTENDING
Everyday, visualize how you'd like your day to go. Revisit your intentions throughout the day.

GRATITUDE
Practice gratitude daily. Bring to mind what you already have and what you appreciate, to cultivate greater peace-of-mind.

MINDFULNESS

ABILITIES
Develop a clear awareness of talents and skills. Continually hone and develop ways of utilizing as income source.

LIFE VISION
Regularly spend time developing and refining life vision. Review on a regular basis.

GOALS
Practice setting both short and long-term goals. Regularly celebrate wins.

SERVICE
Offer your energy and talents to organizations and causes you believe in. Become aware of your role in society.

PURPOSE (FUEL)

DIET
High Protein / Low Carb Organic Fruits & Veggies No: Refined Sugar, Additives, Preservatives.

SUPPLEMENTS
Omega 3: Flax Oil or Fish Oil Healthy stimulants (green tea, yerba mate) Good multi-vitamin

EXERCISE
45 min cardio workout at least 3 times a week. Choose exercises that are enjoyable and not a "chore"

NATURE
Spend time in nature a few times a week – ideally combined with exercise and/or meditation

HEALTH

14

PULLING IT ALL TOGETHER

We've covered a lot of ground. As mentioned in the opening of the book, don't concern yourself with attempting *all* of this right away. Ease in. Give yourself some time to absorb this information. Use the various exercises in the book to clarify and illuminate the specific areas of your life you'd like to improve.

> "Always bear in mind that your
> own resolution to succeed is more
> important than any one thing."
> **– Abraham Lincoln**

The Final Product – What It Looks Like in Practice

So, what does it look like having integrated all of this into your day-to-day life?

First off (and most importantly) the intended result is:

> your life becomes *far more enjoyable and productive.*

That's the goal. The "how" will be different for each one of us. But, it will probably look something like this:

- You have a *clear* understanding of how your unique brain chemistry and neurology functions as a "hunter-type." [*Chapters: 2. Hunter-Farmer Theory, 3. The Hunter-type Brain, 7. Navigating Emotions*]

- You've developed a vision for your life, consisting of both short-term and long-term goals, that you regularly refer to. [*Chapter: 6. Life Visioning*]

- Your diet is optimized to bring you a greater ability to focus, and more consistent energy levels. [*Chapter: 9. Exercise, Diet, and Supplements*]

- You exercise multiple times a week in ways you really enjoy. [*Chapter: 9. Exercise, Diet, and Supplements*]

- You have systems in place (time management, organization, finances, etc.) that make your day-to-day life easily manageable. [*Chapters: 10. Time Management, 11. Tips and Practices*]

- You have set aside time in your regular schedule to receive life coaching sessions. [*Chapter: 12. Creating a Support System*]

- You've tracked what works, what doesn't work, and turned "the good stuff" into habits and routines. [*Chapters: 7. Navigating Emotions, 9. Exercise, Diet, and Supplements, 11. Tips and Practices*]

- You've integrated some form of daily mindfulness practice into your life that strengthens your awareness, ability to focus, and your overall willpower. [*Chapter: 8. Spirituality*]

- You've put your creative gifts, outside-the-box thinking, and ability to hyperfocus, to work for you – earning a living doing what you love. *[Chapter: 13. The Creative Life]*

It's Never Going to Be "Perfect"

As mentioned numerous times throughout this book, accept the fact that you'll never "have it all together." No one does.

You may set up a whole host of good systems, stay with them for a month or two, then slip back into old patterns. *These slip-ups are normal.* Don't let them discourage you. Just keep coming back to those habits that most support your well being. Remember the Japanese proverb:

fall down seven times, get up eight.

Keep this book by your bedside. Flip through it regularly. If it's within reach (and not lost on some shelf) you're far more likely to read it and get yourself back on track.

It's a Lifelong Journey

Keep in mind, this is a *lifelong* journey. It will be a continual act of refining, updating, shifting, and adjusting your habits to be optimized for who you are in that moment.

The good news is, the basic information covered in this book won't change. No matter what discoveries take place as technology and medical science evolve, your body will always require the same basic kinds of maintenance. Over time, you'll see what works, and naturally gravitate towards those activities and practices that make your life more enjoyable and productive.

It doesn't have to be a fight. If it is, you need to rethink your strategies. "Smarter not harder" should be your mantra.

Learning through Teaching

If you've found the ideas and tips in this book helpful, I *highly* encourage you to share them with someone else. Through the act of teaching, you'll understand them more thoroughly. And you may just help turn someone else's life around in the process.

Share this book with a friend. Hold a small group at your home or school. Feel free to leave out those items you don't understand, or don't agree with. Find what really works for you, then share it.

Keep in mind, we're all in the same boat. Hunter-type or not, just about everyone can benefit from a better diet, a time and place to receive support for their goals, and optimal daily habits that make life more enjoyable.

Finally, I encourage you to expand on this information. Question it. Research, refine, and come to your own conclusions. Then share what you've learned.

BIBLIOGRAPHY & RESOURCES

1. Introduction

"An Hour With U2 Frontman Bono", *The Charlie Rose Show*, June 21, 2001, http://www.charlierose.com/view/interview/3063

Meade, Michael. *Thresholds of Change.* [Audio Cassette] Oral Traditions Archive, 1997.

2. The Hunter-Farmer Theory

Hartmann, Thom. *Attention-Deficit Disorder:A Different Perspective* [Second Edition]. Underwood Books, 1997.

———. *The Edison Gene.* Park Street Press, 2005.

Mander, Jerry. *In the Absence of the Sacred.* Peter Smith Pub Inc, 1999.

Estés, Clarissa Pinkola. *Women Who Run with the Wolves.* Ballantine Books, 1996.

Some, Malidoma Patrice. *Of Water and the Spirit: Ritual, Magic and Initiation in the Life of an African Shaman.* Penguin Books, 1995.

Meade, Michael J. *Men and the Water of Life: Initiation and the Tempering of Men.* Harper San Francisco, 1994.

Zimmer, Carl (2007, February 22). Woman the Hunter? *Discover Magazine Online,* http://blogs.discovermagazine.com/loom/2007/02/22/woman-the-hunter

"Hunter-Gatherer." *Wikipedia*: The Free Encyclopedia. Wikimedia Foundation, Inc. February 25, 2013. http://en.wikipedia.org/wiki/Hunter-gatherer

Robinson, Sir Ken, "RSA Animate: Changing Education Paradigms," *YouTube* video, posted by theRSA.org, October 14, 2010.

Hemenway, Toby, "The 5 Methods of Human Persistence," *YouTube* video, posted by bpjammin, August 26, 2012.

3. Am I A Hunter-Type?

Chapter photo: Museum Expedition 1922, Robert B. Woodward Memorial Fund, *Brooklyn Museum.*

Coelho, Paulo (2007, November 9). Attention Deficit Disorder. *Paulo Coelho's Blog,* http://paulocoelhoblog.com/2007/11/09/attention-deficit-disorder/

Silver, Larry, M.D. Can A Blood Test Diagnose ADHD? *ADDitude Magazine Online,* http://www.additudemag.com/q&a/ask_the_add_medical_expert/6126.html

"Adult attention deficit hyperactivity disorder." *Wikipedia:* The Free Encyclopedia. Wikimedia Foundation, Inc. July 11, 2013. http://en.wikipedia.org/wiki/Adult_attention_deficit_hyperactivity_disorder

"Attention deficit hyperactivity disorder controversies." *Wikipedia:* The Free Encyclopedia. Wikimedia Foundation, Inc. July 24, 2013. http://en.wikipedia.org/wiki/Attention deficit_hyperactivity_disorder_controversies

4. The Hunter-Type Brain

McCauley, Dr. Kevin, "Is Addiction Really A Disease [Series of Videos]", *YouTube* video, posted by kevintmccauley1965, December 6, 2009.

Bouchez, Colette. Serotonin: 9 Questions and Answers. *WebMD,* http://www.webmd.com/depression/features/serotonin

Carver, Joseph M., PH.D., Clinical Psychologist. Attention-Deficit Hyperactivity Disorder (ADHD). http://www.drjoecarver.com/clients/49355/File/Attention-Deficit%20Hyperactivity%20Disorder%20%28ADHD%29.html

Walsh, Karen McNulty and Peter Genzer (September 8, 2009). Deficits in Brain's Reward System Observed in ADHD Patients. *BNL Newsroom,* http://www.bnl.gov/bnlweb/pubaf/pr/PR_display.asp?prID=998

(February 27, 2010). Why Eating Protein Increases Serotonin Levels. *3 Fat Chicks On A Diet,* http://www.3fatchicks.com/why-eating-protein-increases-serotonin-levels/

J M Lusher, C Chandler and D Ball (2001, September). Dopamine D4 receptor gene (DRD4) is associated with Novelty Seeking (NS) and substance abuse: the saga continues... *Molecular Psychiatry,* September 2001, Volume 6, Number 5, Pages 497-499.

Attention-Deficit/Hyperactivity Disorder: Causes of ADHD. *WebMD,* http://www.webmd.com/add-adhd/guide/adhd-causes

Nikolaidis, Aki and Jeremy R. Gray (2009, October 19). ADHD and the DRD4 exon III 7-repeat polymorphism: an international meta-analysis. *Oxford Journals,* Social Cognitive and Affective Neuroscience, http://scan.oxfordjournals.org/content/5/2-3/188.full

L Baydala, J Sherman, C Rasmussen, E Wikman and H Janzen. ADHD characteristics in Canadian Aboriginal children. University of Alberta and Misericordia Hospital, Canada, May 2006. *PubMed.gov.* http://www.ncbi.nlm.nih.gov/pubmed/16648231

Liponis, Mark. *The Hunter-Farmer-Diet-Solution.* Hay House, 2012.

L Caixeta, P B Azevedo and C H Reimer. P-425 - Does attention deficit hyperactivity disorder exist in isolated indigenous children living in tribes from the brazilian amazon? *European Psychiatry,* Volume 27, Supplement 1, 2012.

(May 19, 2010). Dopamine System in Highly Creative People Similar to That Seen in Schizophrenics, Study Finds. *Science Daily,* http://www.sciencedaily.com/releases/2010/05/100518064610.htm

Schwartz, Casey (2011, February 8). ADHD's Upside Is Creativity, Says New Study. *The Daily Beast,* http://www.thedailybeast.com/articles/2011/02/08/adhds-upside-is-creativity-says-new-study.html

Chermahini, SA and B Hommel (2010, April 14). The Creativity-dopamine (b)linkage: more brains and bonkers connections. *The Mouse Trap,* http://the-mouse-trap.com/2010/04/14/the-creativity-dopamine-blinkage-more-brains-and-bonkers-connections/

Flippin, Royce (2005, October/November). Learn About ADHD: Focus on Hyperfocus. *ADDitude Magazine Online,* http://www.additudemag.com/adhd/article/612.html

Scicurious (2010, April 21). Anorexia, Dopamine, and Experimental Confounds. *Scientopia,* http://scientopia.org/blogs/scicurious/2010/04/21/anorexia-dopamine-and-experimental-confounds/

Osborne, Charlie (2010, December 15). Low Dopamine in ADHD. *Live Strong,* http://www.livestrong.com/article/335431-low-dopamine-in-adhd/

Carver, Joseph M., PH.D., Clinical Psychologist. Causes of Attention-Deficit Hyperactivity Disorder (ADHD). *Womens Accounts,* http://www.womensaccounts.com/adhd_Carver_causes.html

Juhasz, Francine (2011, March 23). Symptoms of Dopamine Deficiency. *Live Strong,* http://www.livestrong.com/article/346030-symptoms-of-dopamine-deficiency/

Carver, Joseph M., PH.D., Clinical Psychologist (2002, January). The "Chemical Imbalance" in Mental Health Problems. *drjoecarver.com,* http://www.drjoecarver.com/clients/49355/File/Chemical%20Imbalance.html

Phend, Crystal (2009, September 8). Low Dopamine Implicated in ADHD Attention Symptoms. M*edPage TODAY,* http://www.medpagetoday.com/Pediatrics/ADHD-ADD/15872

Dellwo, Adrienne (2008, July 27). What Does Low Serotonin Feel Like? *About.com,* http://chronicfatigue.about.com/b/2008/07/27/what-does-low-serotonin-feel-like.htm.

Kay, Jerald and Victor Schwartz. *Mental Health Care in the College Community.* Google eBook, 2011.

5. Addiction

Ross, Julia. *The Mood Cure: The 4-Step Program to Take Charge of Your Emotions—Today.* Penguin Books, 2003.

B. Lomas and P.S. Gartside (1997). Attention-Deficit Hyperactivity Disorder Among Homeless Veterans. *Homelessness Resource Center,* http://homeless.samhsa.gov/Resource/View.aspx?id=22567&AspxAutoDetectCookieSupport=1

Victoria Schlesinger, Steven Johnson and Gary Panter (2007, July 9). This is Your Brain on Video Games. *Discover Magazine Online,* http://discovermagazine.com/2007/brain/video-games#.UegfKMV5GSo

Wilson, Gary (2008). REVIEW - Evidence For Sugar Addiction: Behavioral and Neurochemical Effects of Intermittent Excessive Sugar Intake. *Your Brain on Porn,* http://yourbrainonporn.com/review-evidence-for-sugar-addiction-2008

Quily, Pete (2011, January 12). ADHD and Crime. 21% To 45% 0f Prisoners Have ADHD 15 Peer Reviewed Studies Show. Crime & Jail Are Costly, Treatment Is Cheap. *adultaddstrengths.com,* http://adultaddstrengths.com/2011/01/12/adhd-and-crime-ignore-now-jail-later-15-clinical-studies/

Diana, Marco (2011, November 29). The Dopamine Hypothesis of Drug Addiction and Its Potential Therapeutic Value. *Frontiers in Psychiatry,* http://www.ncbi.nlm.nih.gov/pmc/articles/PMC3225760/

Miriam Melis, Saturnino Spiga and Marco Diana (2005). The Dopamine Hypothesis of Drug Addiction: Hypodopaminergic State. *International Reveiw of Neurobiology,* Vol. 63, http://66.199.228.237/boundary/SA/dopamine_review.pdf

de Leon, George and Nancy Jainchill (1981). Male and Female Drug Abusers: Social and Psychological Status 2 Years after Treatment in a Therapeutic Community. *The American Journal of Drug and Alcohol Abuse,* http://informahealthcare.com/doi/abs/10.3109/00952998109016931

AA Efficacy Rates. *cbtrecovery.org,* http://www.cbtrecovery.org/AAefficacyrates.htm.

Baldwin Research Institute, Inc. (2004). Adolescent Treatment Research 2004: Drug and Alcohol Addiction Treatment Research. *Sober Forever,* http://www.soberforever.net/researchadolesc.cfm

Wilson, Gary, "The Great Porn Experiment: Gary Wilson at TEDxGlasgow", *YouTube* video, posted by TEDxTalks, May 16, 2012. http://www.youtube.com/watch?v=wSF82AwSDiU

Blankenship, Richard and Mark Laaser. *Sexual Addiction and ADHD: Is There A Connection?* Taylor & Francis Health Sciences, 2004.

6. Life Visioning

Chapter photo by *Georges Jansoone.*

Hartmann, Thom. *The Edison Gene: ADHD and the Gift of the Hunter Child.* Inner Traditions – Bear & Co., 2010.

Hemenway, Toby. *Gaya's Garden: A Guide to Home-Scale Permaculture.* Chelsea Green Publishing, 2009.

Lehrman, Fredric. *Prosperity Consciousness [Audio].* Nightingale Conant, 1999.

7. Navigating Emotions

Rosenberg, Marshall B. *Nonviolent Communication: A Language of Life.* Puddledancer Press, 2003.

Goleman, Daniel. *Emotional Intelligence: Why It Can Matter More Than IQ.* Bantam, 2006.

Choquette, Sonia. *Your Heart's Desire: Instructions for Creating the Life You Really Want.* Potter Style, 1997.

MacMillan, Amanda (2011, July 26). People in affluent nations may be more depression-prone. *CNN.com,* http://www.cnn.com/2011/HEALTH/07/26/affluent.depression.prone/index.html

Lieberman, Matthew (2010, March 18). Putting feelings into words. *UCLAToday,* http://www.today.ucla.edu/portal/ut/putting-feelings-into-words-155536.aspx

National Suicide Prevention Lifeline: (800) 273-8255

8. Spirituality

Shinzen Young (Meditation Teacher) http://www.basicmindfulness.org/ http://www.shinzen.org/

(1998, February 27). Quantum Theory Demonstrated: Observation Affects Reality. *ScienceDaily* http://www.sciencedaily.com/releases/1998/02/980227055013.htm

Chopra, Deepak. *The Seven Spiritual Laws of Success*. Amber-Allen Publishing & New World Library, 1994.

Fortanasce, Dr. Vincent (2009, February 19). Depression & Meditation. *Dr Fortanasce: Personal Blog,* http://drfortanasce.com/?p=68

9. Exercise, Diet, and Supplements

Chapter image:
Photo of fruit and vegetables by *Jina Lee*.
Photo of yerba maté by *Lucas Hirschegger*.

Pollan, Michael. *The Omnivore's Dilemma: A Natural History of Four Meals*. Penguin Press, 2006.

Carper, Jean. *Your Miracle Brain*. HarperCollins, 2000.

Young, Robert O. and Shelley Reford Young. *The pH Miracle: Balance Your Diet, Reclaim Your Health*. Wellness Central, 2003.

Slagle, Priscilla. *The Way Up from Down*. St. Martin's Press, 1992.

Carter, Beth (2012, May 25). Study: Exercise Improves Memory, Helps Alleviate ADHD. *Wired Magazine,* http://www.wired.com/playbook/2012/05/exercise-memory-and-adhd

Boris, M. and F.S. Mandel (1994, May). Foods and additives are common causes of the attention deficit hyperactive disorder in children. *Us National Library of Medicine, National Institute of Health,* http://www.ncbi.nlm.nih.gov/pubmed/8179235?dopt=Abstract

Liponis, Mark. *The Hunter/Farmer Diet Solution*. Hay House, 2012.

Kobylewski, Sarah and Michael F. Jacobson (2010, June 29). CSPI Says Food Dyes Pose Rainbow of Risks. *Center For Science In The Public Interest,* http://www.cspinet.org/new/201006291.html

(2004). The Human Brain: Nourish – Proteins. *The Franklin Institute,* http://www.fi.edu/learn/brain/proteins.html

Shayne, Vic, PH.D. (2009, March 2). You Wouldn't Believe What Goes Into Non-Organic Meat!! *Nutrition Research Center,* http://nutritionresearchcenter.org/healthnews/if-youve-ever-needed-to-know-about-organic-meats/

(2012). The Relationship Between Sugar and Carbohydrates. *FitDay.com,* http://www.fitday.com/fitness-articles/nutrition/carbs/the-relationship-between-sugar-and-carbohydrates.html

Sharma, Rishi, M.D. (2012, April 26). Are Berries the New Brain Food? *AbcNEWS,* http://abcnews.go.com/blogs/health/2012/04/26/are-berries-the-new-brain-food/

Hutchison, Courtney (2011, February 4). ADHD From Allergy? Study Shows Benefit From Diet Changes. *abcNEWS,* http://abcnews.go.com/Health/Allergies/adhd-food-allergy-case-restricting-diet/story?id=12832958

Mayo Clinic (2012, October 16). Eating lots of carbs, sugar may raise risk of cognitive impairment, Mayo Clinic study finds. *Science Codex,* http://www.sciencecodex.com/eating_lots_of_carbs_sugar_may_raise_risk_of_cognitive_impairment_mayo_clinic_study_finds-100231

(2012, February 22). What's Your Reaction? *bewellbuzz.com,* http://www.bewellbuzz.com/superfoods/16-superfoods-you-should-know-about-part-1/

Hampton, Julia (2011, March 9). Does Omega 3 Fish Oil Thin Your Blood? *Live Strong* http://www.livestrong.com/article/399910-does-omega-3-fish-oil-thin-your-blood/

"Ginkgo Biloba." *Wikipedia:* The Free Encyclopedia. Wikimedia Foundation, Inc. July 19, 2013. http://en.wikipedia.org/wiki/Ginkgo_biloba

"Chamomile." *Wikipedia:* The Free Encyclopedia. Wikimedia Foundation, Inc. July 24, 2013. http://en.wikipedia.org/wiki/Chamomile

(2011, May 27). The Top 10 Best Herbal Sedatives. *Revitalise Your Health,* http://www.revitaliseyourhealth.com/the-top-10-best-herbal-sedatives/

Fogarty, Carole (2009, March 30). 3 Potent Natural Herbal Sedatives. *The Healthy Living Lounge,* http://thehealthylivinglounge.com/2009/03/30/3-potent-natural-herbal-sedatives/

Roberts, Susan B. (2009, March 18). Ask The Professor. Why does caffeine give you energy? *Tufts Journal,* http://tuftsjournal.tufts.edu/2009/03_2/professor/01/

M.R. Lyon, M.P. Kapoor and L.R. Juneja (2011, December 16). The effects of L-theanine (Suntheanine) on objective sleep quality in boys with attention deficit hyperactivity disorder (ADHD): a randomized, double-blind, placebo-controlled clinical trial. *US National Library of Medicine, National Institute of Health,* http://www.ncbi.nlm.nih.gov/pubmed/22214254

Jacoby, Christopher. Benefits of Green Tea for ADHD. *HealthGuidance.org,* http://www.healthguidance.org/entry/13347/1/Benefits-of-Green-Tea-for-ADHD.html. Green Tea. *Wikipedia,* http://en.wikipedia.org/wiki/Green_tea

A.J. Dulloo, C. Duret, D. Rohrer, L. Girardier, N. Mensi, M. Fathi, P. Chantre and J. Vandermander (1999, December). Efficacy of a green tea extract rich in catechin polyphenols and caffeine in increasing 24-h energy expenditure and fat oxidation in humans. *US National Library of Medicine, National Institute of Health,* http://www.ncbi.nlm.nih.gov/pubmed/10584049

Becker, Anne (2003, June 10). Green Tea on the Brain. *Psychology Today,* http://www.psychologytoday.com/articles/200306/green-tea-the-brain

(2007, November 13). ECGC In Green Tea Is Powerful Medicine Against Severe Sepsis, Lab Study Suggests. *Science Daily,* http://www.sciencedaily.com/releases/2007/11/071108115608.htm

R.E. Weiss, M.A. Stein, B. Trommer and S. Refetoff (1993, October). Attention-deficit hyperactivity disorder and thyroid function. *US National Library of Medicine, National Institute of Health,* http://www.ncbi.nlm.nih.gov/pubmed/8410504

Carr, Kris. *Crazy Sexy Cancer.* Morris Publishing Group, 2007.

Owens, Elsie (2011, January 23). List of Veggies with High Protein. *Live Strong,* http://www.livestrong.com/article/363483-list-of-veggies-with-high-protein/

Sleep Inducing Foods as Insomnia Remedies. *Nutrition Breakthroughs,* http://www.nutritionbreakthroughs.com/html/sleep_inducing_foods.html

(2010, March 12). ADHD and Vitamin D Deficiency: Any Evidence? *ADHD Treatments,* http://adhd-treatment-options.blogspot.com/

Clark, Dr. David (2010, July 12). ADHD linked with 2 Vitamin & Mineral Deficiencies. *Dr. Clark's Brain Based Blog,* http://drclark.typepad.com/dr_david_clark/2010/07/adhd-linked-with-2-vitamin-mineral-deficiencies-.html

(2008, September 30). Zinc Deficiency Causes ADHD and Depression. *Novus Medical Detox Center,* http://www.novusdetox.com/press/dependence.php?include=136975

Doyle, Marek (2010, November 3). Will Caffeine Affect Adrenal Fatigue? *Live Strong,* http://www.livestrong.com/article/295168-will-caffeine-affect-adrenal-fatigue/

Graef, Nyomi (2009, June 15). Is the natural antidepressant SAMe a safe option for depression, arthritis, and other health problems? *ExtraHappiness.com,* http://extrahappiness.com/happiness/?p=1632

O'Meara, Alex (2011, September 30). Does Running Increase Dopamine? *Live Strong,* http://www.livestrong.com/article/545302-does-running-increase-dopamine/

Amen, Daniel. *Making a Good Brain Great: The Amen Clinic Program for Achieving and Sustaining Optimal Mental Performance.* Harmony, 2006.

Amen, Daniel. *Healing ADD: The Breakthrough Program That Allows You to See and Heal the 6 Types of ADD.* Berkley Trade, 2002.

"Stimulant." *The Free Dictionary:* by Farlex. Farlex, Inc. 2013. http://www.thefreedictionary.com/Central+nervous+system+stimulants

Bennett, Connie (2010, September 10). The Rats Who Preferred Sugar Over Cocaine. *Huffington Post: Huffpost Healthy Living,* http://www.huffingtonpost.com/connie-bennett/the-rats-who-preferred-su_b_712254.html

(2010, May 21). In the Green of Health: Just 5 Minutes of 'Green Exercise' Optimal for Good Mental Health. *Science Daily,* http://www.sciencedaily.com/releases/2010/05/100502080414.htm

Wallis, Claudia (2007, September 6). Hyper Kids? Cut Out Preservatives. *TIME Magazine,* http://www.time.com/time/health/article/0,8599,1659835,00.html

Philpott, Tom (2012, July 23). Vaccines on Chicken Farms Create Supervirus. *Mother Jones,* http://www.motherjones.com/tom-philpott/2012/07/antibiotic-use-vaccines-factory-farms-creating-new-pathogens

(2004). Your brain, just brighter. *The Franklin Institute: Resources for Science Learning,* http://www.fi.edu/learn/brain/fats.html

Weatherby, Craig (2007, October 22). Omega-3 Brain Evolution Theory Gets a Boost. *Vital Choice,* http://www.vitalchoice.com/shop/pc/articlesView_old.asp?id=535

Dakota, Milo (2010, October 5). Green Tea vs. Yerba Mate Antioxidants. *Live Strong,* http://www.livestrong.com/article/270715-green-tea-vs-yerba-mate-antioxidants/

Veracity, Dani (2005, October 11). The hidden dangers of caffeine: How coffee causes exhaustion, fatigue and addiction. *Natural News,* http://www.naturalnews.com/012352_caffeine_coffee.html.

10. Time Management

Free Calendar Software:
http://www.essentialpim.com/
http://www.mozilla.org/en-US/thunderbird/
https://www.google.com/calendar/

11. Tips & Practices

Chapter photo by *Istvan Takacs.*

Hathaway, Warren E. (1992, February). A Study into the Effects of Light on Children of Elementary School-Age: A Case of Daylight Robbery. *Center for Green Schools,* http://www.centerforgreenschools.org/docs/study-into-the-effects-of-light.pdf.

Hallowell, Edward M. and John J. Ratey. *Driven to Distraction: Recognizing and Coping with Attention Deficit Disorder from Childhood to Adulthood.* Touchstone, 1995.

Viegas, Jennifer (2009, October 15). Brain Power Improves Right After Drinking Water. *Discovery News,* http://news.discovery.com/animals/brain.htm.

12. Creating A Support System

13. The Creative Life

14. Pulling It All Together

INDEX

NOTES

Notes

Notes

Made in United States
North Haven, CT
23 June 2024

53977955R00239